MASAO

A Nisei Soldier's Secret and
Heroic Role in World War II

by

Sandra Vea

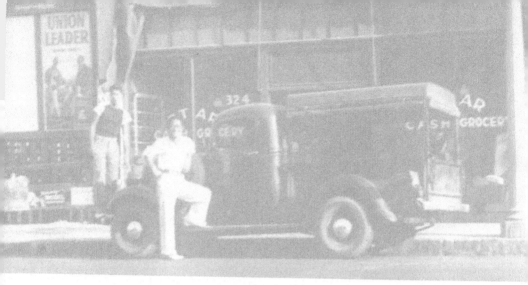

MASAO: A Nisei Soldier's Secret and Heroic Role in World War II
© 2016 by Sandra Vea

Cover Photo Credits:
front: Courtesy of the Abe Family photo collection
back: Courtesy of the Franklin D. Roosevelt Presidential Library

Book and Cover design: Vladimir Verano, Third Place Press

PUBLISHER/AUTHOR CONTACT:

www.dmabooks.com

ISBN: 978-0-692-57558-1

First Edition

For Alan

CONTENTS

ACKNOWLEDGMENTS

I am forever grateful to Masao Abe for humbly sharing his life story and recollections as a Military Intelligence Service (MIS) soldier during World War II. Before he died, Masao was one of the last three soldiers of the ten-man Interrogation/Interpretation Team that was attached to the 81st Infantry Division. The two remaining MIS soldiers have also provided great insight: Saburo Nakamura generously shared his memories before he died in 2015, and Hiroki Takahashi has shared poignant stories via the written hand. It was an honor to gain knowledge from all three of these brave and venerable men.

Doris Okada Abe, Masao's wife of sixty-three years, was kind enough to describe bits of her life. Alan Abe made this project possible and kept propelling it forward. Michael Abe and Kathie Abe were sources of strength. Pat and Stephanie Abe have provided valuable input and shared family photos. Sherman Abe, Anna Pusina, and Kathleen Greinke, the children of Tatsuo Abe, have been wonderful guides and provided intricate details and documents about their parents' internment and imprisonment. Phyllis Mizuharo Hirata was gracious with encouragement and information. Dawn Marano was invaluable as an editor as were Leah Campbell and Barbara McPherson.

Richard Thompson, Librarian for City of San Bernardino Historical and Pioneer Society, and Sue Payne from The California Room in the San Bernardino Public Library sent information and pictures. Mark Vanderveen, University of Washington professor, was helpful with regard to military affairs in Japan during the 1930s. Mark Wittow, intellectual property attorney, provided wisdom and expertise with regard to some of the photos. Lieutenant Colonel Michael Yaguchi, United States Air Force, retired, has been an integral part of the development of the book. Michael provided feedback and also connected me with others. He has been a constant source of encouragement. The input and suggestions by Bobby C. Blair, co-author of *Victory at Peleliu*, and Terry Shima, World War II veteran and recipient of the 2012 Presidential Citizens Medal, were so valuable with regard to military and/or historical accuracy.

My hope is that these fine soldiers of World War II, soldiers who fought in near isolation in the South Pacific, finally have their loyalty, valor, and accomplishments recognized.

INTRODUCTION

THIRTY YEARS. He couldn't speak of his specific assignment in World War II for thirty years after the war ended. Masao, like six thousand other Military Intelligence Service (MIS) soldiers, almost all Japanese-American, were operating under a shroud of secrecy during the war. Masao's assignment in the MIS was unique as he was embedded in a combat unit on the ground, facing an enemy that looked like him and surrounded by the mindset that "the only good Jap is a dead Jap." Only a handful of the MIS soldiers served in this way. They are among our bravest combat soldiers from that time and their stories remain untold.

Masao's medals speak to his heroics during the war. Among the many medals he wore on his service cap were: Combat Infantryman Badge, Purple Heart Medal, Bronze Star Medal, three Bronze Battle Stars, one Bronze Arrowhead, Asiatic Pacific Campaign Medal, Army Good Conduct Medal, WWII Victory Medal, Army Commendation, American Defense Service, and the Philippine Liberation Medal. He was bestowed the Congressional Gold Medal in 2010, an honor he was proud to receive. After Masao passed, we discovered that he had not earned just one Bronze Star Medal, but three. All three Bronze Star Medals were awarded for meritorious achievement as a result of active and heavy ground combat in the South Pacific. Masao died not knowing what a hero he was but had he known, he would have humbly shrugged it off.

By the time Masao was in his nineties, I had entered the picture and started to ask questions about the war. Not only was he was delighted to have an interested listener, he could remember details from seventy-five years ago with little effort. His war stories were fascinating, but he also had poignant memories of his uncle with whom he lived in California. His uncle was imprisoned during the evacuation while his aunt and little cousins were interned. Like thousands of other Japanese and Japanese-Americans who lived along the west coast, their lives were forever changed.

A word concerning the genre of this book: I was honored to meet, and come to love, Masao Abe during the last years of his life. It quickly became clear to me that his was a story that deserved to be told in its own right, but also because one of its central messages concerning the respectful, civil, and humane treatment of Americans, immigrant-Americans, and others in our country of various ethnicities, races and religions is as critical today as it was in Masao's time. The book is a biography, faithfully representing the hundreds of hours of Masao's vivid storytelling that I recorded over time. Taking my creative license from the genre of the "nonfiction novel," first introduced by Truman Capote in his book *In Cold Blood*, I have reimagined portions of Masao's story, rendering those in fictionalized form, although again, carefully attending to the "facts" of those stories as he told them.

After his precious Doris passed away, I spent two days a week with Masao, mostly to keep him busy as he was lost without his wife of sixty-three years. What started out as simple interviews to record his thoughts about the war turned into a friendship unlike any I've ever experienced. In the end, I realized what I had in my time with Masao was a gift. Those three and a half years, the last of his life, were an absolute treasure. He shared so many untold anecdotes about what happened on the islands of Angaur, Peleliu, and Leyte in the South Pacific, but I also saw a warrior who had become vulnerable to the inevitability of aging. That he let me walk with him during these moments of loss is what I remember most.

Masao is gone now. I miss him every day. And I miss his stories about World War II.

PART I

THE FINAL JOURNEY

NOVEMBER 4, 2013

WE APPROACHED THE TSA OFFICER, ATTEMPTING TO MAKE EYE CONTACT. Like so many of those guys, he looked as if he was sick of his job and worked pretty hard to avoid meeting our gaze. Clearly, he didn't want to answer yet another stupid question or take one more insult about the ridiculous security measures from an airline passenger.

Alan stopped in front of him, holding up the line. "The ticket agent told us to check in with you. I have an urn."

"What?" He looked beyond annoyed.

"An urn. You know. An urn." Alan's voice was anything but confident.

"We have his father's ashes." I meant to sound un-intimidated by this guy, but my voice almost quivered, which surprised me. *Shit*, I thought, *I hope this guy isn't going to be an asshole. That's the last thing we need.*

I saw Mr. TSA peek over Alan's shoulder to the pack on his back. The American flag, folded into the military triangle and protected in a plastic cover, protruded from his backpack. He softened and gave the slightest nod.

"Follow me."

At the conveyor belt line, he motioned for us to stop.

"Go ahead and get your things in the bins." We did as instructed, a little confused, but he seemed to have a plan, so we went along. He motioned for his fellow TSA workers to join him as he pulled out his wallet to remove a shiny coin. Two other TSA workers, both young men, gathered near him.

"These folks are taking a loved one to his final resting place." He looked at us, "Here's what we're going to do. We will place this coin underneath the urn while it goes through the scanner. We need to make sure the coin is visible." We nodded, indicating we understood. He gestured to me, "You'll go first. After your things are off the belt at the other end, we'll send your father through alone. Nobody else will have anything on the conveyor belt." His eyes shifted to Alan, "Only your father. Out of respect."

Alan and I looked at each other. My eyes started to sting.

"Okay," I heard Alan squeeze out, trying to avoid a complete break down. I fought to choke back my own tears. It would have been so much easier had the guy just been an asshole.

"I'm so sorry for your loss." We both nodded. Our faces must have revealed the long trail of grief we had followed for weeks.

At the far end of the conveyor belt I glanced back at Alan while I collected my bins and waited for the people in front of me to remove their items. It seemed like they were taking forever. I bit my tongue and smiled at them when they looked at me and they eventually moved on. I turned toward Alan and the TSA officer on the other end. The TSA officer motioned that the conveyor belt was clear.

Masao's urn was carefully placed on the belt that then started to move. In the few moments as the urn came through, a silence fell around us. Fellow passengers seemed to take note and were quietly observing. I watched as the urn lit up the security screen, the coin visible on the bottom. I hadn't realized that the two younger TSA workers were now beside me; both donned fresh gloves. The urn came through, and the TSA officer carefully picked it up to retrieve his coin. He then brought the urn in my direction.

"Excuse me, ma'am, we'll take it from here." One of the younger TSA workers took the urn, "We just need to scan the outside as well."

"Of course." I was relieved that there was more to the process so Alan could get through security and join me on the other side. Alan picked up his bins, and we hurried to follow the young TSA men to a nearby station.

"This won't hurt anything," one of them said as the other used a cotton-like swab to rub the outside of the urn, "we're just testing for certain materials." They couldn't have been any more careful or sensitive.

Alan and I both nodded, each trying hard to control the emotion that was in our throats. I looked at Alan and saw that his eyes were moist but his tears were contained. He looked at me, too. We didn't have to say a word. This was hard.

"Sandie," he whispered. I softly put my hand inside his. "I'm glad you're doing this with me."

I nodded. "Me too."

The TSA workers completed their scan, gently picked up the urn and walked over to Alan. "We're sorry for your loss." Alan took the urn. It was all he could do to nod.

"Thank you," I choked out as I watched Alan arrange his backpack. The TSA guys waited while we organized everything; I think they wanted to be on standby in case we needed anything. It was quite impressive how they treated us that day.

"Thanks," Alan said as he heaved the pack on his back. He looked for the first TSA officer, who was watching from a distance, and we waved to him as well. Step one in the final journey was now complete. Try as I might to hold them in, tears fell from my eyes as we walked to the gate. I looked at Alan only to find him in even worse shape.

CHAPTER ONE

GENERATIONS

Nisei

NISEI. THE LITERAL MEANING IS "SECOND", AS IN, SECOND GENERATION. Masao was born on November 16, 1916, to his parents, Tomie and Yasoshichi, both *Issei* or first generation. They were among the growing population of Japanese people who lived in southern California.

"It was called, uh, Fourth Street School," Masao told me as the waitress poured tea. It was one of the first times I interviewed Masao, quite by happenstance, while we were dining at our regular Japanese place. "I was the only Japanese in my class."

"What? Why? I thought the school was near Little Japan, or Japantown - whatever you called it." I was merely trying to understand his life but quickly found that I would be confused for most of his childhood history.

"Heh!" he chuckled. "It was. But most of the Japanese people lived away from that area. We didn't call it anything. Japanese a-people, they just had their shops there, a-no?"

"So, no other Japanese attended that school?"

"There were a few, a-no? But I was the only one my age."

"So, who were your pals, then?"

"Oh, anyone. A lot of Spanish-speaking people there, you know?"

"I didn't know. Did you speak Spanish?"

"Nah."

"Japanese, though, right?"

"Nah. My parents didn't teach it to me."

"Did they speak English pretty well?"

"My dad did. But my mom, it was kind of hard to understand her."
I was amused by this. I wondered if Masao had the upper hand with his
mom due to her limited English; he seemed like the mischievous type.

"What was it like back then?"

"Back when?" He had almost nine decades to choose from. I quickly
discovered that I would need to be precise in my questions.

"Well, let's start in San Bernardino when you were little. What do you
remember about that part of your life?"

"Heh! I was just a little guy, a-no? Let's see now…"

San Bernardino, September, 1925

The heat was oppressive. It was a sweltering ninety-three degrees outside,
but inside Fourth Street School where Masao attended as a third grader,
the temperature must have hit a hundred. Children sat at their wooden
desks and halfway listened to their teacher. Roughly a third of the students
sitting in Masao's classroom were of color, mostly Latino, one or two African Americans, and one Japanese child – Masao. He glanced slyly at Josue,
the boy sitting next to him. They smirked at each other; seeing or hearing
something that only the eyes or ears of eight-year old boys can detect,
something that amused them.

"Class dismissed," their teacher announced. And with that – the children sprang from their desks eager to get out of the stuffy building.

Masao, already wearing glasses, and Josue erupted through the doors
of the school and ran together like little boys do. They giggled all the way
in a sprint to the end of the sidewalk, their bulky leather shoes not slowing
them down in the least. At the street, they parted ways. Josue would walk
to the barrio, Masao to Little Japan.

"See ya," Masao called after Josue.

"Hasta manana," Josue called back as he trotted off.

Masao walked the five blocks to his house, a two-bedroom, one-bathroom bungalow that sat right behind the San Bernardino courthouse on Arrowhead. The yard was as neat and tidy as the inside of the house which his mom kept spotless. Masao came in through the back door to the kitchen where his mom was working. Like any boy, he tossed his metal lunch pail on the floor and immediately took off his shoes to get some relief.

"Masao. Put pail here." His mother, Tomie, spoke softly in her broken English as she placed her hand on the kitchen counter. Masao complied and hurriedly set his lunch pail on the counter as his mother wanted, part of their afternoon routine. In his bare feet, he scurried to his room to put his shoes away before his mom could get after him about that. Then he came back to the kitchen to eat his afternoon snack that she had carefully prepared and had waiting for him. He sat at the table along with his two little sisters, Yoshiko, then five, and Yuriko, three. He largely ignored them as he ate his sliced apple.

"After snack, you go store," his mother gently demanded.

"Aw, shucks, Ma, I don't want to help daddy today. It's too doggone hot," Masao stammered.

Tomie looked at her only son and smiled. "He need your helping."

"He needs your help," Masao corrected her with a sigh. "Okay. I'll go."

Tomie was trying her hardest to learn the language of the country she had come to a decade earlier, but it was a struggle given that she had limited interaction with English-speaking people. She would sometimes listen to the radio to try to pick up words, but the announcers spoke so fast that she would become frustrated and give up. Besides, she was raising three children, keeping the house clean, cooking meals, and helping in the family grocery store from time to time. Who had the time to learn English?

"My son," she cooed as she gently stroked Masao's thick black hair. Still working on his snack, Masao didn't notice the sadness in her eyes.

A few minutes later, Masao had his shoes back on and was towing his Radio Flyer wagon the half-block down to Third Street. He passed by the dry cleaners on Arrowhead where owner Mr. Kamimura waved to him. Once he turned the corner onto Third Street he was in a different world. This was Little Japan. Japanese merchants littered Third Street for blocks, but the concentration of Japanese businesses was located within the few blocks between Arrowhead and D Streets. He skipped as he made his way inside Star Cash Grocery that was owned and operated by his father, Yasoshichi, and uncle, Tatsuo. The grocery store was as neat and tidy as was the Abe home.

"Little man here!" Tatsuo's English was broken, his having arrived just four years earlier. A strikingly handsome Yasoshichi looked on, admiring the fondness Tatsuo shared with him for Masao.

"Masao. Take these potatoes to Mr. Hirata." He was already loading up Masao's wagon. "Then you come back and sweep." Masao, used to taking orders from his father, helped him load the potato sacks onto the wagon.

Out on the sidewalk, Masao, in an attempt to avoid the chore of sweeping, decided to take the long way to the Hirata Deli that was just across the street. He meandered along, happy-go-lucky, waving to the merchants along the way. They all knew him and greeted him as he passed by: Mr. Sawada who owned the café next door to the grocery store, Mr. Ohashi who owned the barber shop next to the café, Mr. Nakabayashi who ran the pool hall, and finally, Mr. Uyeda who owned the café at the end of the block. Everyone knew Masao and Masao knew them all, by name. It was a tight-knit community.

❖   ❖   ❖

Back in the restaurant, our food arrived and Masao was hungry, so his attention turned to his sushi. San Bernardino of old was gone for now. Back at their apartment, Alan hung up his parents' coats and put their leftovers away. I was in my own world, thinking about San Bernardino in the 1920s. I lingered along the wall that displayed family photos. Then I noticed it: the picture of his school days at Fourth Street School. I took the old photo out of its spot, stuck in the frame of another picture, and had a closer look. There he was. His little face looking back at me from days long gone.

I longed for more of San Bernardino from that time and found myself unexpectedly intrigued by the notion of the west coast in the early 1900s. I coupled my conversations with Masao with research, establishing connections with some folks from San Bernardino who then sent me pictures and maps of San Bernardino from the 1920s. What was remarkable was how well Masao's memory served him. The way he described Little Japan proved to be amazingly accurate, according to historical records. I was content knowing that I had embarked on Masao's story and looked forward to our next dinner with anticipation.

❖   ❖   ❖

We were sound asleep when Alan's phone rang. He jolted awake and grabbed the phone, glancing at the number.

"It's dad," he was alarmed. "Dad?"

"Mommy fell," I could hear Masao's voice in the stillness of the night. He sounded shaky and the fear in his voice was evident. "She's bleeding from her head," he continued.

"I'm on my way. Call 911." Alan was quickly getting dressed while holding the phone with his neck.

"What?" Masao sounded confused.

"I'm on my way, Dad. *Call 911!*"

❖   ❖   ❖

Doris was in the hospital for days, then she was moved to a long-term care facility. Unfortunately, she had entered that "health impairment limbo": lacking an ailment that can be treated, she was sent to a place, it seems, where folks go when they are waiting to die, depressing places despite the efforts of those in charge to create a positive and upbeat atmosphere. Doris hated it there.

I visited her with Alan, and sometimes with Alan and Masao, and even by myself. The interviews with Masao had all but stopped. The attention was on Doris and her health. That was all that mattered to Masao and it was all that mattered to Alan.

"How did your dad get here from Japan?" I asked Masao over lunch one day before going to visit Doris. It was an attempt to regenerate our conversation about his life.

"Well, let's see now. He came here when he was just a youngster. Fifteen or sixteen, I guess."

Ignorant to history, I had no idea what circumstances would bring someone to the United States during that period, but Masao, too, was probably uncertain of the context. As it turned out, the year Masao's father stepped ashore in Seattle was the same year the U.S. started to turn up the heat to stop Japanese immigration.

"He came to work on the railroad, I think," Masao said, attempting to piece together his father's history.

1907, Fukushima-ken, Japan

Sixteen-year-old Yasoshichi balanced on the top rung of a wooden ladder and reached for ripe cherries in the thick of a tree. He came down the ladder, loading his burlap bag to the top with his last handful of cherries. As he carefully poured the cherries from his bag into a wooden bin, he noticed his father approaching. Something about his father's face concerned Yasoshichi, so he put his bag down.

"Ohayou gozaimasu." Yasoshichi met his father with the formal "good morning" greeting. His father, Mataemon, nodded. He admired his son's handsome young face.

"Let's walk," Mataemon motioned. Yasoshichi brushed off his hands and joined his father. They strolled through Mataemon's apple and cherry orchard as Mataemon contemplated how to phrase what was on his mind. Yasoshichi, the oldest of ten children, had been on walks with his father before. Usually, these thoughtful walks meant the introduction of some rite of passage he would soon experience, such as how to properly pick cherries, then apples, then how to sell or barter their goods with others in the small village of Senoue in the prefecture of Fukushima-ken. One such walk introduced Yasoshichi to the art of barter with folks from other villages, an exciting event for Yasoshichi since he had never traveled outside Senoue. But this walk seemed different. It was clear his father's heart was heavy.

"My son. The time has come for you to work away from the family orchard." This caught Yasoshichi's attention. He had heard of other young men traveling to glorious far away places. Maybe his father would send him to Tokyo or other parts of Japan to work on the railway. He listened with much anticipation.

"There is a group going to America. You will go with them." Mataemon gazed at the ground as he strolled and spoke, as though he was carefully choosing his words while thinking through the necessary steps of his plan. Yasoshichi could hardly believe his ears. America! He had heard stories about this land. A land where gold lined the streets and every man had the chance to earn money beyond his wildest dreams. He could surely make enough to make his father proud; he would return to Japan a wealthy man and be the envy of everyone in Senoue – no – Fukushima!

"When will I go?" Yasoshichi tried to control his excitement, but it bled through in his voice, and his father detected it.

"There is a long process. Be patient."

"Yes, father."

The long process included an extensive board examination of character. The Japanese government wanted their subjects treated better, once in the U.S., than Chinese countrymen had been treated previously. This examination was intended to ensure ethical, virtuous, and conservative behavior while abroad. It was a laborious course of action that exhausted the mental capacity of many young men. Yasoshichi endured, but not without question.

"Why must they put me through all of this?" Yasoshichi asked while he and his father waited in the hall of the local municipality for yet another board review.

"America is growing rapidly," Mataemon explained. "It has been necessary for them to gather workers from around the world to fill the jobs."

Yasoshichi nodded, waiting for his father to continue.

"For many years, Chinese countrymen filled much of this demand, especially on the shores of the west, where you will go. But problems occurred with the Chinese."

"What problems?" Yasoshichi asked after giving this some thought. He wanted to be aware so that he wouldn't make the same mistakes.

"I am not certain. I have heard that United States people became angry that the Chinamen were taking all the jobs. And the Chinamen were working harder and working longer hours. So it made the United States people uncomfortable with Chinamen. They made laws to prevent any more travel from China to America. So for many years, no more Chinese people go to America. Only Japanese can go. But that is ending soon."

Yasoshichi didn't know what to make of this. "Why?"

"Same reasons. Taking jobs, working hard. Only Chinese countrymen got in a little bit of trouble with drinking and gambling. The Japanese government wants to make sure Japanese countrymen don't do those sorts of things. That's why you go through all of this."

Yasoshichi nodded. The last thing he wanted to do was to bring shame to his family or to Japan.

"Will I be treated well in America?"

"If you act well, you will be treated well."

"Then I will act well," Yasoshichi assured him. And this made Mataemon smile.

Yasoshichi, having been a good student, son, and citizen, passed the exam and was cleared for travel to the U.S. And so, in November of 1907, Yasoshichi's journey began from his small village. Some friends had a horse-drawn carriage and took Mataemon and Yasoshichi to the train station in Fukushima, eight kilometers away from Senoue. Yasoshichi was happy to get the ride so he wouldn't have to walk with his luggage along the dirt roads. Besides, this way, his father could come along to bid him farewell.

At the Fukushima train station, Mataemon handed him a roll of money.

"Spend wisely. Act honorably."

"Of course, father." Yasoshichi bowed out of honor. In his western suit that they had bartered for, he looked out of place at the train station where everyone else was in traditional kimono wear.

"Go now," Mataemon said with a wave of his hand. Yasoshichi locked eyes with his father while he picked up his luggage. His eyes spoke for him; he was both eager and anxious about the journey that awaited him, not to mention the new world. He bowed again and headed to the train.

When Yasoshichi stepped off the locomotive at the Shimbashi Station in Tokyo, his eyes were wide with wonder at the huge buildings, the vastness of the city, and streets littered with people who bustled along in the growing and industrialized metropolis. On his long walk to Yokohama Harbor to meet the Methodist Missionary group, and ultimately to catch the Kaga Maru steamship, his feet craved a ride on a *jinrikisha*, or rickshaw. But he remembered his father's words, "spend wisely," so he kept his money in his pocket and lugged his suitcase along.

Yasoshichi could not begin to imagine how grueling his voyage across the sea would be. He endured days of travel in steerage, bearing living quarters no larger than a coffin and experiencing seasickness throughout the journey. On November 14, the ship finally pulled into the Port of Seattle.

Seattle, in 1907, was sprawling. While having half the population of Tokyo, it was a busier city. Construction was going on in just about every block. Cable cars whizzed by, people filled the streets, and there were more motor-powered vehicles than Yasoshichi had ever seen. Just a few blocks from the pier where he disembarked stood the Pike Place Market, having opened for the first time earlier that year. It bustled with merchants including Japanese farmers. As the missionary group made their way to the flourishing Japantown, or Nikkei, he noticed where cable track had been laid in a massive expansion. *My fortune is coming*, he thought.

The main passenger terminal for the interstate railway system was located a short distance from Japantown. As a result, numerous hotels were built in the area surrounding the terminal; some of those hotels would be standing as long as a century later. Yasoshichi stayed at one of them, but not for long. It was less than a week before he found employment on a railway. He worked on various railroads from that point forward and for the next several years, moving his way south.

He soon found out that there was nothing glorious about working on a railroad. There were no streets lined with gold, and he was toiling long hours for practically nothing. Although he saved every penny and rarely spent money on anything other than absolute necessities, it dawned on him that it would take years for him to become the wealthy man of his dreams. He also began to notice that he, and other railroad workers who were of color, were treated quite differently than their white counterparts. He was doing his best to act honorably; he didn't gamble, he didn't drink, and he worked hard. And yet, he was treated as though he was some sort of a scoundrel. He was eager to find a different vocation that would allow him to follow his dream and be treated well because, after all, he was acting well.

The railroad work led him to the San Diego area where he found his way to Imperial Valley and the town of Brawley, the site of the Takahashi Company, a farm and packing enterprise. Yasoshichi, happy to find a Japanese employer, worked for Takahashi and was eventually promoted to management. As a manager he was able to save more money, and when the Takahashi Company changed hands, Yasoshichi moved on. Through networking, he discovered that there was a small store in San Bernardino that he became interested in purchasing. San Bernardino was considered a small town at that time yet already boasted a Chinatown, and a strong Nikkei community was forming. It was the perfect setting for him to make his mark. So, in 1920, at the age of twenty-nine and with his hard-earned savings, Yasoshichi became the proud owner of Star Cash Grocery. The block on which his store was located would eventually become the central area for Japanese businesses. It must have been comforting for a young Yasoshichi to settle in a town that had welcomed other Japanese businessmen in its ranks and had such a strong Japanese presence. He had established his home in America.

❖   ❖   ❖

Back in the restaurant, Masao ate the last bit of rice in his bowl. I was always amazed at the artful way the elder Japanese people used their chopsticks. He gently set them down. He was still deep in thought, back in San Bernardino all those years before.

"Maybe it was because his own life was so tough that my old man did what he did to me," he said thoughtfully, looking off in the distance at nothing in particular. But what he said caught my attention, and I waited for him to continue. He sipped his tea. It was the kind of sip he would take before telling another story. But instead of telling me the story about his dad and some mysterious and awful deed he had committed, Masao snapped out of the past and looked at me as though I had just entered the room and sat down.

"Well. Shall we go?"

"Wait. What?" I stammered, "I want to hear about what your dad did to you."

"Ah. It can wait," He waved me off, got himself up, and maneuvered his cane to hobble out from the table.

I helped him get his jacket on. "Mas. You can't just begin a story and then not finish it. Especially when you start it like that, it sounded like something important," I insisted, waving my tape recorder.

"Heh! We'll get to it. My wife is waiting. She wants those little crackers."

"What little crackers? Did you bring the little crackers?"

"We need to stop at the store."

"Stop at the store! Why didn't you tell me this before? When can I hear about your dad and what he did?" But my pleas fell on deaf ears. He didn't care about my interest in his story or about leaving me in the lurch with questions in my mind. He was on a mission to go visit the love of his life and was determined to bring her the crackers she craved.

A few minutes later, we were in an aisle of Uwajimaya, a Japanese grocery store. I took a package of crackers off the shelf, "Are these the ones?"

He inspected the box. "Nope. That doesn't look right." He hobbled along looking for a recognizable box, but couldn't seem to locate what he was looking for. "They are just small crackers." He was using his index finger and thumb to make a small circle. I had no idea what he was talking about, but I took a guess.

"Do you mean, like, oyster crackers?" I asked.

He whipped his head around and looked at me like I was on to something. "Oyster crackers. That's it."

I found your basic variety of oyster crackers and showed him the box. He approved but didn't look too confident in our choice. "Are you sure these are the right ones?"

"I don't know, you know? She used to like a certain kind." *Uh-oh. She's not going to be happy with these. No matter what we buy, it will be wrong.* I felt bad for Masao already.

"Should we go to a different store?"

"Nah. No need."

So, we bought the somewhat iffy crackers and got on our way to visit Doris. My theory was correct. He offered up the box of oyster crackers he had carefully picked out and Doris practically threw the box back at him.

"Those aren't the right ones!" she hissed just as Alan came through the door of her room. I cringed and moved to the corner while Doris bossed both men around. It was a flurry of activity as her husband and son scurried to get things in order for her. I wondered how this eighty-pound woman had so much power. Alan left to go get something and Masao sat down, using his cane as a resting place for his hands. I think Doris wanted me to leave too, but I wasn't sure and didn't know where to go, so I tried to become invisible.

She looked at her husband and reached for his hand. "They don't like Japanese people here," she said. *No wonder she's crabby*, I thought. She looked vulnerable for the first time since I had met her. I got up and meandered off so Masao could comfort her. In the hall, Alan was talking to a nurse about her mattress being too stiff. When he was done, I reported what I had heard.

"Okay," he said, "we'll need to figure something out. We can't leave her here if that's how she feels." Alan was already planning a way to make his mother feel more comfortable.

❖   ❖   ❖

The moving truck was outside the retirement home when I pulled in. I spotted Alan's car and knew he'd already been there for hours. I glanced around the garage and recognized other cars. From the looks of it the entire family had arrived. I wondered what I might do to help in the move and pondered different scenarios as I made my way through the halls. *They'll probably have me clean out the refrigerator or some other horrid chore.*

The door to Masao's apartment was ajar. "Hi there!" I announced as I walked in. Alan was in the bathroom packing up his parents' toiletries. His brother, Mike, was cleaning out the refrigerator, much to my relief, and his other brother, Pat, was in the bedroom. Masao looked up from his Japanese show that was blaring on the TV.

"Hey, Sandie."

"You ready for the move?" I sat down on the couch adjacent to his recliner.

"Ah. Makes no difference where we live. As long as we're together, a-no?"

Doris had been in the long-term care facility for weeks. It was hard on her, but maybe even harder on Masao. When she was at home, they would socialize far more. She would insist that they eat in the community dining room with other residents. Without Doris, Masao was not willing to make the trek to the dining room alone. He clearly missed her and was excited to be with her again. She needed more help, physically, than Masao was capable of providing for her though, so they were moving to a facility that provided assisted living.

"How can I help?" I called out to Alan.

"You can take him to lunch if you want." Masao and I looked at each other and both simultaneously shrugged.

"Okay," I said, "I guess I get out of working." Masao's eyes lit up, and he chuckled. After we settled in the car, I asked him where he wanted to go.

"We go casino."

"Casino? I was kind of hoping you would tell me more about your parents."

"Ah. We talk on the way." Then he motioned with his hand. He was in some sort of a hurry to go gamble. While he missed his wife, I sensed that he felt his freedom vanishing and wanted to have one last day to do as he wanted. I took out my tape recorder and turned it on hoping to hear more details about his childhood. There wasn't much conversation in the beginning of our twenty-minute drive up the mountain to the closest casino. I was caught off guard and didn't have any questions prepared. After about five miles, I remembered our last conversation. About that same time, Masao decided on a topic.

"Did I tell you about my mom?" he asked. I could tell that he wanted to provide me with something about his life to make my time worthwhile, interview-wise. I think he felt he was manipulating me in some way by having me drive him to the casino. I was just happy to get out of cleaning toilets, though, so we were both benefiting.

"No, not yet. We were last talking about your dad." I was trying to steer him back to the terrible deed, but no such luck.

"Heh!" He was somewhat embarrassed by what he was about to reveal. "My mom, she was a picture bride." He looked at me for my reaction. There wasn't any reaction other than confusion. I had no idea what he was talking about. I shook my head and shrugged, like a five-year-old would shrug, to indicate my ignorance.

"My dad. He wanted a wife. So he sent for her."

"What? Like some sort of mail-order bride?" Masao laughed at this while nodding, still uncomfortable with this piece of his family's history.

"How did that work back then? I can't even imagine."

Masao was really amused. "Well, he wrote letters back home and there was a woman, a-no, who arranged marriages. Heh!" He chuckled more. "My mom. She was a *picture* bride!"

1914, Tsukidate, Fukushima-ken

Seventeen-year-old Tomie Haga had closed herself off in the far end of the home so she could concentrate on her sewing. Considered quite the seamstress, once she was working on a project she didn't like to be interrupted. Weeks before, her mother had surprised her with a trip to the city of Fukushima to buy fabric for a new kimono. Her mother let her pick out a beautiful purple-and-light blue fabric that boasted stripes. Used to wearing drab gray kimonos, Tomie was thrilled to finally make something that would get her noticed.

Her mother approached her so quietly, Tomie didn't even notice.

"Tomie." Tomie stopped and turned toward her mother. "You are making good progress, yes?"

"Yes, Mommy. I will be done well before New Year's Day," Tomie reported proudly.

"Come, please. I have someone I want you to meet." Tomie's mother motioned with her hand.

In the sitting area, tea had been served. A woman in a stunning kimono sat on her knees. Tomie had never witnessed anything like her.

She had her hair worn *shimada* style, up off her face in elaborate buns and adorned with *kanzashi*, various styles of hairpins. Her make-up was flawless and her skin – perfect. Tomie immediately felt "country" and unsophisticated. The woman looked up. Tomie instinctively lowered her eyes and bowed out of respect.

"Tomie, this is Hayashi-san. Hayashi-san, my first daughter, Tomie." Tomie's mother was talking but Tomie couldn't hear anything; she couldn't take her eyes off this woman.

Hayashi-san's eyes slowly assessed Tomie's appearance from head to toe. Tomie tried not to notice.

"She is pretty, Haga-san." Her voice was like silk. Tomie blushed, felt herself blush, and then looked down.

"You are kind, Hayashi-san," Tomie's mother was saying as she poured more tea. Tomie felt trapped in her body, not sure if she should sit or simply run out of the room under the pressure of being in the presence of someone so magnificent and who was attributing any beauty at all to her. Tomie was naturally beautiful although completely unaware of it. There was softness in her perfectly almond-shaped, mocha-brown eyes. Her face was put together in an almost symmetrically perfect way, and her nose was small – not too pointy, not too short. She felt herself bow to signal appreciation for the compliment.

"Tomie, your mother tells me that you sew." Hayashi-san's silky voice filled the room.

"Yes, Hayashi-san, I make my own kimonos, of course, and for those of my siblings," she reported.

"Very good." Hayashi-san smiled and that elicited another bow from Tomie. Then Hayashi-san gave the slightest of nods to Tomie's mother.

"Tomie, you can continue on your project," Tomie's mother suggested, an order put in a polite manner. Tomie understood. She bowed again as she made her way out of the room.

From behind the *fusuma*, sliding rice paper walls, Tomie peeked out and stared at Hayashi-san. She couldn't hear what they were talking about but she couldn't take her eyes off this handsome woman in her spectacular kimono and perfect hair. *Why did my mother have to shoo me off?*

A few days later Tomie modeled her newly made kimono for her mother and father. She had finished it a week ahead of the big day.

"I will be the envy of all the girls on New Year's Day," Tomie announced. Her parents smiled; their oldest daughter was their pride and joy.

"Tomie. Come, sit." Her father patted his hand on the pillow next to him after she had finished her debut. Tomie did as she was told, it was a perfect chance for her to see how this new kimono would wear. She decided, as she sat, that it was perfect.

"Tomie." Her father's voice was suddenly compromised.

"What is it, father? Are you ill?"

"No, my child. My health is fine." He paused before he continued. "Tomie, the time has come for you to marry."

Tomie was confused by this. "But I have not been courted, father," she reminded him.

He nodded that he understood. "We have arranged for you to marry."

At first she thought she was hearing things. She had barely talked to boys much less anticipated being courted. But *married!* "I don't want to marry, father, I want to stay with you."

Her father scratched his head. This was going to be more difficult than he thought. "My dear, Hayashi-san has arranged for you to marry the son of a councilman."

The son of a councilman! Her mind started to spin. Maybe this would mean that she would take on the attributes of someone as grand as Hayashi-san.

"In Tsukidate?"

"No, Senoue." Her mind settled a little bit with this. Senoue was just a carriage-ride away; she could even walk home if she was desperate.

"I don't want to leave my family," she succumbed, "but if I must, I'm happy I will be close by."

Her father looked helplessly at his wife. "Tomie, this son of a councilman lives - in America."

"America!" The breath was sucked out of her body. She couldn't even imagine how far away this was. "I – I don't want to go. I won't go! Haven't you heard the stories about the brides they send to America?! Some are left to rot, never claimed by their husband. Some are stuck with an old man who purports to be young in his photos. Is this what you want for your daughter? Helpless and alone in a country that is foreign to her?"

Her parents had no answer for Tomie for they had also heard the stories of disappointed brides who had been sent to America. But arranged marriages had become common practice since so many Issei men had taken work overseas. The Japanese government thought it prudent to formulate a strategy to unite Japanese men with Japanese women. The only problem was the Pacific Ocean that separated the men living abroad from the women still in Japan. To complicate matters, Japanese men living in the U.S. had limited means to return to Japan to be married. While earnings were better in the U.S. than in Japan, any savings required hard work and long hours. There was no time for the luxury of traveling to Japan, losing weeks of work, for the purpose of marriage. A much simpler solution was born: the "picture bride."

They let her sob in between them and when she looked up with longing eyes, she didn't get the assurance she was hoping for. They, themselves, were torn about this decision and knew it was a gamble. At the time in Japan, there wasn't much of a future for girls in general, but girls coming from small towns had very little chance of meeting the right man for marriage. They had taken all the precautions they could and had gone as far as traveling to Senoue to meet Mataemon. They felt assured that Tomie would embark on a better life with Yasoshichi in America than she would if she remained in Japan.

"It is decided, my daughter." Tomie's father's voice was gentle but firm.

Later that night, alone in her room, Tomie sobbed quietly. She looked at her new kimono, the one she had been so proud to wear. It was all a farce. This kimono that she had put her heart and soul into making, this kimono was intended only for her first meeting with her new husband, a total stranger. This kimono of beautiful colors would not be enjoyed on New Year's Day; its purpose had been entirely different and unbeknown to Tomie. She now hated this kimono and everything it stood for.

❖ ❖ ❖

Tomie, with a dozen or so other brides, endured the same grueling voyage across the Pacific as Yasoshichi had years earlier. She arrived in

San Pedro, California on February 18, 1915, as Tomie Abe, having been married by proxy in Japan. In the kimono she hated, she was taken to the immigration office on Terminal Island to wait for her new husband. Other husbands came to claim their brides and with each union, Tomie became more anxious. One husband was a good twenty years older than he had portrayed himself in the photo held by his helpless bride. Tomie saw the sheer distress in the young bride's eyes, utterly powerless to do anything but go with the old man. She waited nervously for this son of a councilman.

When Yasoshichi entered the room, she hoped that he was the one, her husband. He checked in with the immigration officer speaking fluent English. The immigration officer shuffled papers around and then pointed at Tomie. Her heart fluttered. Could she have such good fortune? This was a handsome man, seven years her senior, and had secured a good vocation. He looked over at Tomie, and their eyes met for the first time. With papers in hand, he walked over to her and extended his hand to help her up.

"Tomie. I am Yasoshichi," he said in perfect Japanese. She bowed. He continued, "You must be tired after such a long voyage."

"Thank you, yes."

"We have three hours travel ahead of us," he said as he picked up her suitcase, "much easier travel than the steamship, however." And with this, he smiled at her, and her heart knew in this moment she was with a good man.

Yasoshichi took great care of Tomie as they arrived at the train station. Tomie's eyes were wide with wonder at the modern Los Angeles of 1915. While railroads in Japan were plentiful, Los Angeles boasted a whopping fifty-two rail routes and sixty-one hundred departures a day, making this city one of the busiest hubs in the country. Los Angeles county possessed the highest number of automobiles in the state – something that was astounding for Tomie to see.

"Much to learn, no?" Yasoshichi noticed how intrigued Tomie was with the modern state of America. Tomie nodded. Indeed, she had much acclimation ahead of her – a new world, a new language, and a new husband.

❖   ❖   ❖

I sat in a chair next to Masao, who was making two-dollar bets on a slot machine that was making all sorts of noises, but my mind was still with Tomie. I marveled at the strength of the young woman who made the voyage across an ocean to an unknown life that waited for her. How brave she must have been.

At the new retirement home, Alan greeted us in the lobby, and we all headed up to see their new place. Masao hobbled along at lightning speed on his cane — I had never seen him move so fast. I figured he had to go to the bathroom, but I was wrong. He was in a hurry to get to Doris. That was all he wanted.

Doris was in a hospital bed in her room. Masao was excited to see her and immediately went to her without even so much as looking around at the new place his sons had arranged so nicely. When Alan and I peeked in on them, Masao was sitting by the head of her bed. They were holding hands and comforting each other. The way they were looking at each other seemed to transcend time; it was as if they were young and seeing each other for the first time.

CHAPTER TWO

THE LOSS OF HOME

It had been months of recovery for Doris. She was still extremely frail, but Alan insisted on taking her out even though it required a wheelchair. He was careful and loving as he helped his mom so she could enjoy meals out. Masao was so content having her back at home that it didn't matter to either of us how much work was required for the outings.

I always had my tape recorder on hand in case a story broke out. I was still waiting, not so patiently, to find out what Masao's dad had done to him. It was a question that was always burning in my heart but that I stifled on a regular basis for the sake of keeping peace with Doris. Finally, I couldn't take it any more. We were at a Ginza, their favorite Japanese restaurant in old Bellevue, and I thought I'd give it a shot.

"Mas?" I asked in a surprisingly meek voice. He looked up from the local Japanese newspaper he was reading. I felt Doris look at me too. And she didn't seem thrilled.

"Do you remember when we were talking about your dad?"

"My dad. Jeeeeezzz." He started to go down the trail of thought from his childhood. I was happy to see the look on his face that told me he was ready to revisit the past. But just then, Doris pulled on Masao's arm and took his attention away from his thoughts.

"Tea," she ordered. He immediately reached for the tea, but Alan beat him to it and was already pouring hot liquid into her cup.

"Let's hear about your dad," Alan encouraged him. Alan made sure that he took care of his mother's needs so that it freed Masao up to go back into his mind and pull forward some more of his history.

"My dad. He was a different kind of father than I am."

"What did he do?" I asked, almost afraid to hear the answer. Masao settled into a thinking posture, his eyes drifted off into the distance, and I knew he was reliving something. He shook his head.

"When I was eight," he started, looking at me to make sure I was listening. "When I was just a little boy, my whole family took a trip to Japan." I nodded; I was with him so far. I was eagerly waiting for the punch line and was about to get it.

"The whole family, we went. We were there a few weeks, maybe months, I don't remember. I didn't know any Japanese but for some reason, my dad started me in school over there. The kids – they were mean, boy, reaalllly mean."

1925, San Bernardino

Masao and Josue sprinted to the end of the school sidewalk as usual. Josue won by a hair.

"See you tomorrow," Josue puffed as he caught his breath.

"Uh-uh. Remember? I'm taking a trip with my family."

"Oh, yeah. Where are you going again?"

"Japan." Masao could tell by Josue's confused face that he needed to fill in the details a little bit more. "It's where my parents are from."

"Is it by Mexico?"

"Nah. I don't think so. We have to take a boat to get there."

"When are you coming back?"

"I don't know. By Christmas, I hope."

"Shucks, Mas. That's too long."

Masao shrugged, "See ya, Josue."

"See ya, Mas."

Masao kicked a can all the way home, then picked it up and put it in the trash behind his house. He came in through the back door and set his lunch pail on the counter. His mother, who was always in the kitchen to greet him, was not to be seen.

"Mommy?"

Tomie came out of the bedroom, wiping her eyes and nose with an embroidered handkerchief. Masao wondered if he was in trouble.

"What's wrong?"

"No. I okay," she lied. "I fix snack." And she immediately busied herself at the kitchen counter.

Masao went to put his shoes away and noticed that his mom had been packing his suitcase. He slowly swung open his closet door and saw that there was nothing left inside. On his bed, two suitcases were waiting to be closed up.

Back in the kitchen, his snack of apple slices was waiting. He sat at the table and ate, not thinking too much about anything.

"After snack, you go store," his mother was saying.

"Okay. Hey, Ma, why are you packing all my stuff? Are we going to be there that long?"

But his mom didn't answer him. She was at the sink with her head down. Masao figured she didn't understand him, her English was a little on the sparse side and sometimes this was how she coped – by ignoring.

A few minutes later, he was on his way to Star Cash Grocery, wagon in tow. As usual, all the merchants along the way waved to him. He rounded the corner to Third Street and pulled his wagon inside his father's store. Tatsuo was the first to greet him.

"Ah. Masao!"

"Hi, uncle." Masao eyed the fresh apple-bananas that had arrived. Sweeter and smaller than a regular banana, it was Masao's favorite fruit.

"Take one, they good," Tatsuo encouraged him. Masao pulled an apple-banana off its stock and peeled it. He sat down in his wagon to enjoy the treat.

"You excited for trip?" Tatsuo took a piece of the fruit for himself and peeled it.

"Nah, what's so special about Japan anyway?"

His dad came out from the back of the store and was ready to bark out orders but decided to give Tatsuo and Masao their moment. When he saw that they were done eating, he gathered some produce.

"Masao. Take this to Mr. Uyeda," he directed as he loaded up Masao's wagon, "then come back to sweep."

Masao pulled his wagon into the café at the end of the block where Mr. Uyeda was waiting for him.

"Ah, thank you, Masao-chan," Mr. Uyeda warmly greeted Masao, helping unload the goods.

"Okay, see ya, Mr. Uyeda." Masao started to leave when he felt a tap on his shoulder.

"I have something for you. For your journey," Mr. Uyeda was saying as he reached behind the counter and pulled out a small neatly bundled package. "It's candy."

Masao's eyes lit up. His parents rarely let him eat candy. "Thanks, Mr. Uyeda!"

"You take care, now," Mr. Uyeda was saying to an oblivious Masao who was clutching his little candy package as though it was a bag of gold.

And as Masao walked back to Star Cash Grocery, the sun was setting.

❖   ❖   ❖

The voyage to Japan took forever, in Masao's mind. Finally, land appeared in the far off distance. He stood at the rail with his father and felt the chill of the sea breeze. He wondered what this new place would be like. But mostly he wondered when he would return to San Bernardino, to school, to Josue, and to Little Japan.

The ship docked inside Yokohama Harbor, and there was a mass exodus. Masao, holding his mother's hand tightly, thought he might get lost in the swarm of people disembarking the ship. As he looked up and around, he noticed for the first time that he was surrounded by Japanese people. Only Japanese. There were no Caucasian people, no brown people like Josue, only Japanese. There was a lot of chatter going on around him but he couldn't understand a word of it. He strained to comprehend anything but all he could hear was Japanese.

There were more people here in Japan, yet in a way, it was as if he had stepped back in time. He noticed that men were loading their automobile engines with wood, something that he had never seen back home. The automobiles were clumsier than those in California. There were odd contraptions that men pulled to carry passengers, and these seemed to be the most common way for people to get around. They made their way to the train station where they would begin the eight-hour journey to Senoue, over two hundred miles north of Tokyo.

The next morning Yasoshichi was up early. He and his father had tea together and then walked in the orchard as they had done many times when Yasoshichi was young. Yasoshichi was impressed with the expansion of roads in the little village since he had departed some seventeen years earlier.

"Was the harvest good this year?" Yasoshichi asked, noticing that the trees had not been pruned. This would be at the top of his list to accomplish while visiting.

"Yes."

They walked along in silence.

"This town in California, it's a good place to live?" Mataemon pondered.

"Yes. Many Japanese live there, father. Tatsuo is quite content," Yasoshichi said. It was important to ease his father's mind.

Mataemon nodded. He hadn't intended for his sons to live in America permanently. But out of economic necessity, that was exactly what happened. And now, two of his sons had chosen America as their home, and a third son was entertaining the idea as well.

Back in the house, Masao woke up. He examined the odd house, one huge room with flimsy doors that slid to cordon off sections. It was bitterly cold inside. He wandered around until he found his mother in the kitchen along with an older woman who was decrepit and had a sour face. The woman whirled around to look at him with such hostility it made him jump.

"Mommy?" He instinctively went near his mother wondering who this horrible old lady was and more—wanting to get far away from her.

"Ah, Masao. Good morning." She kissed him on the head. The old woman spattered out something in Japanese, her voice was as harsh as her looks. Tomie listened respectfully to this old woman, then nodded.

"Masao, this is grandmother to you," she said. Masao cringed, then tried to hide it. He glanced at his little sisters who sat quietly nearby. Evidently, they had already met this sour woman.

"Nice to meet you," he said and extended his hand to shake hers. But the old woman, his grandmother, pulled back and spat some other Japanese words out at him. Tomie gently guided his hand back at his side.

"In Japan, must have great caring for grandmother. No – this," she motioned with her hand. Masao got it: don't shake hands with old people here.

"Mommy, where is the bathroom?"

"Ah," she guided Masao to the window that overlooked the orchard. She pointed to a little shack in the back area. Masao couldn't believe his eyes. His little sister, Yuriko, muffled her giggles.

"Out there?" He was mortified. This elicited more Japanese that seemed to vomit from his grandmother's mouth. She was the most unpleasant woman Masao had ever encountered. His grandmother was grabbing newspaper from a pile and abruptly handed it to Masao. Then she sharply motioned for him to go.

"I can't read Japanese," Masao was confused but did as his grandmother ordered and headed for the door.

In the outhouse there wasn't a toilet, just a hole in the ground. There was no toilet paper either. That was when it dawned on him: the newspaper *was* the toilet paper. From that first morning, Masao couldn't wait to get back home. He longed for San Bernardino, for their house that had a regular bathroom and no grandmother to torment him.

That night at dinner, Masao quietly observed his grandparents and stuck close to his mother. He had been raised using chopsticks so that was natural to him and seemed to please his grandmother. But that was the only thing that pleased her.

The meat they served was unlike any Masao had ever tasted. He didn't like it and instead ate the rice. His grandmother noticed this, of course, and that ignited more of her wrath. She spat some Japanese out at his dad who then took note.

"Eat your meat, Masao," he said firmly.

"I don't like it," Masao responded respectfully. "What kind is it?"

"Horse. It's good for you." This made Masao set his chopsticks down. Then there was an eruption of Japanese from his grandmother. His parents went into some sort of explanation, evidently on Masao's behalf, but his grandmother was visibly angry.

"What's the matter, Mommy?" Masao asked timidly.

"She thinks you're a spoiled American," Yasoshichi answered for Tomie. Masao leaned into his mother. He felt ashamed but didn't know exactly why. "Tomorrow, we start you in school." Yasoshichi continued. Clearly, this was not the time to argue. He tried to sink away into his mother's side. He didn't want his grandmother's eyes on him any more.

The next morning, his father woke him up early. He had some clothes laid out for Masao, a drab, gray outfit.

"It's your school uniform," Yasoshichi explained.

"Daddy, I don't know Japanese. What am I going to do in school all day?"

"You go to school to *learn* Japanese."

"Are we going to be here that long?"

"Get dressed. Don't argue."

Masao and his father walked the half-mile on a trail through a wooded area. Children also walking to school stared at the newcomer. His dad delivered him to the schoolmaster and the two spoke in Japanese. Masao looked around noticing the stark difference from his school in San Bernardino where there were a variety of faces and the teachers were nice. Here, everyone looked the same, and there was a harsh feeling to the place.

"Do you remember your way home?"

Masao nodded. His father nodded back, took a moment to assess his son's strength, then left.

The first day was the worst. Masao didn't understand anything that was going on in the classroom, and to make matters worse, children made fun of him. They couldn't understand how someone could be Japanese and not speak the language. At lunchtime, they surrounded him. Although he couldn't understand a word, he knew he was being taunted.

He ran all the way home, holding in his tears. When he came to his grandparents' orchard he slowed down. He sat down by a tree and it was there, in the safety of the orchard, where he cried. Things didn't get any better as the days wore on. Even on his ninth birthday in mid-November, when one is supposed to celebrate their own life, their own existence, Masao endured the relentless teasing.

Over the next several weeks, Masao suffered the same punishing treatment, day after long day. Kids teased him endlessly and every day after school, he sat alone in the orchard. But he began to pick up words, one of which was *chitai*. It was something that the kids yelled at him persistently in the schoolyard. He decided that he wanted to know what this word meant.

"What does chitai mean?" he asked his father at dinner. His grandmother gasped at this and mumbled something under her breath. Tomie's eyes filled with tears. She quietly got up and left the table. Yasoshichi watched her go and then looked at his father who nodded slightly.

"Where did you hear this word?"

"The kids at school call me that all the time. What's it mean?"

"Masao, you are not chitai. It means – slow."

"Slow?"

"Retarded. It means retarded."

Masao swelled with anger. His grandfather noticed and said something in Japanese to which his father nodded and agreed.

"Masao, it won't be long before you are able to speak two languages. The children here, they only have one. You, Masao, you know what it is like in two worlds — they only know one. You are not chitai." His father's words calmed Masao for the moment. Yasoshichi gazed at his son. His eyes spoke only love as he softly followed with, "You are brave. Brave and smart."

At bedtime, when his mother came to kiss him goodnight, Masao noticed that she had been crying again.

"Mommy, it's okay. I'll be okay," but this just made it worse for her. She sat down next to him and stroked his hair, choking back tears. Masao didn't know what to say to her to make her feel better.

"I'll be okay. I promise," he assured her. He already had a plan for how to deal with the mean kids, and besides, they couldn't stay in Japan forever.

"My son," her tears persisted, "you good boy." She kissed him on the head and quietly got up. Masao watched his mother's silhouette behind the fusuma. She collapsed into his father's chest as he shut the fusuma that closed off his room. Masao was confused about why the situation with the mean kids bothered his mother so much, but he would show her that he was strong. He would show her that she had nothing to worry about.

The next day at lunch, in the courtyard, he was again surrounded by children. But he was ready.

"Chitai!" They shouted from every direction.

"Watashi wanaidesu chitai!! I am not retarded!" Masao yelled back. "Watashi wa American! I am American!! I'm from America!!! I will know things you will never know!" And this stifled their voices. They backed down, every last one of them. He had found a way to get some relief from this horrid vacation that seemed to last forever.

In his mind, he must have thought the nightmare would end someday soon, when he and his family would return to the United States, to San Bernardino where everything made sense. But that would not happen. His nightmare would only get worse. That afternoon when Masao returned home, things had changed. It was the first day he didn't need to stop in the orchard on his way home. He felt vindicated somehow. Maybe now they could go home, content in knowing that he could survive in Japan if need be. Maybe now, his stupid grandmother would let him be.

He walked in the back door and spotted his horrid grandmother at the sink.

"Mommy?" he called out. Something felt different. His annoying little sisters were not there to bother him, he hadn't noticed his father or grandfather outside where they usually were, and his mother wasn't answering him.

"Mommy?" he called out again. He ran through the house looking for anyone; his sisters, his father, his mother, anyone at all.

"Mommy?!" His voice was becoming frantic.

His grandmother gave him a sly look from the sink and sputtered something in Japanese. The only thing he understood was "inaku natta" —gone. His little heart pounded. *This can't be happening*, he thought as he ran to every last corner in the house. Not one piece of luggage remained; even his own suitcases had been taken.

"Mommy? Daddy? Where are you??" His grandmother was saying something else in her ugly, shrill voice. He didn't try to understand her words as he ran passed her out the door. Outside, he scanned the orchard.

"Daddy!" He ran through the rows of trees. He was in a sheer panic now as he ran passed the house to the dirt road. He ran as fast as he could to the end of the village and then, desperately fraught, he fell to his knees. On the first day he didn't need the orchard to absorb his tears from bullying, his tears fell for a different reason. He used the dirt road to sop up the sobs that were from the deepest part of his broken heart.

"Mommy, where are you?" He slowly and unwillingly succumbed to the reality that he was left behind, alone. He could not begin to stop his deep sobbing. "Mommy…"

At the rail of the ship that was ready to depart Japan, Tomie could not stop her sobs either.

"Masao…my Masao…"

❖   ❖   ❖

Back in the restaurant, I was almost driven to tears listening to Masao. I imagined that his little body must have been filled with confusion, with fear, and with grief that day, searching for his mother. I looked over at Alan. He was as entranced as I was. I think this might have been the first time he heard his dad narrate this part of his life. What haunted me the most were his calls for his mother. There he was, a little boy, scared to death, and hollering for the one person in the world who was supposed to protect him at all costs. I felt for Masao, for what he had endured. And I felt for his mother. It must have been agonizing for her to leave him.

"I was scared. I was just a little boy, just turned nine years old, a-no?" His voice wasn't angry or bitter; he spoke as if speaking of someone else, of some little boy he knew long ago and for whom he felt incredible empathy.

"Why did they do that?" *There must be a good reason.*

"Gee, I don't know. I would never do that to my boys." He was genuinely bewildered by his parents' decision. The mood fell upon the table; a sadness, even grief, about a child who had been left behind. Masao felt it, Alan felt it, and I felt it. Doris nibbled away on her rice.

"It took a long time before I could even communicate with my grand-parents," he said as he ate a piece of *sashimi*. "But my grandmother was mean, boy, reallllly mean."

"What about your grandpa? Was he mean?" I asked, hoping for some sort of silver lining to this depressing story.

"He didn't talk much. But I remember that he always ran for village councilman. He was always nervous about winning. Heh!" It's funny that Masao remembered a detail like this. His grandfather's position in the village also factored in to Masao's future in a way that nothing else would.

At home, I pulled up the ship's manifest that showed it all. December 14, 1925. Masao's name is vividly absent from the list that contains every other Abe family member on the ship returning to the port of San Pedro, California: Yasoshichi, Tomie, Yoshiko, Yuriko.

No Masao.

CHAPTER THREE

MASAO'S HOME IN JAPAN – TAKEN

"I think my dad wants to eat at the casino." Alan was preparing me as we pulled into the parking lot.

"The casino?" I looked over at him. "It's not the best place to interview your dad."

"It's where he wants to go," he said with a shrug, "Are you getting anywhere with him?"

"What do you mean?"

"Is he talking much about the war?" He shut the car off and rested his hand on the back of my car seat.

"We haven't even gotten to that point. We're still talking about his childhood."

Alan chuckled at this. "The best stuff is the war. Talk to him about that."

"I'll get to that. I will. But I'm enjoying this part of his life, too. It's really interesting to me how his family got here, and his life as a youngster."

"Sounds boring to me," he said with a smile, "but it's your deal. And at least my dad has someone to talk to about his life."

After gambling and eating, the four of us headed home. On the way back down the mountain to Seattle it was quiet in the car, so I decided to ask more questions about Masao's childhood in Japan.

"Hey, Mas," I said to get his attention. From the front seat, he turned his head to the side so his ear was facing the back. That was his signal to keep talking. Alan held out his hand for the tape recorder; I handed it up.

"Can you tell me more about your time in Japan?"

"What do you want to know?" he asked, needing a little more help with a direction but definitely in the mood to talk.

"Hmmm. Well, what was school like over there?"

"Heh! It was a lot different then. That was a long time ago. Geeee… now…let me think. Well, middle school, that's like high school here, a-no? I was in, ah, ROTC, military training." He glanced back at me.

"Was everyone in military training?"

"Nooo," he said his *no's* almost like it was an explanation rather than a finite answer. It was a soft and thoughtful no and the inflection went up at the end.

"A lot of us boys were in ROTC, military training. I was in *officer* training. A big shot, a-no?" Masao chuckled at himself. "The military in Japan was taking over a-everything. There were a lot of assassinations during that time. Jeeezz. Tough times in Japan."

Fukushima-ken, 1932

As Masao grew up he learned the Japanese language as well as the culture. The school system in Japan, at that time, was a tracking system. Students attended primary school and subsequently took a test to enter a specific middle school for five years. Students were tracked depending on how they tested and whether or not they showed promise of academic success for college. For Masao, it was the military track.

In 1931, Japan had become more aggressive in its invasion of China with the Manchurian Incident whereby Japanese troops overran the Chinese province of Manchuria despite treaties previously signed. During this time, the military grooming of Japan's children intensified in an attempt to prepare Japan for ultimate expansion. Masao, going on fifteen, was in his final stages of being primed for the military. He had entered the officer's training program and, upon graduation, could enter the Japanese

Imperial Army as a Second Lieutenant once he reached the age of the draft, which was twenty.

During this period, the Ministry of Education compiled and produced all textbooks studied by children in schools. Essentially, the government was choosing what to feed the minds of its young. The military had a strong influence throughout Japan and permeated education. The heavy emphasis was placed on loyalty to the emperor and the Empire of Japan. Spartan discipline and national spirit also ranked high on the agenda. Most extra curricular activities and social customs revolved around the notion of loyalty to the empire as well as the superiority of the Japanese race or *yamato*.

Masao's training included military tactics and weapon instruction. He was even involved in sword fighting as part of his school day ritual. In the all-boy program, Masao was indoctrinated into a brotherhood that was often divided, as was Japan as a nation. One day Masao walked with his buddies, Akira and Kunio, through the wooded area near their school. They all wore military uniforms but were kids at heart, joking and laughing. Although they were just fifteen, they had been in training as warriors and when serious topics emerged, the men in them would come out.

"What do you think about the coup attempt in Tokyo? Our prime minister – gone. Just like that," Akira inserted into their banter. The laughing all but stopped as the three young men debated this.

Masao took a stance. "Those militants are short sighted."

"Masao, those guys are the future of Japan," Kunio shot back.

"It's going to be hard for them to be the future of Japan from jail," Masao laughed, retorting. But Kunio wouldn't have it.

"Maybe their 'short-sighted' ideas are the right ideas. Maybe their goals for Japan are the correct goals for Japan. Those brave men are going to be the leaders of Japan one day, you'll see. Then we'll go in as officers, and it will be up to *us* to protect our country and the purity of our people."

"No country is pure, Kunio. Look how many countrymen we have living here from around the world. Look at me."

An infuriated Kunio cut Masao short. "You! You are not Japanese! You never have been! It's only nationalists, like myself, who are pure in our blood, and who will fight to the death for Japan!"

All three boys stopped in their tracks. Kunio often went into tirades, but this personal attack on Masao was unprecedented.

Kunio positioned himself physically and became more of a threat. "You and your American blood will one day have to choose. Do you have the spirit of Japan in your heart? *Do you*?!"

Masao was mortified. Never once had Kunio referred to Masao as an American.

"Kunio, he is one of us. He can't help where he was born." Akira came to Masao's defense.

Masao stood speechless, unable to believe that his friend of so many years had turned on him in an instant.

Kunio deliberated for a moment then stomped off.

"He just gets caught up in the movement," Akira assured Masao, then he ran to catch up with Kunio.

Masao, now alone, looked around. He decided to change his course and instead of following the trail home he took a different way, to the all-girl school. Masao waited patiently outside. Finally school let out and girls poured from the building. A pod of girls, all wearing drab school uniforms, appeared. Masao perked up when he saw her. Miyoko. She approached Masao, and he stood up. It was Masao and Miyoko, in public, yet alone.

"Hello, Miyoko," Masao greeted her with a smile. Miyoko smiled back.

Masao carried her books as they walked the dirt road toward Miyoko's house.

"You look handsome in your uniform." Miyoko admired the boy who had come from America.

"And you...look pretty," Masao stumbled on his words.

"Please, tell me more about America."

"I don't remember much about it."

"I love to hear about America."

Masao saw the genuine curiosity in her eyes. It was understandable. Living in Japan at this time was bleak, particularly for women. Ambitious young men had the military waiting for them, but young women had little to motivate them other than young men. Masao wanted to please her, so he pulled up a recollection in his mind.

"I was only eight when I left. But I remember it was always sunny, sunny and warm. It was like a little Japan in the middle of a city. It was nice the way all the Japanese people knew each other. I remember everyone was happy."

"Carreefornia," Miyoko said, trying to impress Masao by reiterating the name of this place where he had lived long ago. Masao smiled at this.

"I think that's how you say it. I've forgotten my English."

"Herreewood," Miyoko continued showing off her knowledge of American places and names of cities. Masao was confused by this one, though.

"What?"

"Herreewood. You know, where the movie stars live."

Masao chuckled, both at Miyoko's pronunciation and at the fact that he couldn't remember the correct pronunciation.

"I can't remember how to say that either," he admitted. "Hollywood. That's it. Hollywood. California."

"Horr-i-wood."

"Holl-i-wood."

"Har-i," Miyoko was trying her hardest.

"You have to go like this, with your tongue," he tried to show her how his mouth and tongue were positioned in his mouth.

"Har-har. Har-he," Miyoko made another attempt but, try as she might, she couldn't pronounce the L.

"Herreewood is fine," Masao assured her.

"Your family, so far from you. Do you miss them?" Her question elicited a gaze on Masao's face that said it all. He was in love.

"Not any more."

"And the warm, sunny days of Carreefornia?"

"Japan is my home now."

After spending time with Miyoko, and even though it was just the few minutes to walk her home, Masao felt elated. He practically skipped along the wooded trail back home, his confrontation with Kunio a distant memory. When he got to his grandparent's orchard and had the house in sight, he sensed something. He ran up the stairs and into the house planning his strategy to avoid talking to his grandmother. He still did not care for the old woman, even after living with her for years.

Masao entered the house to find his entire family from America. They had just arrived, their luggage littered the house. Tomie immediately choked up when Masao walked in — she barely recognized her oldest son who she hadn't seen in eight years. She embraced him and spoke in Japanese to him for the first time in her life.

"Masao, my son. You're all grown up." She smiled at him.

"Mommy." Masao held her tightly. He had missed her. By the looks of the luggage they had brought everything with them. His two sisters, now thirteen and eleven, stared at the big brother they barely remembered. His new little brother raced by in a flurry.

"What's his name?"

"Jiro," Tomie responded. She smiled. She couldn't have been happier. All of her children were together at last.

Yasoshichi stepped toward Masao, he examined his son in the military uniform. Masao felt the judgment but didn't care. He was just happy to see his mother again.

"We stay here now," his father stated.

Masao nodded. He understood why. Masao's grandfather, Mataemon, was becoming frail and could no longer care for the orchard or garden. As the oldest son, it was Yasoshichi's responsibility to take care of his ailing parents and oversee the family orchard business. Tatsuo would assume responsibility for the store in San Bernardino.

That night the entire family gathered to eat. His younger sisters seemed terrified of their grandmother. Masao, now used to the old lady, largely ignored her but knew it would take his sisters awhile to get to that point.

"You will take your sisters to school tomorrow," Masao's father stated matter-of-factly.

"Yes," Masao obeyed.

"You have entered military training?"

"Yes. I can join the military as an officer once I am at the age of conscription." Masao stated this confidently thinking it would make his father proud. Instead, his father looked doubtful.

"Hmm." His father appeared to deeply reflect on Masao's plan.

The next morning, Masao and his father took Yoshiko and Yuriko to school. Masao left them at the primary school and walked to his school, wondering what Kunio's mood would be like. His prediction was that whatever had been bothering him would be long forgotten. Still, it would be hard for Masao to get the image of Kunio's wrath out of his mind.

Kunio was waiting outside the school for Masao. Masao strained to see his friend's face from the distance and felt relieved when he saw him smile. He relaxed even more when he saw Kunio walk his way with his hand out.

"Good morning, Masao," Kunio said gently as they shook hands. "Please forgive me for yesterday. I get emotional when I think about the current state of our country."

"Of course," Masao responded as the gentleman he was. They both understood, though, that they were leaning toward vastly different political ideologies. Masao had the gift of living in two enormously different cultures and had fond memories of America. Kunio had never been outside of Senoue. Their friendship would be forever compromised and they both knew it.

❖   ❖   ❖

"So, you were kind of liberal among your peers?"

"I guess," he chuckled, "I didn't think too much about it. I just didn't want to get all wrapped up in what they were teaching us in school, that's all. Some of what they taught us was just bullshit," and then he chuckled again and quickly added, "sorry for the language." Oddly, Doris perked up and chuckled too. I made a mental note: Doris likes cuss words.

"Were there a lot of liberal people in Japan? Or just the ones who had lived other places?" I felt ignorant asking the questions.

"Heh! There were a lot of liberal Japanese. Most, I think. Just a small group of military extremists."

I saw Alan look at me in his rear-view mirror. "Did you know that?" I asked him, hoping that he was as stupid as I was.

"I didn't study Japanese history," he said.

Genius, I thought, *you didn't really answer my question but I have a feeling you're as stupid as I am.*

Masao looked at his son. "Well. That's enough for now." And once again, I would be lingering in Masao's past, longing for more of the pieces to his puzzle.

❖   ❖   ❖

Several weeks later, Alan and I walked in to find Doris navigating her way around the apartment with her walker. She had made a major comeback with the news of her granddaughter, Taryn's, engagement and upcoming wedding plans.

"Wow!" I was hoping to sound impressed, and evidently I did because she smiled and chuckled. It was nice to see her engaged in life again.

"Mommy wants Italian," Masao announced. That meant one thing and one thing only — Pizzuto's, a neighborhood restaurant in the Seward Park area. It was cozy right down to the red-checkered tablecloths and candlelit tables. I always loved it when Masao and Doris wanted to eat there.

After we ordered, I got out my tape recorder. Masao saw it, and I could see the wheels turning already.

"Okay if we talk more about Japan?" He nodded yes so I turned the recorder on.

"Last time we talked, your family had all joined you in Japan."

"That's right, they moved over there. All of them. My grandfather was getting too old for the orchard," he recalled.

"So then what happened? How long did you stay there before you came back? And…why did you come back?" I so badly wanted to understand the puzzle that was Masao's life I didn't realize that I was peppering him with questions.

Alan glared at me. "Slow down, jeez," he suggested in an attempt to protect his dad from my intrusive curiosity.

"Well," Masao started off, "I graduated from officer training school, a-no? I could go into the army as - second lieutenant."

I nodded that I was still with him. Alan arranged his mom's salad that had arrived.

"But my dad, that son-of-a-bitch, sent me back," he stated as he unfolded the red cloth napkin that protected the warm rolls in the breadbasket. I allowed time for him to get a roll fixed for himself, then continued my inquisition.

"Sent you back here?" I clarified.

"Yep. To the States. He sent me back here," he said while nodding and smearing a huge glob of butter on his roll – my kind of guy.

I was dumbfounded. "Did you want to come back here?"

"Heck no! I wanted to stay in Japan. It was my home by then. I knew the language, my friends were all there. My family was there. I didn't know English any more, so – no use being here. I was ready to go *fight*. In China." He took a bite of his roll as though we were talking about nothing more than the weather.

"I'm so confused," I said. They were really my private thoughts that accidentally spilled out of my mouth. Alan looked at me and smiled at my bewilderment.

"Help me understand the bridge between you wanting to serve in the Japanese military and you actually serving in the U.S. military."

"Heh! I don't know. It just happened that way," he responded. He was sincere about his statement. It was the way life had happened *to him*.

Spring 1934, Senoue, Fukushima-ken

Outside the school, Masao waited for Miyoko. She emerged, happy to see him.

"Your sisters, their Japanese is getting very good," Miyoko reported. Masao nodded in agreement. "Do they like it in Japan, or do they miss the warm, sunny days of Carreefarnia?"

"I don't know, I haven't asked them. It doesn't really matter if they like it or not, I guess, they can't go back. Besides, it's safer for them here.

America's military is weak." Masao didn't really believe this, but like any young man out to impress a girl, he had to boast a little bit. He was being primed by the Japanese military, after all, to lead soldiers in battle.

"Are you coming to the graduation?" he asked her, hoping that she would attend, hoping that she would see him in the spotlight, accepting his diploma, accepting his future as a leader in the military.

"Yes, of course. My family is very proud of my brother," she glanced at Masao before she finished, shy to speak the words her heart was singing. "And I am proud of you."

Masao liked this. It was quiet as they strolled.

"When I am called to duty I will go proudly. And I will come back for you, Miyoko."

❖   ❖   ❖

The drab courtyard at Masao's school had been transformed into a spectacular graduation arena. The Rising Sun flag took center stage along with another flag laden with *kanji* that espoused loyalty to the emperor. Paper lanterns in vivid colors hung from string all across the yard. The front of the courtyard was reserved for the most prestigious men of the village, the schoolmaster, the village councilmen, including Masao's grandfather, and other statesmen. These men were adorned with sashes that crossed the front of their chest and indicated the level of importance they held. On both sides of the courtyard, Taiko drummers waited for the celebration to begin. In the center of the yard, rows of chairs accommodated the young men, future militants, dressed in their officer wear. Behind them the families gathered to watch the glory unfold.

Masao sat, his hands folded in his lap. He adjusted his glasses when the schoolmaster began his speech about the honor and loyalty that had been instilled into the minds of these young men and about how proud the emperor would be. Masao, only halfway listening, glanced at Kunio who was all ears. Without straining his head too much, Masao looked back to find Miyoko. There she was, looking at him. He smiled, and she smiled back. After the schoolmaster finished his exhaustive speech, he stepped to the table that held all the diplomas. As he called each boy to the front, there was no applause or cheering. This was a serious affair.

Masao's name was called. He accepted his diploma and bowed to the schoolmaster, and then smiled his wonderful big smile. This made his mom happy and it made Miyoko smile too. A seventeen-year-old Masao had accomplished a great feat — he had learned a second language, a second culture, and was trained as a warrior for the Japanese military. He felt like a man. Now all he had to do was turn twenty so he could put into action all he had learned.

The summer after graduation Masao worked in his grandfather's orchard alongside his father. One afternoon when the sun and heat wouldn't let up, Masao and his father sat under a tree to cool off. They heard someone approach and thought it might be little Jiro. But it was a man that Masao didn't recognize. His father knew this man, though, and his face contorted as if this was some sort of uninvited salesman. Osamu Fujita, a stocky man in his thirties, approached Yasoshichi. Masao noticed a scowl develop on his father's face. This didn't slow Fujita down in the least. He was no stranger to unwelcoming looks on parents' faces. He was there to serve the emperor and took great pride in that effort.

"Abe-san." Osamu greeted Yasoshichi with a bow. Yasoshichi stood up and nodded — he motioned for Masao to stand up as well. Osamu dabbed his sweaty forehead with his handkerchief. "You must be proud of your son," Osamu continued, taking out a small notepad and pencil.

"Yes, very proud," Yasoshichi nodded. Masao had no idea what was happening.

"Tell me, what are your plans this summer, Masao-chan?"

"His plans are to work in the orchard," Yasoshichi answered for Masao. "He is but seventeen, Fujita-san."

"Yes, I am aware," Osamu snapped back, "and this fall, what are your plans this fall?"

Masao shrugged, "I will help my father in the orchard, as he said."

Osamu recorded this in his notebook. Masao looked at his father who was staring daggers at this man.

"Are you planning travel of any kind?"

"No, no travel," Yasoshichi assured him.

Osamu was skeptical. "And his passport. Where is it located? I would like to take a look at it," Osamu wasn't going to back down from his interrogation.

"It is packed away, Fujita-san, it will take some time to locate. We can have it for you on your next visit," Yasoshichi stated.

Masao was surprised to hear his father bend the truth like this. His passports, both his Japanese passport and his American passport, were tucked away in one of his mother's hatboxes, along with all the other family passports.

"Hmm," Osamu said with suspicion. "I will need you to report any travel directly to me," he ordered as he looked directly at Masao.

"Yes," Masao replied as he bowed, feeling his father's overwhelming urge to whack Masao for being so cooperative.

"I will be back at the end of harvest. Have that passport ready for me to examine. Good-bye for now." Osamu tucked his little notebook away and dabbed his forehead again.

When Osamu was safely out of hearing range Masao looked at his father. "Who was that?"

"Osamu is the military affairs clerk for Senoue," his father said in a dejected tone. "He is here to keep tabs on you for the next two years."

The Japanese military had placed over ten thousand military affairs clerks in villages throughout Japan. These men, like Osamu Fujita, were wholly in charge of keeping track of the young men in the village, their whereabouts if they had moved, and their ages. Twenty was the age of conscription. Osamu Fujita certainly had Masao on his list of future soldiers who were primed for service in the military. Masao's grandfather, Mataemon, had been the village councilman for a number of years and this brought even more attention to Masao's name. Not only that, but since Masao had just graduated from officer training, Osamu was not about to let him out of his sight. He would continue to check on Masao, his conduct, his appearance, his mental state of mind, his whereabouts, and most importantly, his intentions to maintain loyalty to the emperor. With every visit, Masao would become more enthusiastic and Yasoshichi would become more agitated. But the visits continued, season after season.

In November 1935, after Masao had turned nineteen, his younger sister, fifteen-year-old Yuriko developed acute appendicitis. It came on suddenly. The village doctor provided only minimal relief, but the prognosis was grim and, sadly, Yuriko died within weeks. The grief of losing little Yuriko permeated the home, and it was during this time that Osamu made another one of his routine visits. The family had just gathered to eat when they heard the knock at the door. Yasoshichi, who had aged years in the span of a few months, opened the door.

"Fujita-san, please, we are mourning the loss of our second daughter. Leave us in peace," Yasoshichi asked somberly.

"Of course, Abe-san. I only come to express my condolences," Osamu said as he bowed. The door was opened enough for Osamu to see inside and take note that Masao was still in Senoue. This didn't get by Yasoshichi who felt like pushing Osamu out of the house and grinding him into the dirt. But Yasoshichi was a smart man and knew that he had to keep this military affairs clerk happy and confident in his findings.

"Thank you." He called to Masao, "Masao, please come." Masao went to the door and greeted Fujita-san with a bow.

"You are nineteen, now, yes?"

"Yes," Masao said proudly.

"No travel plans?"

"No, of course not," Masao answered confidently. Yasoshichi looked on.

"Very well. Again, my condolences, Abe-san," Osamu bowed. Yasoshichi nodded and closed the door. He glanced at Tomie who looked at her husband helplessly. She couldn't bear to lose another child. They had only one more year before the military would claim her oldest child and from what she knew, he would have little chance of coming out of the military alive.

In early 1936, unrest in Japan was growing, and in February of that year, some nationalistic military officers attempted another coup in Tokyo, assassinating several ministers and hoping to start a new regime. While the coup did not succeed entirely, it managed to marginalize the political system, polarize parties, and make it possible for the military to gain control over the political direction of Japan.

This coup attempt, combined with the recent loss of Yuriko, drove Yasoshichi and Tomie to make the decision to send Masao back to San Bernardino. To make matters even more urgent, in Yasoshichi's mind, that persistent Osamu Fujita was visiting more and more often. He knew exactly when Masao would turn twenty, on November 16, 1936. There would be no turning back once the military had a hold of him. Yasoshichi must have known all of this and, acting in his son's best interest and at great risk to himself, he arranged for Masao's return to San Bernardino seven months before his twentieth birthday.

It was a cold winter evening in the Abe home. Masao was putting more wood in the stove in an attempt to heat up the house. Grief still lingered from the sudden passing of Yuriko and Masao was attentive to his mother during this time of deep sorrow. The family gathered at the table to eat; Masao closed up the wood stove and joined them. His father cleared his throat and looked at Tomie, who then looked down.

"Masao. The time has come for you to leave Senoue," Yasoshichi stated as he focused on his bowl of udon.

"Not now, father, I cannot join the military until I am twenty." Masao thought his father was confused.

"No military. You go back to States." The table fell quiet. This was shocking to everyone except for Yasoshichi and Tomie.

"No. Father. I have trained as an officer. The military is expecting me to join, as second lieutenant. I must join. Fujita-san is expecting me as well."

"You go. Tomorrow. Arrangements have been made," Yasoshichi responded without skipping a beat. There was no emotion at all. This was an edict.

Anger descended upon Masao, but Japanese culture defined his actions: respect your parents. He defiantly stood up and stormed out. Tomie started to get up to follow him but Yasoshichi gently held onto her arm and shook his head.

"He will be fine, let him be," he gently persuaded her. She succumbed and sat down next to her husband. Tears filled her eyes and with that, her children felt her sadness. "It is best." And in her heart, she knew he was right.

That night, in the pitch black, Masao ran through the dark trails and along dirt roads to Miyoko's house. He carefully placed a letter near her door. The following afternoon, just as the Chichibu Maru departed Yokohama Harbor, Miyoko found the letter. At first, she smiled, excited to hear from her love, Masao. But tears soon followed as she read his words.

Miyoko. Our walks together have filled my heart with joy. But in one moment, my father has changed my life forever; he has torn me from the country I love and the girl I adore.

And while she read his words, Masao was at the rail of the ship, anguishing as he watched Japan, and his Miyoko, disappear.

By the time you read this I will be on my way to America. Your military officer, his destiny unclear. I will return to Japan someday, I feel it. I can't ask for you to wait for me. But I hope you will. Fondly, Your Masao

Masao's intuition about returning to Japan one day would come to fruition; it just wouldn't occur the way he envisioned.

❖   ❖   ❖

It was the night of their granddaughter, Taryn's, wedding. They were a stunning couple: Masao in a tux, Doris in a shimmery pink dress. It was an exquisite wedding from beginning to end. Doris was having the time of her life. She loved having her entire family around. She even danced with Masao.

I watched them in each other's arms. *There must be a story there too*, I thought. I wondered if she would ever share it with me. She would not. I would discover her story almost entirely through Masao. Had I met Doris at an earlier point in her life, she probably would have bubbled with information about herself. But by the time I came into the picture, she was nearing the end and was uncomfortable most of the time.

On the ride back to the retirement home their spirits were high and jubilant after such an affair.

"Sandie." Mas looked back at me.

"Yeah?" I wondered if he needed something. It seemed like an odd time for one of his stories, and I wasn't prepared with my tape recorder.

"Do you know the movie, *Gone With The Wind*?"

"I do." *Where is* this *going*, I thought.

"Heh. When that movie came out, I wanted to go see it." He paused after this as he often did when telling a story. I waited with great anticipation and glanced at Doris who was listening with a smile.

"I wanted to take a girl. Hana." He chuckled again as he said "Hana". *This is going to be good*, I thought. I was smiling already.

San Bernardino, 1939

Now back in the United States, Masao tried to acclimate to life in California. He had to re-learn English and become re-acquainted to the more relaxed Western ways. His Uncle Tatsuo, with whom he lived, had since married Yukie, also Issei. But Masao wasn't settled. He longed to return to Japan and made it known to his Uncle Tatsuo who became like a second father to Masao.

While Masao had been in Japan, Tatsuo had established himself as a pillar in the Japanese community. He had become the president of the local Japanese Association and had developed a strong customer base for the little grocery store. Many of his customers were Mexican, and Tatsuo had even learned some Spanish so he could better relate to them. The nickname his Latino customers gave Tatsuo and Masao was "Chappo" and Masao soon developed a fondness for the Latino customers just as Tatsuo had.

Tatsuo also had a soft heart for those who struggled and would help out the American Indian locals who would occasionally come around for a serving of wine. Even though it was forbidden to sell cigarettes, wine, or alcohol to persons of Indian descent, Tatsuo always took the time to care for these individuals. Other American Indians who were down on their luck came to know Tatsuo as someone who would never turn them away. One day a local American Indian came into the store in need of groceries. Without any money, the woman had with her a hand-woven basket and asked if she could possibly trade the basket for supplies. It wasn't long before Tatsuo had quite the collection of intricately woven and beautifully designed American Indian baskets. At one point, he realized that one of the baskets he had been given was, in fact, a family heirloom. Being the good man he was, he promptly returned it to the family.

Tatsuo was the first, and perhaps the only, merchant to extend credit to local customers. His customers appreciated this about him and always paid him back. On the day they came in to settle their bill, Tatsuo made sure they had a bag of produce and staples, free of charge. He was known throughout the San Bernardino Valley as a good and caring soul and treated others with respect and kindness.

There were things in San Bernardino that Masao enjoyed. Whenever there were community gatherings they were light-hearted and fun, a stark difference from the militant Japan he had been torn away from. Annual picnics occurred every summer along the Santa Ana River. Folks would come together to enjoy Japanese food, play games, have races, and socialize.

The summer months in San Bernardino were plagued with oppressive heat. To cope with it, Masao would take a break from the grocery store around mid-afternoon. He took ten cents and went to the theater that was air-conditioned. Occasionally Masao would go to the movies with Jimmy Shimizu, a friend whose father owned the barber shop down the street. Masao thought of Jimmy as a really sharp guy because he attended the San Bernardino Valley College and was majoring in chemistry. While Masao idolized others because of their ability to master college-level courses and pursue post-secondary studies, he was viewed as a *Kibei.*

Kibei was a term used to describe people like Masao, born in the United States and therefore Nisei, educated in Japan, and then returned to the United States. While it would seem that Kibei would imply great skill and wisdom, as this small group of Japanese-Americans were not only bilingual, but also understood and empathized with two vastly different cultures, the term Kibei was more often used in a derogatory sense. While Masao should have been honored for his survival and accomplishments in Japan, he was actually looked down upon. He was literally caught between two worlds. The more he encountered dismissive attitudes from both Caucasian and Japanese people in America, the more he wanted to return to Japan.

In San Bernardino, life was complicated for the Japanese population. The Nisei children who had been born of Issei parents, were now well into their twenties or thirties and had western ways baked into their personalities. While they appreciated Japanese traditions, they lived in the west. Their parents would often look on, helplessly, watching their Japanese blood become diluted. But once in a great while, Japanese traditions would take hold and be enforced by the elders. This was the case with Masao asking the girl named Hana out on a date.

Hana's father owned a restaurant a block down Third Street from Star Cash Grocery. Masao would routinely see Hana in town. One day when Masao and Tatsuo were stocking a delivery of fresh vegetables, Hana walked by the store with some other girls. Masao stopped what he was doing and watched them pass by, instinctively waving, which then prompted Hana to smile and wave back. Tatsuo took note.

"You like her, no?" Tatsuo asked when the girls were safely out of sight.

"Heh! Well, she's cute," Masao was slightly embarrassed. His English was back, only a slight accent remained.

"You should take her out."

"Nah." Masao quickly shut the idea down.

"No, really. Take her to that new movie that's out. *Gone With The Wind.*"

Masao hadn't really thought about a girl in a serious sense since Miyoko back in Japan. The letters with Miyoko had stopped within a year of his return home. The last he heard from his friends in Senoue, Kunio had turned radical and both Kunio and Akira had been conscripted and were serving in China. Miyoko was working in a factory somewhere making military uniforms, and life in Japan was generally hard.

Masao looked at his uncle, who had never steered him wrong, and pondered the notion of taking this cute girl out on a date.

"Heh, maybe I will."

❖   ❖   ❖

Masao was recollecting the details about his big date with Hana. Doris, it seemed, had not heard this particular story.

"So I asked her father, Mr. Kobayashi, he, ah, owned a restaurant, a-no? In Japantown. Anyway, I asked Mr. Kobayashi, 'Say, I'd like to take your daughter, Hana, to see the movie.' And he said, 'Okay, you can take.' Heh heh." Masao was recalling the details so the story would be complete. His voice fluctuated and changed to represent himself as a young man and Mr. Kobayashi as an authoritative father.

"So, I got myself prepared for the *date*. I was excited, boy. Hana was cute," he chuckled more. "When I went to pick her up, her mother answered the door. She told me, 'You can't take Hana. I have three daughters. You will take first daughter, Kay.'"

With this punch line, Masao chuckled loudly. Doris, Alan, and I joined him.

"I didn't want to take Kay, a-no? But, I had to." He was still chuckling at his younger self.

"That's Japanese tradition," Doris explained to me while she giggled along with her husband.

Japanese culture took over; Hana's mother dictated which daughter would be courted. The two cultures inside Masao must have clashed. The Japanese part of Masao, succumbed, and said, "Okay, I'll take Kay out," and he dutifully took out the first daughter. But the American part of him must have been saying, *Eh? What's this now?*

"That was the last time I approached Mr. Kobayashi about dating Hana." Masao again chuckled, then looked out the window as he remembered this funny anecdote. I watched him; his ninety-year-old face was about the kindest I had come to know. I smiled inside, happy that he was sharing these little stories about his life.

"It's hard to believe," his voice had changed. It was more serious and reflective. "At the theater in those days, there was a rope. Right in the hallway. On one side, the left side, I think, it's only for white people. Only white people go on that side. And the other side, the right side, is for oriental people and colored people. We had to go on the right side. If you try to go to the other side, the left side, they chase you out and say, you know, 'go to the other side'." He shook his head slightly.

Masao, still back there, in San Bernardino with a date he didn't like in a racially segregated, cordoned-off line at the theater, made that sound with his mouth, the sound you make when you're thinking, *What a shame* or *What the hell*, but don't want to say the words. He glanced out the window at the lake as we crossed the floating bridge.

This generation of his - they are the salt of the Earth, I thought. *They know that it was on their backs that current generations have liberties. And they seem to be okay with that, happy to have been the pawns in the evolution of humans so that their children and their children's children won't have to be treated in such a humiliating manner.*

I felt uncomfortable with the notion of segregation. It must have shown on my face because Masao glanced at me and seemed to understand what I was thinking.

"Well, it was the times. Nothing you can do about it," he said in a tender voice.

CHAPTER FOUR

THE PASSING

"HER APPOINTMENT IS AT TWO," ALAN WAS TELLING ME. IT WAS ONE OF the many appointments Doris had endured with her dentist to adjust her dentures that never seemed to fit right. "Why don't you just go to their place at three thirty and wait with my dad."

"He's not going with you?"

"It's too hard for me. I can't manage both of them." His voice sounded almost shrill; I could tell he was really stressed.

"Okay, okay," I replied trying to get him to calm down, "I'll hang out with your dad."

"Take your tape recorder," Alan insisted.

"He doesn't want to talk, lately, Alan," I reminded him. Masao could barely function due to the worry he had for Doris. He was like a lost man most of the time. Doris was shriveling down to nothing because eating had become such a chore. It would take her ten minutes to chew a grain of rice. Masao could see her fading away, and it distressed him to no end. It was painful to watch Doris struggle and agonizing to watch Masao witness the deterioration.

"Well, he might, you never know. Take it just in case."

❖ ❖ ❖

I had arrived a little early. "Mas?" I called out as I went in. He was sitting in his recliner with the TV blaring and didn't hear me.

"Hi, Mas," I said again. He jumped, which made me jump.

"Oh! Heh! I didn't hear you!" He was embarrassed. His hearing was becoming compromised, but he didn't want to admit it. "I guess I had the TV on too loud." He adjusted the volume.

I sat down on the couch adjacent to his recliner and looked over the snacks he had on the end table between the couch and his chair. He often had goodies that I adored; Nutter Butter cookies, peanuts, chestnuts, chocolate.

"Help yourself," he encouraged me. This was my favorite time, when it was just me and Masao and his snacks. I tend to put weight on by just looking at a Nutter Butter cookie and can never stop at just one for some reason. But Masao didn't care about such things; he didn't care if I weighed a hundred and twenty pounds or four hundred and twenty. He was beginning to like my company, and I loved his. So I helped myself to a Nutter Butter and glanced at the TV.

"My wife is at the dentist, a-no?"

I nodded while I savored the cookie.

"I don't know why that dentist took out all of her teeth. She can't eat any more." His voice was weak and tainted with fear.

"I don't know either," I empathized with him.

"She's just skin and bones, a-no? She must be down to about seventy-five pounds. She needs to eat."

I nodded in agreement, suddenly acutely aware that my teeth worked perfectly fine on the Nutter Butter and in addition, I had many excess pounds that I could donate to Doris.

"Where should we go for dinner? What do you think she could eat tonight?" I asked as my mind ran through the series of chores that went along with taking Doris out to dinner lately. She was back in the wheel chair and was so weak that she needed help with literally every movement, including her trips to the restroom. Alan was a powerhouse with all of it. Our dinners would last for at least two hours because it would take her that long to finish. Many times, Alan and I opted to just pick up dinner and eat with them at their place. You'd think this would shorten the evening, but it didn't because Alan always wanted to stay until he was sure his mother had eaten enough. His dedication to his parents was remarkable.

"Gee, I don't know. We have to wait for her." Masao thought about this. He seemed helpless somehow. I thought about my tape recorder and wondered if a trip to the past might help him get his mind off his worries.

"Hey, Mas?"

He looked over at me.

"Can I ask you something about when you were drafted?"

He nodded. I would come to find that Masao was up for talking about the war and the military just about any time. It was a subject he loved and about which he was very proud.

"So, when we last talked you were still working in the store on Third Street."

"Third Street, that's right. Up until the summer of forty-one, I worked in that store."

His mind started churning and I was glad to be going back to San Bernardino.

Summer 1941, San Bernardino

Masao, now twenty-four, stocked shelves in the grocery store. He had all but succumbed to a life as a would-be grocery store owner. He had watched other Nisei peers go on to college and earn degrees that would lead them to important professions. But with the two languages mixed up in Masao's head, college was too hard. His slight accent had only earned him condescension from his peers. While other Issei had sent their children, mostly their boys, back to Japan for their education, it wasn't that common, and Masao knew of no one else in the area who had lived in Japan as a youngster. Here he was, a Kibei, unique in a culture that left him out.

He wondered often if he would ever belong.

His uncle returned to the store with the mail in hand. "Masao. A letter for you." There was some excitement mixed with stress in Tatsuo's voice. Masao thought it might be word from Japan. Maybe his father had finally decided to let him return, although he was now used to San Bernardino and wasn't sure he wanted to start all over again back in Japan. What hateful word would they have back there to describe him now, being bounced back and forth across the Pacific? Masao took the brown envelope that Tatsuo carefully handed to him and looked at the outside.

"From U.S. Army." Masao was surprised, he looked at Tatsuo.

"Open it!"

Masao slowly opened it and glanced inside. He smiled. "I've been drafted." He looked at Tatsuo, who was also smiling.

"You finally get be a soldier!" Tatsuo assured Masao as he patted him on the back. Masao smiled while he mulled this over. He had wanted forever to be a soldier, but all of his visions had been with the Japanese military, wielding swords and bayonets. He had never once given thought to serving in the U.S. military with a bunch of Caucasian guys.

"Well, at least we're not at war," Masao said.

"Not yet, but soon. With Germany or Italy." Tatsuo patted Masao again, and this time Masao nodded.

It was September 10, 1941, when Masao caught the train that would take him to the induction center. On the train platform, Masao said his good-byes to the many residents and shop owners from Little Japan who showed up to send him off. He shook hands with each one, thanking them for their good wishes. They were all very proud of their Masao Abe. He saved his last good-bye for his precious Uncle Tatsuo. Tatsuo shook his hand and looked directly in his eyes.

"You are American. You must fight like an American and honor this great country."

"Of course, uncle," He didn't want to say good-bye to this wonderful man who had been such a great father figure so he did what he often did, he ended on a high note. "At least I'll get to see Europe, a-no?" Tatsuo smiled and nodded. Masao picked up his bag and boarded the train. He sat next to the window so he could see all his friends and family. The train slowly started to move.

"Banzai! Banzai!!" The townsfolk yelled as the train pulled out. *Banzai* – ten thousand years, a traditional Japanese battle call used to wish warriors luck as in "May you live ten thousand years." Masao waved to his family and friends who were dressed in their best attire.

Dressed in a suit and tie, he sat on the bench and watched the San Bernardino train station until it was no longer in sight. He felt a sadness that he attributed to leaving this world behind. He tried to shake it off with thoughts about the adventures that awaited him but the sadness wouldn't leave. Somehow he knew things would be different when he returned.

As it turned out, this would be the last time he would see all of his friends in such fine spirits. This would be the last time he would see Little Japan in its current state. The next time he would see San Bernardino, Little Japan wouldn't exist.

❖   ❖   ❖

I was on my fourth Nutter Butter when Masao came back to the present.

"I can still see them, a-no? So many people came to bid me farewell that day. That was really something." His voice was warm; clearly he had fond memories of his American hometown.

"That must have been something," I smiled. I was about to ask him about boot camp when the door swung open, and Alan maneuvered Doris in her wheel chair through. Alan looked utterly exhausted from the afternoon at the dentist.

"She needs to go to the bathroom," he abruptly announced as he wheeled her down the hall. I could hear them in the bathroom, wrestling about, trying to get her on the toilet. Masao hobbled on his cane down the hall to look on. I got up and went over to Masao's wall of pictures. I had remembered seeing something that I wanted to check out. I perused each image until I saw it. There he was, a twenty-four-year old Masao waving from a train window. A young man full of ideals, full of energy, ready for training that would lead him to battle. He was proud.

I looked down the hall and saw the man he had become. He supported himself on his cane and watched his wife struggle to use the toilet, helpless to do anything. He could hardly bear to see the love of his life in such a state. The worry filled his face. In that flash of an instant I felt only sorrow; sad for the young man leaving his life behind, heading for distress and uncertainty in the years ahead, and sad for the elder Masao who was watching his wife of sixty-three years wither away.

For each Masao, his near future was inevitably heartbreaking.

❖   ❖   ❖

It was a shock, but not a surprise, to receive Alan's text message. "Mom died this morning." She had died in her sleep. Masao discovered her in the morning when he woke. Fortunately, she slept in her own bed, and Masao had not been next to her at the moment of her passing. My immediate concern was for Masao. I thought about Alan too, but knew that he would be consumed by supporting his father and his grief would have to take a back seat. Masao, though, I wasn't confident at all that Masao would make it through this.

"How's he holding up?" I asked when Alan finally called me in the afternoon.

"Not too good." His voice sounded drained. He had gone home for a bit of relief. "I'm going to pick up some Japanese food and take it back a little bit later."

"Are you staying with him tonight?"

"I haven't thought about it. Do you think I should?"

Someone needed to be with Masao that night. The grief would be too heavy. "He can't be alone tonight, Alan. He just can't."

"You're probably right." He knew I was right. I was beginning to understand Masao at a level that his own sons did not. I wasn't sure when or how it happened, but it had. "Dad said something about moving back to the facility on Mercer Island. I want him here, though. It's closer to me."

"Move him back, Alan. He wants to be in a space where memories were good. It's where he and your mom were living when things were better. That's why he wants to move there."

Alan spent that night with his dad, and the next night as well. He described the feeling of their apartment as being weighted down with immense sadness, explaining that he and his dad were taking turns sobbing. Masao appreciated having Alan there by his side during this trying time. By the third day, arrangements had been made to move Masao back to the

Mercer Island facility. The third day was also the day we all gathered to say good-bye to Doris at the funeral home.

There, the family, Masao at the helm, was escorted to a room where Doris was waiting, dressed in the pink dress that she had worn at her granddaughter's wedding. I stood at the back of the room while family members mourned. I could hear the sobs of Doris's children and grandchildren, but I could not hear the sobs of her husband. I watched him as he made his way to her casket where he brought his handkerchief to his eyes every few seconds. I knew he was feeling grief from the deepest part of his soul and that was what finally brought me to tears. I watched him, this man I was learning history from, this man who had endured great losses from the time he was eight and who had braved it all, and I worried that this deep grief might be too much for him. It might be too much.

After several moments, Masao, with his head lowered, turned and made his way out of the room. Alan was right next to him. The rest of the family took more time with Doris, but I left the room after Masao and Alan and looked for them in the hallway. They were already outside and were sitting, in the February cold, on a stone bench. I don't think either of them could feel the bitter weather. They couldn't feel anything but sadness.

From the day that Doris's ashes were ready, Masao wore three things on a gold chain: his Bronze Star Medal, her wedding ring, and a fragment of bone selected from her ashes.

He wore these items, and these items only, around his neck for the rest of his life.

❖   ❖   ❖

The weeks following Doris's death were incredibly difficult. Alan and I took Masao out, often times ending up at the casino. It was the only place where Masao could get any relief from his sorrow. We discovered that he wouldn't go downstairs in the retirement home to eat, relying completely on leftovers. Both Alan and I were deeply concerned about him, afraid he might have a secret plan to starve himself to death. In reality, he was just depressed. He missed his wife.

In April after Alan and Masao returned from Hawai'i where they had laid Doris to rest, Alan and I had a conversation about his dad.

"I don't know how to help him," Alan was saying. He was absolutely exasperated and exhausted from trying to keep watch over his dad, petrified that if he didn't, his father would perish.

"You know," I started out gently, "your dad is pretty social. He needs to be around people."

"I know that," Alan snapped back, "but I can't spend every day with him." He was tired so I ignored his pissy-ness. Alan had absorbed the brunt of looking out for his father. His brothers, both of whom had children and even grandchildren, didn't have the luxury of spending as much time with Masao. Alan was the most dedicated son I had ever known.

"I'm just saying, we should all coordinate and have a little routine with your dad."

"You'll never get my brothers to have a routine with dad," Alan stated adamantly.

"Well. Can we try?" I was always the optimist, something that really irritated the pessimistic Alan.

"How?" he spat back at me.

"Well, let's email everyone with our idea and see what happens."

With begrudging delight, Alan reported that the plan worked and a weekly routine was born. We split up days so Masao would be out of his apartment five or six days a week. I volunteered for two days: Tuesdays and Saturdays.

Unfortunately, my interviews with Masao had stopped completely. The only thing that relieved his hurting heart was gambling and I was happy to take him to the casino, content knowing that I could help him in some small way. I didn't pressure Masao into talking about his past. When it was time to resume our conversations I would be ready with my tape recorder, always tucked away in my purse—just in case.

PART II

THE FINAL JOURNEY

NOVEMBER 4, 2013

Now at the gate at the airport in Seattle, we sat waiting, making idle conversation with other family members and keeping Masao's urn packaged neatly in Alan's backpack. Taking Masao to his final resting placed was trying to say the least. Alan and I were relying on each other in ways we hadn't before. Alan had taken the time to make the entire voyage special, right down to flying first class, which is something we don't often do. Finally the announcement was made to load the plane. Because we were first on, we had time to figure out how to best arrange his father's urn. It wouldn't fit under the seat, the flag was too tall. Alan needed some relief so I took charge.

"I've got this," I said as I picked up his backpack and went to the front of our section. A flight attendant, used to taking orders from first-class passengers, was all ears as I approached her.

"Say, these are the ashes of a soldier. We're wondering if we can have them in a closet or something. They won't fit under the seat."

"Oh, of course." She went to the closet and opened it, but something didn't sit right with her about the closet idea. She frowned and looked at her co-worker who jumped right in.

"Let's see if it will fit in this cupboard up here." She opened a cupboard in the galley area. It was empty. I lifted the backpack up but the protruding flag was too tall to fit. I brought it back down to adjust. Meanwhile, passengers were backing up waiting to get through.

"I'm sorry." I started to get flustered.

"You take your time." The passenger at the front of the line said in a sensitive, genuine voice.

I nodded, removing the flag and carefully arranging the urn in the pack next to it.

"I think that will work."

The flight attendant smiled. "That will be a private cupboard for the duration," she said as she closed it securely.

I nodded, my eyes starting to sting again. She patted my shoulder. The passengers who had been waiting patiently for me smiled empathetically. I waved thank you to them and made my way back to my seat just as the tears broke free.

❖　❖　❖

The beautiful turquoise waters that surrounded Oahu had always thrilled me, but when it occurred to me that this would be the first time in years we'd be landing in Hawai'i without Masao beside us, the usual delight of seeing Honolulu below us had a different feeling. Once we touched down, even the warm Hawaiian air with that sweet smell to it didn't break me out of my funk. It all seemed so surreal, being surrounded by excited tourists while we waited for the shuttle. Somehow the elation of others only intensified the sorrow.

On the shuttle the sadness swelled. Part of the fun of traveling to Hawai'i with Masao had been watching his eyes light up when he saw different landmarks that sparked memories.

"See that place?" he would ask me, pointing to a dilapidated building sitting in a marina. I would nod, knowing the story he was about to tell because he had told me the same one a dozen times before.

"Doris and I used to meet there for lunch every Wednesday." Then he would look at me for my reaction.

"Wow! Every week?" I would ask sincerely.

"Every week. Doris loved oysters, and they had the best oysters. So every Wednesday, I would come from work, and she would meet me there." And then he would smile and be lost in the memory with his beloved Doris.

Passing the same building now, it just hurt. I strained my neck a little bit so the other passengers on the shuttle couldn't see my tears. Alan felt it, though: the soft jolts of my body, my hands going up to my cheeks to wipe my eyes. He felt it all and put his hand on my leg to comfort me. I was a little pissed at myself for getting all worked up, solely because I had wanted to stay strong for Alan. But our hearts seemed to have an agreement; one heart would hurt, the other would comfort. And that was how we operated. It worked for us.

Our condo had a breathtaking view of Waikiki Beach. Alan arranged Masao's urn and flag in a nice little shrine on the desk by the lanai.

"He would want the view," he told me as he placed Masao's medals around the urn. I nodded and helped him clear everything else off the desk. We sat on the lanai, watched tourists avoid all the homeless people loitering on the sidewalks, held hands, and soaked up the afternoon sun. That was a Monday. The ceremony was in two days.

CHAPTER FIVE

U.S. UNDER ATTACK

WE WERE ALL WORRIED SICK ABOUT MASAO. OUR STRATEGY HAD BEEN working, though, and we managed to get him out of his apartment six nights a week. Now that it was summer break and I had days free, I could pitch in a little bit more, and I was happy to do that, given how my enthusiasm for gambling had grown. I still waited patiently for Masao to resume his stories. The last time we talked, he had been drafted and was heading for boot camp. I longed to know more about his experiences in the military, but resigned myself to the fact that he would have to let me know when he was ready.

"Masao?" I called out as I went in. No answer. The TV was on, but he was not in his recliner, and I immediately got nervous.

"Masao?" I called, a little louder this time.

"Hey! I'm in bathroom!" I noticed the door to the bathroom was wide open. I maneuvered my way to the couch and sat so I couldn't see.

"Okay! Uh, take your time." After a few minutes I heard the flush and out he came.

"Hey, Sandie."

"Hi, Mas, how's it going today?"

"Oh, same old, same old," he plopped down in his recliner with a sigh and clicked the TV off. I often got the feeling he was just waiting to join Doris and that was the feeling today.

"Are you okay?" We both knew what this meant. I was asking how his heart was.

"I had a dream about my wife last night." He looked at me, and I nodded with anticipation, letting him know I wanted to hear more. He was happy to have someone who wanted to listen. "I think she's waiting for me, a-no?" he continued.

I nodded. "Of course she's waiting for you. She misses you."

He was still looking at me in a way that was asking for my participation in his belief that he was somehow communicating with Doris. And, of course, I did believe him. "She misses me, I think," he pondered. I smiled and nodded. His words lingered in the room. He was off in another world now, thinking about happier times with his Doris. It was quiet except for the ticking clock on the wall. We both sat for a few minutes in the silence; I wasn't about to ruin his connection to his wife.

Finally he looked at me. "Well. Shall we go?"

"Sure! Where to today?"

"We go casino," he replied, already walking somewhat unsteadily to the closet to get his jacket. I should have known that would be his answer. The casino continued to be the best way for him to get relief. I no longer tried to talk him out of it.

We were on our way up the mountain when I thought, *There's no harm in asking him about the army.*

"Hey, Mas? Remember when you told me about leaving for boot camp?" He nodded, it looked like a go. "What was that like for you?"

"Heh! Well, it was hard work, a-no?" He looked out the window, calling his history forth.

September 1941, Induction

A dapper twenty-four-year-old Masao sat on the Southern Pacific locomotive. The train would take him from the sweltering heat of San Bernardino to the cooler climate of the California coast. He sat with the window open and enjoyed the three-hour journey that included several stops, picking up other draftees from small towns along the way. As the train approached the seaside, Masao recognized landmarks from the times he had been there before. He reminisced about arriving in San Pedro from Japan and how he hated being back in the States. All of that was behind him now. He needed to let go of Japan. He was moving farther away from that life from this point forward, and he knew it.

The train slowed and rolled along the piers in San Pedro. For a moment, Masao thought he spotted the *Tatuta Maru*, the last ship that had transported him from Japan across the Pacific. His thoughts drifted as he watched the busy port go by, spotting a little fishing village that seemed to be filled with Japanese residents. He'd heard about a Japanese place along the coast, a small town populated almost exclusively with fisherman from an even smaller village in Japan. *This must be it*, he contemplated.

He let that thought drift by and wondered what life in Japan was like now. He wondered about how his life would have been different had he remained in Japan. He assumed he would still be courting Miyoko, maybe even be married to her by now. He would be a proud officer, probably stationed in China, writing to his beloved Miyoko from a great distance, promising her his safe return.

The recruit next to him nudged him and pointed out the window, bringing Masao back to 1941. He looked ahead and spotted what his fellow passenger had noticed, a sign for Fort MacArthur.

"There's no turning back now," the other recruit was saying.

"I guess not," Masao smiled. The draftees on the train had kept to themselves, each of them nervous for what was to come.

Fort MacArthur was like a well-oiled machine. Recruits were unloaded from the train and funneled into different buildings for the series of tasks: uniform issue, scheduling of the aptitude tests, receiving the appointed time for the medical and physical examination. Masao got sucked along in the crowd doing his best to follow orders.

On September 11, 1941, Masao took his oath of enlistment and was sworn in. His aptitude test and interview with a career counselor resulted in a path of army medic. He had not considered this before, being a medic, but wasn't opposed to the idea. This meant that he would be sent to a different facility for training.

It wasn't but a few days before Masao was on his way to Camp Grant, located on the outskirts of Rockford, Illinois, about seventy miles west of

Chicago. In its day Camp Grant sprawled over eighteen thousand acres and was boot camp for soldiers during both World War I and World War II.

The train ride had been days long. A young and spry Masao, dressed in his military uniform, looked out the window of the train as it passed through farm land. One of only a few Asians on the train, he sat with a guy named Bob Fukui. In an attempt to be funny, Bob nicknamed Masao "Kibei Abe." Masao hated this and made a goal to avoid Bob at all cost.

Masao enjoyed the breeze through the open window. The air was a lot cooler than in San Bernardino and not quite as dry. He speculated what this new world of the U.S. military would be like. He hoped he would get the chance to experience real combat if the U.S. did engage with Germany as his uncle had predicted.

The train slowed as they passed an air strip, then he saw a white sign ahead: Recruit Reception Center. Masao would learn that the town of Rockford was about four miles north of the camp. He hoped there might be a Little Japan or a Chinatown. He was already craving rice, having gone five days without it now.

Boot camp lasted for weeks. Masao felt as if he was the only Japanese-American on base. During field endurance training, he was the only Asian in a sea of white privates. As much as he couldn't stand Bob, he would sometimes look for him for a tiny bit of camaraderie.

He eventually met a few Japanese, among other Asians, and so he was able to build a group to call his own. One of their favorite things to do on one-day passes was to head to Rockford to search out anything resembling rice. They had to strike out many times before they found a small Chinese restaurant. Masao wasn't terribly fond of Chinese food, but in the absence of Japanese food for weeks, Chinese seemed like heaven.

His new-found buddies, Rokuro and Shinji, were happy-go-lucky, just like Masao. They would sometimes include Bob, who became more mindful about negative Kibei talk, since both Masao and Shinji were Kibei. Rokuro, one of the few Nisei who lived inland, didn't relate to the concept of Kibei and was happy to ignore the whole thing. They eventually ventured all the way to Chicago when they were awarded weekend passes. Travel to Chicago would become their motivation to do well during the week so they could earn weekend passes. Together, the four endured boot camp and medic training. Although they were aware that war could erupt at any moment and they could be shipped out to Europe, for now things were peaceful.

November 3, 1941 - Fourth Army Intelligence School

Located on the northernmost point of San Francisco, the Presidio had been built by the Spanish in 1776 specifically to protect the inner harbor. That small fort had grown into a magnificent post for the Spaniards, then Mexicans, and finally for the U.S. In 1941 the Presidio was a highly efficient military base with a sense of purpose. Jeeps were used to transport generals around the facility. Just built in 1937, the Golden Gate Bridge hovered over the many military operations that were in the works on the Presidio.

It was a Monday morning when the first Military Intelligence Service Language School (MISLS) opened under the wing of the Fourth Army which was headquartered on the Presidio. The school was housed in Building 640 on Crissy Field, the airstrip. Building 640 was constructed as a hangar but had been converted into classrooms and barracks for this highly secret operation that had been developed months before and rolled out at the very time Masao was in boot camp some two thousand miles away.

Fifty-eight Nisei soldiers and two Caucasian soldiers were the first to be trained in specialized interpretation and translation of Japanese. The Nisei soldiers had been carefully handpicked from recent draftees in the army as well as from academic institutions through military contacts. However, there was concern from all sides. Military officers wondered if these Japanese soldiers could be trusted, as many of them had strong ties to Japan, and there was worry about Fifth Column activity along the west coast. On the other hand, Japanese-American recruits had heard rumors that this operation was developed to implant spies into the Japanese-American communities, and they wanted no part in that. Eventually, Nisei soldiers would come to realize that the mission of the intelligence school was for something much larger than the west coast, and they became eager to prove their loyalty.

Once the sixty soldiers were selected, they were on a strict daily schedule and took their training seriously. Most of the Nisei soldiers had limited Japanese, having learned the language in Japanese school in the States. But there were some Nisei who were fluent in Japanese because they had lived in Japan, the Kibei. All of the soldiers worked hard, day and night, to memorize key Japanese kanji and become experts in interpretation and translation.

When the soldiers had free time they were welcomed in San Francisco. Japantown was a short bus ride from the Presidio and the Nisei soldiers naturally gravitated to this part of the city. Residents in San Francisco recognized the U.S. Army uniforms and had the utmost respect for these soldiers, no matter what ethnicity they happened to be. The language school soldiers, though, were sworn to secrecy regarding their training and mission. They themselves assumed that this training was purely precautionary on the part of the U.S. military. Or perhaps, in a worst-case scenario, they would be involved with allies in the Philippines.

Life in California was good — good for San Franciscans and good for these Nisei soldiers.

November 21, 1941 - Wai Momi

Doris Kimie Okada, eighteen, was born and raised in Honolulu. She was third-generation Japanese, or *sansei*. Japanese people had immigrated to Hawai'i many years earlier out of economic necessity. The first arriving Issei Japanese then stayed in Hawai'i when they realized they were welcomed by the local residents.

Fishing and farming on Hawai'i wasn't dissimilar to Japan, and it made the transition easier for those Japanese that chose to settle there. The weather was far more pleasant than the extreme seasons in Japan, which was another lure to making Hawai'i a permanent home. By the 1930s, the Japanese were by far the largest race inhabiting Hawai'i, besides native Hawaiians. Numerous Japanese schools were prevalent, along with clubs, movie theaters, and community centers dedicated to Japanese traditions.

In 1941 Hawai'i was considered a U.S. territory but would not become a state until 1959. A former kingdom, Hawai'i had been quietly, and without any bloodshed, overthrown by the U.S. in 1893. The reigning monarch, Queen Lili'uokalani, under protest, gave up her throne to avoid having any of her people compromised through military strife. The U.S. was big and powerful compared to the peaceful country of Hawai'i and the queen knew her monarchy didn't stand a chance against the superpower.

Waikiki, in 1941, was still somewhat undiscovered and considered exotic. The famously pink Royal Hawaiian Hotel was one of two notable hotels on Waikiki beach. They sat alone, surrounded by pristine beaches and lush greenery. The absence of merchants and stores is what drew tourists from the mainland. The closest city was downtown Honolulu, several miles away. Tourists came to surf and sun on the beautiful and untapped wonder of Waikiki, but it was home to Doris.

The oldest of three children, she lived with her parents, both Nisei, in Manoa Valley, a short distance up the hills from Waikiki. Manoa Valley was a different world from Waikiki. It was cooler than the beach resort area and received more rainfall so the foliage was lush, green, and beautiful.

Doris attended McKinley High, located on King Street in Honolulu, less than a mile from the beautiful Ala Moana Beach and a mere eight or so miles from Pearl Harbor. The magnificent Iolani Palace, where the last reigning Queen Lili'uokalani had held prisoner by the United States, was just down the road.

One of the things Doris loved to do was to pick up oysters off the beach. In Hawai'i, there was one place and one place only to do that – Wai Momi, Water of the Pearl, or Pearl Harbor. Hawaiian legend had it that the water in this area was the home to the Shark Goddess, Ka'ahupahau, who was believed to live in sea cave at the entrance to the harbor, protecting the waters against sharks that preyed on man. Whatever the folklore, these waters were known for generating a wealth of pearl-producing oysters and had been popular among locals for generations.

It was the Friday after Thanksgiving and Doris, along with her friend Helen, arrived on the beach, buckets in hand. Doris loved oysters and she loved to cook, so the combination of collecting and preparing oysters was the making of a great day. They waded along in bare feet and rolled up dungarees searching for the delectable oysters that they would make for lunch with other friends. It was the perfect November morning. Even with U.S. battleships in the background, it was a peaceful, Hawaiian day.

December 1, 1941 - San Bernardino

Tatsuo swept the floor of the store. Now that Masao was gone, and Yukie was taking care of their newborn daughter, he was manning the store almost entirely by himself. It was chillier than normal that afternoon, so he went to the storage-area office and found the sweater that he kept in the back. He glanced at the only picture in the store, a picture of himself, his older brother, Yasoshichi, and their father. It had been taken when Tatsuo first arrived in the United States in 1920. He could hardly believe he had been in the States for twenty-one years already. He admired a younger Tatsuo who looked innocent. He chuckled at his youth.

Only the railroad-style wall clock made any sound with its continuous and serene ticking, the polished brass pendulum swaying back and forth behind the glass door of the old wooden case. The hand of the clock struck twelve and the prompt but calming chimes sounded the top of the hour. He wondered where that clock came from. He only remembered that his brother, Yasoshichi, had purchased it to remind himself of the harder railroad times. Tatsuo's thoughts were interrupted when he heard someone enter the store so he put his sweater on and hurried out.

Ben Miller, a disheveled looking American Indian, was trying to remain invisible just on the inside of the establishment. He wasn't supposed to be there, he knew that. Nobody of Indian blood was to be in a store that sold alcohol or cigarettes. In other establishments, signs were posted to that effect. But in Tatsuo's store, things were different. Tatsuo smiled.

"Ben, my old friend, how are you?" Tatsuo held out his hand.

"Okay. And you?" Ben's hand reached out to meet Tatsuo's. He tried to control the shaking as much as he could but Tatsuo noticed it anyway. He gently took Ben's hand in both of his and then motioned to the back of the store.

"Come on. Let's get you fixed up." Tatsuo encouraged Ben to follow. In the storage area, Tatsuo reached for a bottle of whiskey and a tin cup stored there, pouring a shot for Ben who chugged it down in one swallow, closed his eyes and waited for it to kick in. Tatsuo poured another shot and looked at Ben to see if it was helping. It seemed to be. Tatsuo pondered Ben's age; he figured that he was in his early forties although he looked much older. Tatsuo attributed his weathered appearance to the rough life

Ben led. He was a man down on his luck and no matter what he did to elevate himself, society wouldn't have it.

"Thank you kindly." Ben's voice was timid, almost ashamed.

"Don't mention it," Tatsuo assured him. And the two sat quietly. When it was time, Tatsuo made sure Ben had groceries before he left.

"See you again," Tatsuo bid him as he made his way out the back door into the alley. He watched Ben limp away and wondered what came first, the alcohol or the shame placed on American Indians from the dominant society in a land they once themselves had ruled. In that moment, Tatsuo felt fortunate to have made his way in a country where he was considered a foreigner.

Friday, December 5, 1941 - The Presidio

While Masao endured boot camp and the rest of the country prepared for the holidays, the highly secret operation on the Presidio amped up. The Military Intelligence School had been put together by three army officers: Captain Kai E. Rasmussen, Captain Joseph A. Dickey, and the lead officer, Lieutenant Colonel John Weckerling. All of these men had lived in Japan and were as expert as possible with regard to military tactics involving that country. It was these three men who screened all sixty recruits for the language school.

The daily operation of the MISLS was under the direction of John Fujio Aiso, a graduate of Harvard Law, a practicing attorney, and a Private First Class in the Army Reserves. Aiso spoke flawless English and Japanese, was college educated, well-traveled, and was now the chief instructor of a highly classified operation. Lt. Col. Weckerling would occasionally visit the language school but left the administration and operation detail up to Aiso.

On the morning of December 5, 1941, a black sedan pulled up to the curb in front of the newly established Western Defense Command post located up the hill from Building 640. A soldier rushed to open the car door, standing at attention and saluting the emerging general, admiring the three stars on either shoulder of the man. General DeWitt returned the salute and headed into Building 35, followed by an entourage of officers.

DeWitt was aware that a special language school was well into operations on the base but had not yet visited the school. He decided that today was the day he would check on the progress of these Japanese-American soldiers.

Although a short walk, he was driven by Jeep to Building 640 on Crissy Field. As they drove, DeWitt envisioned the necessary construction to house the potential increase in training and deployment of military personnel. They arrived at the small building just along the airstrip. The general got out and gaped at the enormity of the Golden Gate Bridge, just a short distance away. His escorting officer led him into the building and introduced him to Aiso. After garnering the appropriate amount of information, DeWitt was ready to get back to his important job. Before he left, though, he patted Aiso on the shoulder and told him he was doing a good job. He also offered his assistance if Aiso ever needed anything, something that was both astonishing and highly valued. If these guys had the support of General DeWitt, after all, they must be doing something right.

December 7, 1941 - Honolulu, Hawai'i
7:15 a.m. Hawai'i Time

It was a beautiful Hawaiian morning. The air was a tad crisp in Manoa but Doris didn't mind. Her parents had finally been letting her use their car occasionally, something she had been badgering them about for months. Dressed in a cute tennis outfit, she flung her tennis racket into the back seat and jumped in the front. She drove the few blocks to Helen's house where her friend was waiting.

"Good morning!" Doris greeted Helen who threw her tennis racket in the back and hopped in.

"Hi-de-ho, let's go!" Helen smiled.

Doris grappled with navigating the four-door Model T Ford through the narrow neighborhood streets. It was a short drive to get to the tennis courts at their old high school. The trick was to get there early because everyone in Honolulu had the same idea on the weekends. They were the third car in the parking lot, and there were only four courts, so they hustled to claim one.

On the court, they chose sides, knowing one side would inevitably face the rising sun. They positioned themselves on the court where Doris served the first ball.

December 7, 1941 - San Bernardino, California
9:45 a.m. Pacific Standard Time

7:45 a.m. Hawai'i Time

Tatsuo kissed his wife, Yukie, and baby Kathleen. Just as he did every day, he walked the short distance from his home on Fourth Street to his store on Third Street, greeting other merchants along the way. He opened the store, turned on the lights, and straightened out some of the produce as he made his way back to the office where he would brew coffee for himself.

Once his mug was filled, he decided to sit down and read the newspaper as he did almost every morning before the first customer arrived. Sometimes he would meander down the street and chat with one of the other Japanese merchants, but this morning he just wanted to read the newspaper in peace. He brought his coffee cup and his newspaper out to the front of the store and sat on a stool. It was the perfect location for him to keep an eye out for customers and enjoy the morning at the same time.

December 7, 1941 – San Francisco, California
9:50 a.m. Pacific Standard Time

7:50 a.m. Hawai'i Time

As Japanese fighter planes were almost above Pearl Harbor, operations were status quo in San Francisco. The Fourth Air Force was conducting air defense exercises that began on the 6th and were planned to continue until the 11th. As war heated up around the world, the military had implemented precautions. The Navy took over Treasure Island in San Francisco Bay as a military base. Routine test firing of coastal defense guns occurred at Fort Barry, just across the Golden Gate Bridge from the Presidio. And on the Presidio, the military practiced war exercises. There was a heightened sense of alert, and while military personnel felt it, they were not privy as to why.

For most of the citizens of San Francisco and most soldiers who called that area home, it was business as usual at 9:50 a.m. on December 7th.

December 7, 1941 - Chicago, Illinois
11:50 a.m. Central Standard Time

7:50 a.m. Hawai'i Time

The four soldiers left base early that morning on a one-day pass. They were eager to get to the city and away from the strict regimental training they had endured for weeks. The bus was full of privates looking to do the same thing that Masao, Rokuro, Shinji, and Bob wanted to do – eat good food. They found a diner that served breakfast all day. The place was packed, though, so they would have to wait their turn.

December 7, 1941 - Honolulu, Hawaii
7:55 a.m. Hawai'i Time

Doris was ahead forty-love in the first game of their second set when, all of a sudden, they heard loud, cacophonous blasts.

"What's going on?!" Helen was running toward Doris who looked up when she heard the sound of airplanes flying toward them. She shielded her eyes from the sun to take a closer look. She spotted the distinct red dial on the white background on the underside of each airplane wing — the Rising Sun emblem.

"Are those Japanese airplanes?" Doris uttered. The shock was too much to bear. The airplanes flew overhead while explosions continued in the distance. She instinctively looked off to where the blasts were coming from and saw billowing, black smoke rising. The ground seemed to shake beneath her as she watched the scattered Japanese planes circle and head back toward the smoke. Horrified, she looked at Helen who was frozen, her mouth hanging open.

"Come on!" Doris shouted as she grabbed their belongings. Helen stood, paralyzed by fear, staring at the sky. Doris took charge, physically taking Helen's arm. "Now, Helen! Let's go!!"

As Doris pulled Helen to the car, she looked back in horror. The Japanese planes looked like a swarm of bees over Pearl Harbor. More of the thick black smoke rose as the ruthless attack continued. She pushed Helen in the car from the driver's side and jumped in after her. She shoved the car in reverse and it lurched back; the tires spit up gravel as she floored it forward. She glanced over at the others who had been playing tennis, and they just stood there, staring at the sky.

"What the hell are they waiting for?" Her voice was shrill.

Helen looked over and saw what Doris was talking about, so rolled down her window and stuck her head out. "Get out of here!! Get out!!" But her shrieks did little good; the others didn't seem to feel any urgency. Residents of Honolulu were used to air maneuvers by the American military and even though this seemed different, they seemed blissfully confident that this was routine. But Doris knew. This was real.

"Don't take Kapi'olani! King Street! Take King!!" Helen was shouting.

Doris used all her might to crank the wheel. They flew by more onlookers who appeared confused and were gazing at the sky in a daze. "What are they doing? Why don't they leave?!"

The heavy Ford dashed down King Street. Doris swerved to go around cars that had stopped so drivers could get out and gawk at the sky.

"I'm taking McCully," Doris stated. Helen looked confused by this. "It's going to be faster!" Helen nodded. She looked out the back of the car and watched the black smoke rise up from Pearl Harbor.

"Do you think the Japanese really just attacked us?" Helen uttered.

"What else could it be?" Doris answered. But Helen was shaking her head in doubt, unable to digest the thought. "I saw it. You saw it too. Those were Japanese airplanes. This is no drill, Helen!"

They finally came to McCully and the tires squealed as Doris hurled the car making the hard left and heading up to Manoa Valley. Little did they know that just a short while later, King and McCully, the very intersection they had just passed, would be under assault, a casualty of anti-artillery shells being misfired. Businesses and homes would go up in flames and the owners would be helpless to do anything. Fire personnel would all be dispatched to Pearl Harbor. It would be too late by the time they made their way to King and McCully. In all, thirteen buildings would be completely destroyed, an entire block decimated. Thirty-one people would lose their homes and/or businesses and four people would die. Several other neighborhoods in greater Honolulu, including Waikiki, would feel the direct impact of defense missile misfires.

Doris sped all the way up to Manoa and pulled into her driveway with a screech. Her dad came out of the house with a scowl on his face — this wasn't the way he wanted his car treated. But before he could open his mouth to lecture her, Doris cut him off.

"Dad, something's happened! Look!!" She took him by the arm and pulled him out in the street where there was a view of Honolulu and the billowing smoke.

The blood ran out of her father's face, his eyes widened with fear.

"Dad. Those airplanes, they are Japanese. I saw them with my own eyes. They are Japanese." Doris was shaken. Her father took the girls inside the house and immediately tuned the radio to a news channel. The announcer was calling for calm although he sounded highly anxious and disoriented himself. At about half past eight, the radio announcer proclaimed that the bombing had stopped. There was a collective relief throughout Honolulu that was short-lived. It would turn out to be a short lull in an otherwise furious attack that would continue for another hour or more. The second wave of 170 Japanese airplanes appeared over Pearl Harbor and continued the relentless assault.

All the citizens of Hawai'i could do was watch and wait helplessly.

December 7, 1941 - The Presidio

11:00 a.m. Pacific Standard Time

9:00 a.m. Hawai'i Time

Military communications were swift, and commanders in the Bay area wasted no time to establish defense strategies. The order came to lay mines in San Francisco Bay almost immediately. All members of the Armed Forces in the Bay area were recalled to duty and man battle stations. Local police were solicited to find all soldiers and sailors in the San Francisco area and have them report to their stations at once. Maritime operations in the bays and harbors were ordered to a halt. And, sadly, Japanese citizens who had previously been considered members of society were now considered suspect.

December 7, 1941 - Chicago, Illinois

1:25 p.m. Central Standard Time

9:25 a.m. Hawai'i Time

Their mouths watered as they watched thick Belgian waffles topped with strawberries and fresh whipped cream being served at the table next to them. They figured that their order must be next up. The hungry soldiers had all ordered The Farmer's Breakfast: a stack of hotcakes, two country eggs, ham steak, potatoes, a hot biscuit, juice, and coffee, all for $1.10.

"I'm not too keen on this place. What's taking so long?" Bob sputtered. He had developed the reputation of being a whiner, or a fat-head as others would call him. Masao had gotten used to Bob's inability to cope in the world, but Bob's social ineptitude drove Shinji crazy.

"Ease up, Bob. We're next," Masao assured him. Bob sat back in the booth with a sigh. He was used to being handled by Masao, and as much as he wanted to look down on him for being Kibei, he had actually come to admire Masao's ability to keep things calm, as well as his natural inclination to lead.

"Hey! There she is." Shinji noticed the waitress. They all watched as she retrieved their plates from the heating station, grabbed a bottle of ketchup, and headed their way. She set the hot, steaming plates down in front of the young men. Masao got one big bite of ham in before an army private ran by the front of the diner, instantly stopping when he spotted the military uniforms and darting in.

"You guys got to get back to base – pronto! Something's happened!!" He was motioning with his whole arm, and everyone could tell – this was serious.

December 7, 1941 - San Bernardino

11:25 a.m. Pacific Standard Time

9:25 a.m. Hawai'i Time

Tatsuo was bagging up produce for a customer when he noticed commotion across the street in the Hirata Deli. He walked out to see if it was something he needed to attend to. Mr. Hirata was yelling at anyone who would listen, something about a radio. Tatsuo wondered what had driven him to such a state. Then he heard it clearly.

"Turn on your radio!" Hirata was shouting as he looked directly at Tatsuo. Hirata's face was filled with anxiety. Tatsuo immediately went to the back of the store and switched his radio on, tuning it in. Finally a clear signal and the announcer's voice blared.

"The Japanese have attacked the American Naval Base at Pearl Harbor, Hawai'i…" In shock, Tatsuo couldn't hear beyond this one sentence. He looked at the radio while he processed the magnitude of the announcer's message. He glanced out to the front of the store and Third Street where his Japanese community had, in that instant, been shattered.

December 7, 1941 - Chicago, Illinois

1:45 p.m. Central Standard Time

9:45 a.m. Hawai'i Time

Masao boarded the bus with all the other army personnel who were on leave. They still had no idea what had happened. The bus driver glared at the four as they went by and maintained his glare while they found seats. Rokuro sat next to Masao.

"What's under his skin?" Rokuro's voice was low; he didn't want any problems. Masao shrugged. The driver started up the bus, then fiddled with his portable radio. He found a station, tuned it in and turned it up, then put the bus in gear.

"The Japanese have attacked Pearl Harbor from the air, and all naval and military activities on the island of O-ha-oo, Hawai'i…" The announcer's voice filled the bus with the horrible news. The fact that the announcer didn't pronounce Oahu correctly didn't even register with Masao. His face turned white. He looked at Rokuro who looked like he had seen a ghost.

"My God," was all Masao could utter. He tried to listen to the details of the attack, but all he could think about was the bus driver's glare. He couldn't bear to look around at his Caucasian army counterparts for fear that they would have the same look of hate on their faces. He worried what this would mean for his future in the U.S. military.

The bus ride back to base was the longest of his life. The news reporter kept filling in the details of the morning's attack with gruesome specificity. With each added piece of information, Masao could feel himself sinking further in his seat. The eyes of other soldiers penetrated his existence. Shame grew inside him. While Rokuro sounded American and had no hint of an accent, that wasn't the case for Masao or Shinji. In that moment, Masao envied Bob for having an American name. That made Bob two steps removed from his Japanese ancestry, he didn't have a Japanese name *and* he didn't talk with an accent. Meanwhile, Masao was Japanese. His name was Japanese, his accent was Japanese, and he looked Japanese.

Masao glanced at Shinji and Bob, who were sitting across the aisle. Shinji looked like Masao felt, his head hanging down, his eyes averting any contact with others. Bob, meanwhile, was alert and scanning the bus, seemingly unaware that his roots were Japanese.

"That guy, doesn't he get the connection?" Masao whispered as he nudged Rokuro and motioned toward Bob who was now poking the soldier sitting in front of him and saying something about the attack that, in Masao's mind, made him look stupid. Rokuro watched Bob make a fool out of himself. Shinji, meanwhile, was trying to become invisible.

"He's an idiot," Rokuro whispered back.

December 7, 1941- Honolulu, Hawai'i
12:00 p.m. Hawai'i Standard Time

The attack had stopped just before ten a.m. as the last of the Japanese airplanes headed back to the aircraft carrier from whence they came. The massive attack on Pearl Harbor was an incredible success for the Japanese military: twenty-one American ships had been destroyed or heavily damaged, over twenty-four hundred military and civilian deaths were incurred, and nearly twelve hundred had been wounded in the attack.

After the Japanese airplanes had left the area and some time had passed, people slowly emerged from their homes to assess the damage. Everyone would eventually get to a vantage point where they could see the heavy thick, black smoke rising from Pearl Harbor. Disbelief permeated the area, and a grave reality settled in.

On McCully and King, ashes still smoldered. Buildings had burned to the ground leaving behind homelessness and grief. The trade winds carried burning debris from McCully and King the few blocks down to the Lunalilo School where fire caught hold.

It seemed that one disaster led to another.

December 7, 1941 - Camp Grant, Illinois

4:00 p.m. Central Standard Time

12:00 p.m. Hawai'i Time

All soldiers of Japanese descent were ordered to attend a special meeting at the Service Club on the base at 1600 hours sharp. Masao had only been to the Service Club a few times, once when there was a social mixer for soldiers, and a couple of times when he had wanted to write to his Uncle Tatsuo. Today, the Service Club had been set up for a formal meeting. Chairs were arranged in rows and the space easily housed the few dozen Nisei soldiers who were ordered to report. Masao found a seat next to Shinji and glanced around at the perimeter of the room, noticing that Caucasian soldiers were stationed strategically.

He glanced at Shinji. "This doesn't look too good," he said in a muffled voice. Shinji nodded in agreement.

A door opened at the far end of the room and a one-star general entered, prompting the entire room full of soldiers to stand at attention and salute. The general walked with purpose to the podium that had been set up for his personal use, and took a moment to peruse the soldiers who still stood at attention.

"At ease," he commanded with the slightest nod. His face looked stern. Anxiety grew among the Nisei soldiers who collectively wondered if they would be immediately dismissed from service. Dishonorable discharge: you are not wanted. They understood this as a distinct possibility and, in their hearts, understood why the American military might take such action. The worst part would be that they would then not have the opportunity to prove their loyalty. And for each and every Nisei soldier in that room that had become their primary goal since hearing the horrible news earlier that day. Apprehension filled the room as the general gathered his notes. It seemed to take him forever. There wasn't a sound except for the shuffling of papers at the podium. Finally the general looked up.

"As you know by now, one of our naval bases has been deliberately and suddenly attacked by the Empire of Japan. They attacked by air with over 190 air squadrons in the first wave and 170 air squadrons in the second and final wave. The military casualties were extensive and the assault was long and brutal, lasting almost two hours from beginning to end," the general paused to let his words resonate throughout the room.

"The targets appear to be military, although there were some civilian casualties. The data is not yet conclusive on that. What is clear is that the attack caused severe damage to American military and naval services on that island. While the base in Hawai'i regains strength and prepares for further attack, bases along the west coast are also preparing, strategically, for certain and impending Japanese attacks."

Oh my God, thought Masao. This was worse than he imagined. *What about my uncle? I need to talk to him, make sure he's okay. He's Issei.* Masao worried to himself. He had to force his attention back from San Bernardino in order to continue listening to the general.

"Although I'm not certain what course of action the U.S. Military will take, I am certain of one thing."

Here it comes, thought Masao, *this is where we find out our destiny. Are we going to be soldiers, or are we going to be the enemy?*

"As long as you men are wearing the U.S. Army uniform, you will be treated like any other American. You are Americans. And your country needs you now."

Pride swelled in the room. The Nisei soldiers didn't even try to hide their smiles and their relief to hear that they were still seen as part of the team, part of the society that they were there to serve. Humble but proud, there was a collective relaxation of shoulders. Their hearts pounded waiting for the next words from the general they now revered.

"When you get your orders, remember that," the general concluded. He folded up his papers and gave the room a salute that immediately prompted the soldiers to stand erect, tall and confident, in their salute back. They watched until the general left the room. While they congratulated each other and chatted, Masao glanced at the Caucasian soldiers who lined the walls. They didn't look as happy as the Nisei soldiers felt. While part of him was elated, another part of him had an ominous feeling that things were going to get really tough from here on out.

December 7, 1941 - The Presidio, San Francisco, California

4:00 p.m. Pacific Standard Time

2:00 p.m. Hawai'i Time

Now on high alert, the Presidio bustled with activity. Soldiers knew what was expected and were determined to man their stations with valor. At 1600 hours, military guards were ordered as posts on the Golden Gate Bridge, responsible for scanning cars crossing the bridge and stopping anyone who looked Japanese and searching their vehicle for explosives. The Japanese citizens who were subjected to this were horrified that they would be considered suspect, some of them having lived in the area for many years, if not their entire lives. These were people who considered the United States their home.

Later that evening, President Roosevelt would order the Army to work in tandem with the FBI and assist in rounding up enemy aliens who were considered dangerous. The method used to filter who was dangerous and who wasn't would become confusing and hasty. Potential aliens included a wide swath of people. Anyone Japanese, German, or Italian was at risk of being hauled away on a moment's notice.

December 7, 1941 - Honolulu, Hawai'i

4:00 p.m. Hawai'i Standard Time

The Okada family had remained indoors for most of the day. Doris was getting antsy; owing to her naturally curious nature, she wanted to know what was going on. They had been listening to the radio for information but Governor Poindexter had ordered all commercial radio stations off the air earlier that day. He feared that the Japanese could pick up the radio frequency and capitalize on public reports that were being broadcast on the open air waves. Residents kept their radios on in hopes of getting periodic updates, but only static came through. Yet, Doris continued to mess with the radio. She didn't want to miss anything.

Finally the radio announcer was back on the air.

"The governor has turned power over to the military." The faint voice of the announcer came through as she fiddled with the dial. Her family all gathered close. Lieutenant General Short was introduced and took over the broadcast. He described how the island would now be under martial law. There would be an island-wide blackout starting at six p.m. Nobody would be allowed out of their homes, no lights of any kind should be used. Not even candles. They weren't going to make it easy for Japan to attack again.

By six p.m., the Okada family, like all the other families on Oahu, turned off every last light in their home, locked their doors, and waited for daybreak. Throughout the night, military police patrolled neighborhoods looking for anyone breaking the rules. Even for very minor infractions, people would be taken to military court and fined hundreds of dollars. But the Okada family obeyed the law, as did most of the residents on the island, and remained in the dark throughout the night. It would turn out to be the first night of many dark nights to come.

As the sun set on December 7, 1941, in Honolulu, Hawai'i, it set on a day that would long live in infamy. The deep mourning for those who were lost would be replaced by a determination to become a part of the solution, the clean up, and military response. Doris wasn't sure just how she would do it, but she was determined that she would be included in the civilian effort whether or not her dad approved.

❖   ❖   ❖

Masao returned to the present, looking bewildered. I had pulled off the highway at a truck stop to listen to his riveting account of December 7th.

"Where are we?" he asked innocently.

"I just pulled over, we're almost there, though," I assured him.

"We're going casino, a-no?"

I smiled and nodded. "Yeah, I just needed to stop so I could hear everything you were saying," I explained.

"Heh! You've heard it before, it's nothing new."

"It's new to me. I have never heard this before. Never," I attested. He just shrugged. "I didn't know Doris was just a few miles away from Pearl Harbor, for one thing," I continued. "Picking oysters off the beach just a couple weeks before the attack."

"Yep, two weeks before, that's right," he nodded. I had a warm feeling that our conversation, and my interest in it, gave him relief bringing the past, his military experience, and thus, Doris closer. I was happy to be in this role, an unlikely historian keeping his story alive. I admired his face as he lingered in 1941, no doubt picturing his beloved Doris on the beach, picking the oysters she so loved.

CHAPTER SIX

THE AFTERMATH

"DAD WANTS TO GO TO VEGAS," ALAN ANNOUNCED OVER THE PHONE. At the time I had absolutely no idea that Vegas had been a frequent travel destination for Mas and Doris. It had also been a meeting spot for Masao's war buddies. Traveling with Masao required a lot of equipment. He needed his cane, his walker, and a wheelchair. Alan and I became experts in airport navigation and also became skilled at shielding Masao from ever feeling like a burden. It was worth every last bit of hassle to travel with him, and he was always incredibly gracious and thankful.

This would be the first trip of many to Vegas, and we soon developed a predictable routine that included a lot of gambling and eating. Masao preferred to stay downtown, and I was pleasantly surprised at the beautiful accommodations at the Golden Nugget. For lunch we always ate at Aloha Specialties at the California Hotel. For dinner, we ate at Grotto, a wonderful Italian restaurant at the Golden Nugget with the most delicious desserts one can imagine.

"Hey, Mas," I said at dinner during our first trip to Vegas. He sipped from his coffee cup while he fixed his eyes in my direction. I pushed the sugar toward him, instinctively knowing he would want more. He added another spoonful.

"How did your uncle do after December 7th?"

"My uncle, jeez… He lived in San Bernardino, a-no?"

I nodded. There was the familiar expression on his face that occurred when he called up memories.

"There was a Japanese Association in San Bernardino. And my uncle, he was the President of it. A leader in that community." He paused to formulate his thoughts. "I think that hurt him after the attack on Pearl Harbor, a-no?"

I leaned forward and turned all my attention to San Bernardino, December 1941.

December 8, 1941 - San Bernardino, California

It was a Monday afternoon. Tatsuo locked up Star Cash Grocery a little early that day and headed for the local hall where the Japanese Association meetings were always held. The events of the last two days were to be discussed, and too, some much needed support within the community would be shared. His face said it all as he walked down the street: here was a man feeling ashamed of his race, fearful for his future.

People in Little Japan were still reeling from the horrible news about the attack on Pearl Harbor. They were leaning on each other, trying to understand what had happened and how it might affect their future in the States. The Issei were the most worried as they were not citizens. But the many Nisei had grave concerns as well.

The Japanese who lived along the west coast of the U.S. and in Hawai'i had immediately become suspect. By the end of the day on December 7th, President Roosevelt had ordered the gathering of any Japanese person who was considered a subversive alien. These people would be taken away and detained for two weeks until they were sent to one of the imprisonment camps operated by the Immigration and Naturalization Service (INS).

There were three classifications of Japanese people who were considered suspect. Group A consisted of those thought to be highly dangerous saboteurs: local fishermen, produce distributors, farmers, successful and influential businessmen, Shinto priests, Buddhist priests, and members of the Japanese Consulate. Group B had not been under direct surveillance but were thought of as possibly dangerous. Group C were thought of as likely to be involved in sabotage of American military efforts and were closely watched due to their Japanese ties. Groups B and C included Japanese language teachers, teachers of the martial arts, travel agents, editors of Japanese newspapers, community leaders, and, of course, Kibeis.

Many of the Japanese that fell into the three classifications were rounded up and turned over to the nearest INS office to be processed. By the early morning of December 8, 1941, less than twenty-four hours after the attack, 736 Japanese, German, or Italian "enemies" had been taken into custody.

Tatsuo had heard about the round-ups along the coast, as had many of his friends and business associates. His footsteps were heavy as was his heart. He wasn't sure what he would say to people, but as the leader of the local Japanese Association, it was certain that the community would be looking to him for answers.

The hall was packed with families. The look on each face was one of anxiety, apprehension, and fear. It seemed that some people had aged overnight. As was usual in San Bernardino, everyone spoke English. Tatsuo took center stage at the front of the room.

"Good people of San Bernardino, and my friends. We're going to need to rely on each other now more than ever until this gets straightened out," Tatsuo began. People nodded. "Let's begin by just checking in with each other. Let me ask, what immediate needs do you have?" A man named Tom Mitsuhashi raised his hand. Tatsuo nodded.

"My suppliers have cut me off." Mitsuhashi's voice was compromised and weak.

"Me too," café owner Jimmy Sawada added.

"We just have to do our best. If you need supplies for your café, Jimmy, I have produce, staples, and coffee. What I have is yours." Tatsuo tried to sound reassuring.

"Some our best customers aren't coming around," George Kamimura added.

All Tatsuo could do was nod. There were no answers. It was quiet. "Let's hope this is the worst of it." Tatsuo knew this was not the case, but felt the need to remain positive, no matter how dire the situation.

"We had a good crop last year. We can share all the canned pears and peaches anyone needs," farmer David Yurimoto stated loudly. This one bright thought seemed to change the mood.

"We have plenty of vegetables," another farmer, Ben Omori contributed.

"I've got five hogs I can butcher," added Bessie Tamura.

"Let's stick together through this. Cooperate fully with any authorities that might question you. You have nothing to hide, nor do I. We have been good residents of California and of the United States. Some of our children, indeed, my nephew Masao, have been called to military duty. We have done nothing wrong and we need to stand by that." Tatsuo looked around. Faith in his words seemed to build; maybe, too, a sense of hope.

December 8, 1941 - Honolulu, Hawai'i

"Dad?" Doris hollered as she came through the door. Her dad came out from the kitchen. "A bunch of people are heading to town, I want to go with them." She strode past him and began rummaging through the cupboards and refrigerator.

"What for?"

"What for? Because all the supply lines to Hawai'i have been cut off, that's what for. There will be a shortage of food, don't you see? I'll go with them and get all the groceries I can."

Her dad thought this through, then grabbed his keys. "We'll both go." This was a pleasant surprise for Doris. Her dad usually dismissed any idea she had, even when they were brilliant. Her mom, who had been sitting at the table listening, was already writing a list.

As they drove to Honolulu they witnessed the enormity of the situation. Lines three blocks long formed at gas stations, blocking intersections and creating traffic jams. Everything seemed confusing and chaotic, a drastic difference from the usual relaxed and peaceful Hawaiian ways.

"Try Piggly Wiggly," Doris suggested when they encountered the long lines at May's Market. But at Piggly Wiggly the line wrapped around the block.

"My Lord," Doris said, "Dad, let's try Kaimuki."

"That's a ways out there."

"I know, but probably less people shop there. We might even find a service station to get fuel." Doris persuaded him and he agreed. They made the drive out to Kaimuki only to face the same disappointment with long lines.

"This is no use. I'll wait in line here, you go try to fuel up." Doris was quick with the plan of action. "Pull over here." Her dad did as ordered by his bossy daughter and pulled the Ford over. Doris jumped out and headed for the back of the line at the Central Market.

Four hours later they would return home. The car was filled with fuel, and they had the "appropriate" amount of groceries for a family of four as hoarding was strictly prohibited.

"We're set for now," her dad assessed.

"Yeah, but what about next week?" Doris was already concerned about how to make sure her family would be able to survive what was surely to come, severe shortages of everything.

December 8, 1941 - Camp Grant, Illinois

Camp Grant was alive with purposeful activity. Earlier that morning, soldiers had listened with great anticipation and satisfaction as President Roosevelt declared war on Japan. Action was swift and troops were already receiving orders to be transported to other facilities for combat training. Masao and his friends waited patiently for their orders, watching their Caucasian counterparts pack up and ship out.

No orders came for any of them.

December 11, 1941 - The Presidio

There was a heightened sense of alert on the base. Reports of Japanese submarines off the coast of California were kept from the public, but officers on base were acutely aware of the potential dangers. The entire west coast was declared a Theatre of Wartime Operations by the Western Defense Command, now under the sole authority of Lieutenant General

John DeWitt. One of his first orders as commander in charge – no vessels of any kind were allowed to sail at night in the Bay. Military vessels, of course, were permitted.

The branches of the military wasted no time in organizing efforts. A huge submarine net had already been laid across the San Francisco Bay just inside the Golden Gate Bridge. On the other side of the bridge, layers of an extensive mine field had been laid at the mouth in overlapping arches out into the Pacific. Several army regimental combat units had already been shipped out, their destination – Honolulu. The navy would also send ships loaded with sailors to the same location. Decisions were swift and decisive.

The round up of enemy aliens continued. The Department of Justice, now in charge of this operation, routinely took Japanese, German, and Italian residents into custody. In the coming weeks, the round-up would expand to include all aliens who were fourteen-years-old or older, and who were of enemy nations. All of these aliens were to be moved to the interior of the country and off the west coast. DeWitt believed that there were about forty thousand people along the west coast who fit this description. He held the belief that these forty thousand, and every one of them, posed an immediate and potential threat to defense measures. He was determined to eliminate that threat.

By the end of the month there would be an absolute frenzy by military, local police, the Department of Justice, and the FBI to ferret out enemies. Because of the military alert status, these agencies would err on the side of caution and detain even those who clearly posed no security threat at all. FBI agents, who now had the authority to search homes at will, frequently imposed their will on those suspected as enemy aliens, given little or no evidence that gave cause for concern.

Meanwhile, in Building 640 on Crissy Field, the Nisei language school students kept their noses to the grindstone. Now more than ever, they wanted to prove their worth, their loyalty, and their citizenry. Just days before, General DeWitt had given them the nod of approval. They wondered if his approval still held.

❖   ❖   ❖

Back in Vegas, we finished our meal. "You know, at Camp Grant, I was there for four months," Masao continued. I nodded. "I was never promoted. Other guys, they came in as privates, then promoted to private first class. But me—no."

"What about your friends? Your Nisei buddies. How about them?" I asked. He just shook his head no, and it was a sad no.

"Nope, not a one of us. You know, they said we were American soldiers. But…" His voice trailed off. He didn't need to complete the sentence. It was easy to see what was going on. Pearl Harbor had just been attacked; he and his buddies were collateral damage. They knew it and there was nothing they could do about it.

Just then our waiter brought more coffee, and I pushed the sugar and creamer Mas's way. This took his mind off of that troubling time. I was happy to leave it too. What do you say to a warrior who has been passed over, underutilized? The thought stayed with me until I saw the dessert cart being pushed toward our table. This was no ordinary dessert cart; this was a two-tiered extravaganza featuring a strawberry cassata, tiramisu, a six-layered chocolate cake, and other scrumptious delicacies. Once I saw the strawberry cassata, I failed to see anything else in the restaurant. Alan suggested that we share a piece, but Masao saw my eyes. He knew that I needed a piece all to myself.

"No, no," he said to Alan. "We get our own tonight." And his word was final.

Tuesday, October 12, 2010

He was gazing out the windows at the stunning fall foliage as we drove along the freeway on our way to the casino. "Beautiful day, a-no?"

"It is." Autumn has always been my favorite time of the year especially when it's clear and sunny.

"You know, my uncle, he got arrested," he announced out of nowhere. I was floored by this piece of information. Until then, I hadn't explored the notion of internment and didn't know if his family had escaped that horrible process.

"Arrested? Or interned?" I thought maybe he was confused.

"Arrested." I trusted his memory and wanted to hear more. Looking ahead, I saw the truck stop exit.

Tatsuo's Arrest

Inventory was disappearing from store shelves all along Third Street, as though the shelves themselves detected what was coming — the vanishing soul of Japan Town. Tatsuo's suppliers had cut him off weeks before. He swept the floor of the store and arranged merchandise to give the appearance of a full inventory. It was December 31st and his mind was on the next day. He was looking forward to the annual gathering of the community to celebrate New Year's Day. Yukie was already busy preparing Japanese food for the big event. He noticed a shadow of a man out of the corner of his eye. It almost startled him until he recognized Ben Miller.

"Ben. How are you, my friend?"

"I think I might be faring better than you these days, sadly," Ben said sincerely.

Tatsuo glanced at Ben's shaky hands. "Come." They walked together to the back of the store where Tatsuo poured some whiskey for Ben. He then did what he never did, he poured a shot for himself. "I think I'll join you today."

It was quiet. Two men who had been rejected from American society under entirely different circumstances but with a common thread.

Ben pointed to the picture on the wall. "Who is that, Tatsuo?"

"That's my father and my brother. We look pretty good, don't we? All dressed up." Tatsuo smiled. Ben nodded. The only sound was the wall clock ticking. Ben's appreciation of the picture gave Tatsuo immense comfort.

"I came from Japan in 1920. That picture was taken in San Francisco just after I arrived. My dad, he went back on the same ship that brought me here. It's a long time ago, now."

"It's a nice photo." Ben was genuine in his compliment. The clock ticked. "I feel bad about what's happening here in Little Japan," Ben said. "You're good people. You don't deserve this."

Tatsuo smiled, happy to have compassionate company. "Here's hoping it gets better," he said as he raised his cup to toast.

The next morning, New Year's Day, 1942, Tatsuo was up early to start the wood stove so Yukie could be comfortably warm when she got up. They were well on their way to making sushi rolls when they saw a car park in front of the house. Two men in suits and one policeman emerged from the car. Tatsuo immediately felt this was the worst event possible. He had heard of Issei being picked up and detained for no reason and hoped this wasn't going to be the case.

He opened the door and greeted the men as though they were guests. They were all business, though, and would have nothing to do with Tatsuo's hospitality.

"Tatsuo Abe?" One of the men asked.

"Yes, I am Tatsuo Abe."

The man held up his badge and some other papers that Tatsuo couldn't even begin to read before all three had entered his home.

"We are FBI and have the authority to search the premises," the agent loudly stated. He motioned for the policeman to stay in the kitchen with Tatsuo and Yukie, who was holding their daughter. "You two stay here. Don't talk to one another," he ordered. Tatsuo looked at Yukie and motioned for her to sit down. The policeman watched their every move. The other two men, one from the FBI, the other from immigration, scoured the home leaving a trail of clutter in their wake.

"The stove needs more wood. We have in garage. Can my husband or I go get more to keep the house warm for our daughter?" Yukie asked politely, pointing to the dying fire in the wood stove.

The young policeman looked straight ahead, refusing to let humanity enter the room.

"You stay here," he said without any hint of emotion. Yukie held her daughter more tightly. Tatsuo took off his sweater and handed it to Yukie to wrap around Kathleen. It was an hour or more before the other two men came back to the kitchen.

"Stand up," the FBI agent ordered. Tatsuo did as told.

"We're taking you in."

"Why, what have I done?"

There was no room in this investigation for justice or due process. The three men hastily escorted Tatsuo by his arms out to the car. A horrified Yukie looked on.

"Where are you taking him?" she called out in a frantic and shrill voice, but they ignored her. She watched as they put him in the car, in between the two men in the back seat, and drove off.

After she warmed the house up again and put Kathleen down for a nap, she spent an hour or more working to make the house tidy. She had been looking out the window at the courthouse, just behind their home, to see if they had taken Tatsuo to the county jail. So far, she hadn't spotted anything. Her plan was to enlist the help of other Japanese in the area. Just when Kathleen was waking up, Yukie looked out the window and spotted the car, the one that had taken Tatsuo away. It pulled up in front of the courthouse. She saw Tatsuo get out of the car in handcuffs. He looked okay; no harm had come to him yet. She sighed with relief. They ushered him into the building.

They would keep Tatsuo in the county jail for twenty-eight days. Yukie would be allowed to visit but was warned that if one word of Japanese was spoken between them, the visits would abruptly end. Since they had never spoken English with each other it was awkward. Sometimes it took several attempts just to convey simple things, such as the notion that she was sure she was pregnant again. This piece of information took five minutes to get straight but delighted them both.

"I'm here with heavy criminal people," Tatsuo reported to Yukie during one of their visits. As it turned out, Tatsuo was in jail cells with rapists and robbers, along with the local drunks during weekends. Yukie gasped at the thought, unable to express her emotions in English. Tatsuo was never formally arrested; they kept him for investigative purposes only. Still, he felt enormous shame in having been put in jail at all.

"Tell everyone, I have done nothing wrong. Nothing." Tatsuo pleaded with Yukie.

She had already taken care of that. She had also taken care of the operations of the grocery store, visiting it daily to make sure everything was in order.

The two kept their hopes up that the investigation would be short. Yukie found out that other Japanese men had been incarcerated too, but the men were separated. Tatsuo had been taken to the San Bernardino jail; Mr. Kitagawa, to the Indio jail; and Mr. Okubo, to the Riverside jail. In the coming months, there would be many more men who would be taken into custody; their fate would sometimes be published in the local newspapers making the humiliation that much more potent.

In mid-January, Yukie received a postcard in the mail, it was from immigration. It contained specific instructions for her: take Tatsuo's belongings to the county jail on January 28th at promptly 12:00 p.m. She found out that she could also bring him a meal, and she knew he would be hungry for Japanese food.

She prepared a basket of fried chicken, *gohan* or cooked rice, *takenoko*, or bamboo shoots, and even a few pieces of sashimi. She knew he would be craving rice most of all, so she made sure he had plenty. She made the short walk to the courthouse, carrying the basket, a small suitcase, and pushing Kathleen in a carriage. She arrived at 11:45 and waited patiently for Tatsuo, still unsure what was happening. Nobody had told her anything, nor would they.

Meanwhile, Tatsuo was eager to get out of jail. He proudly stepped onto the elevator, a man about to be free. He had proven himself worthy of living in society, he hadn't done anything wrong, and could never imagine being involved in anything that would bring harm to the United States, the country where he had made his living and enjoyed a good life. The elevator, carrying Tatsuo, an immigration officer, and an FBI agent, arrived at the ground floor, and he stepped off, delighted to see Yukie. He smiled as he approached her and wondered why the law enforcement officers were hovering.

"Here is some food. I make many things you like," Yukie proudly offered as she opened the basket, revealing all the wonderful foods that were Tatsuo's favorites.

His mouth watered at the sight. He was hungry and could have easily devoured everything she brought. Not knowing that Yukie had been instructed to bring a meal and still in the mindset that he must prove his loyalty to the U.S., he thought hard about whether or not to accept the food. He badly wanted to go home, to "make free", he didn't want to be connected with anything Japanese at the moment, not even the food. Besides, the way these officers were hanging around it was clear they thought something important was in the basket besides food, some sort of device that could aid in the sabotage he had been accused of. He wanted to prove them wrong.

"I sure appreciate it you bring gohan, chicken, and the rest. But I not hungry in this moment," he lied, hoping to prove that he was in no way connected with Japan. Yukie, dismayed, nodded that she understood even though she didn't. Tatsuo instinctively went to the carriage to admire a sleeping Kathleen. He leaned down and kissed her on the forehead.

"She's so beautiful," he whispered to himself. His intimate moment with his daughter and wife was abruptly interrupted by the FBI agent.

"You sure you don't want any of that Jap food?" the agent barked. And with this question, Tatsuo thought he was surely making the right move by saying no. Maybe this was the final test. Maybe now they would let him resume his life.

"I'm still full from breakfast." His voice reflected the dejection he felt. Yukie detected it and her heart sank for him.

"Okay, then. Let's go." And before Tatsuo could utter a word the two men whisked him out the door where a car was waiting. Yukie looked on, helpless to do anything and still holding the basket of food she had so carefully prepared.

In the car waiting for him, Tatsuo recognized Mr. Kitagawa and Mr. Okubo. He noticed law enforcement officers on each corner of the block, armed with guns, ready to shoot anything or anyone who looked or acted suspicious. Yukie looked on as the car carrying her husband sped off, watching until she could no longer see the car, then turned to ask someone, anyone, where they were taking him. But things in the courthouse had resumed to business-as-usual. The excitement was over. No one acknowledged her — she had become an invisible presence. She stood there with her basket of delicious food, and although she was proper and quiet on the outside, she was screaming on the inside.

February 1942 - Camp Grant, Illinois

Masao was still waiting for his orders. Bob had been shipped out to some-where, to the relief of Shinji and to the dismay of Masao. He wondered what the military saw in an idiot like Bob.

Rokuro had just been handed his orders and was packing. It was just Shinji and Masao left behind. They couldn't help but think they had been passed over because they didn't sound right, as if they were covering up their Japanese accents, and they were. There was an unspoken understanding between them to never talk about how deeply it hurt to be excluded from orders, time and time again.

❖　❖　❖

Mail call sounded and to his surprise, Masao had a letter from San Bernardino. It was from his aunt Yukie, although the envelope had been addressed in someone else's handwriting. He found a private spot, made sure no one else was nearby, and opened it. He was almost afraid to get the update; she had written to him just after his uncle Tatsuo had been arrested in early January. Grateful that they had kept him in San Bernardino, he wondered if perhaps the connection between Tatsuo and an American military nephew would make a difference to law enforcement. Maybe they would let him be.

He pulled out the letter that was written in Yukie's pen, beautiful Japanese kanji. She explained the entire horrible ordeal at the courthouse and that she still didn't know of Tatsuo's whereabouts. It had been ten days since she had seen him last. She was worried sick but kept things going at the store and managed to keep afloat at home with her little girl. She described how Little Japan had changed, as if it was dying a slow and painful death. Piece by piece, it was withering away, its residents losing faith and hope with each passing day. Many of the Issei men in the San Bernardino valley had been picked up and taken to unknown destinations, leaving the women behind to fill in the gaps of labor and assume the head of the household.

A Caucasian soldier walked near where Masao was sitting, so he lowered the letter inconspicuously, waiting until it was safe again. He continued reading, feeling his aunt's angst, her helplessness, and her attempts to muster strength in the dimmest of conditions. He finished reading and sat there for a moment, unable to function, unable to clearly see the direction he should go. Should he leave the military and go back to California where he was certainly needed? Or should he stay and prove his loyalty as his other Nisei comrades were determined to do?

He looked at the letter in his hands and admired the beautiful, flowing, and elegant Japanese writing. Japanese. He glanced around and realized the enormity of that moment. Any Caucasian person would assume the worst. They would never believe that this was the letter of a hurting heart, from a wounded woman whose family had been ripped apart by the very government he served, by the country to which he had pledged his loyalty.

He knew what he had to do; he slowly and gently ripped the letter into the smallest of pieces, so no kanji was detectable. He would keep it concealed until he could find a barrel fire, either one on base or one in Chicago on a dismal street, to dispose of it for good.

February 1942 - Terminal Island, San Pedro, California

Located between San Pedro and Long Beach in Los Angeles Harbor, Terminal Island was a little Japanese world of its own. It had become a fishing village, first occupied by a group of Japanese laborers who had worked on the Southern Pacific Railroad in the late 1800s, many of whom had originated from Wakayama, near Osaka Bay, in Japan. Born and raised fishermen, these railroad workers were eager to get back to the sea and Terminal Island was the perfect spot for that to happen. As early as 1907, this little fishing village had become established as a productive tuna fishing site, prompting a housing development. Within a few years the word got out and more fishermen of Japanese origin flocked to the village; the population grew to more than six hundred.

The community was very tight knit, due in part to the isolated location. The productive fishing led to cannery operations. It was a thriving economy, bolstering many fishing boats that were owned and operated by Japanese fishermen. Tuna Street would become the main hub for businesses including markets, pool halls, barber shops, and bakeries, many were owned and operated by Japanese businessmen. Elementary-aged children would attend Walizer Elementary School located on Terminal Island. Older students would take a ferry to San Pedro and attended San Pedro High.

The name the Japanese had for their home on Terminal Island was Furusato, the Japanese way of saying "home sweet home". The people of Terminal Island even had their own dialect, a mixture of Japanese and English that further distinguished these folks among Japanese-Americans along the west coast. By 1941 this little Japanese community was idyllic and connected. It boasted a Shinto Shrine, a Japanese Fisherman's Hall where traditions such as martial arts were maintained, and Japanese gardens complete with a *sori bashi*, or arched wooden bridge. The community embraced the American sport of baseball and formed a team of its own, comprised of high school-aged boys and sponsored by local businesses. This little town was quaint, friendly, and inviting. The residents of Terminal Island loved their community and their livelihood.

That livelihood would change forever on December 7, 1941. Many of the adult males on Terminal Island were the first to be rounded up and taken into custody. The community came under scrutiny; the military perceived this little village to be an enemy hotbed and in a prime location for spying on merchant ships and other vessels in the port, as well as partaking in sabotage. These Japanese people were not to be trusted.

The immigration office on Terminal Island, the very office where Yasoshichi had met Tomie for the first time, would now house alien enemies for processing. This is where the FBI agent brought Tatsuo on January 28, 1942. During the two-hour drive from San Bernardino, Tatsuo thought about the wonderful food that Yukie had prepared for him, the food he rejected in an attempt to appear loyal and trustworthy. *What good did that do*, he thought. Now his stomach grumbled as they approached the ocean.

The car pulled up in front of the immigration office and the men were told to wait on the bench outside the office along with their luggage. Then the FBI agent, the INS officer, and the policeman disappeared. It was the first time the three Japanese men had been left alone, and although there were guards in the area, nobody was close by. They could have spoken Japanese and nobody would have heard. But they did not; they spoke only English, and very little of it.

At first, they just sat there looking out at the water in the distance and watching boats bob up and down in the harbor. Then Tatsuo's stomach growled and everyone heard it.

"I haven't eaten since breakfast," Tatsuo explained. Mr. Kitagawa and Mr. Okubo nodded.

"My wife, she brought me good food, gohan, sashimi, chicken. But I said 'no thanks.' I didn't want to connect to Japanese in front of the law officers," he mourned. "Now, I'm hungry. Haven't eaten since six-thirty. Heh! My mistake. Should have eaten."

It was after three p.m. when the men were told to sit and wait. It would be six before they would be ordered onto a bus, equipped for prisoners and half full with other Japanese men. Dressed in suits, they were headed for an unknown destination.

The bus would take them to Tujunga, just north of Burbank, where a detention center had been built to house suspected enemy aliens. Although temporary, the detention center was now holding nearly one thousand Japanese and Italian men. This was where all of the men of Terminal Island had been taken. Tatsuo stepped off the bus with his luggage, his heart sinking. He realized that he wasn't going home any time soon.

Oh how he wished he would have eaten Yukie's food.

❖   ❖   ❖

I was once again mesmerized by Masao's family's legacy.

"He was taken away, just like that." I was astonished.

"Just like that," Mas assured me with a nod.

"Will you tell me more about your uncle later?"

"Oh, sure." He shifted in the passenger seat, producing a wince. I had never seen him do this and it scared me.

"What's wrong?"

"My leg. It's been bothering me today."

"Arthritis?"

"No, gunshot."

My eyes must have popped out of my head. "What???"

"Ah. It's not important, let's go gamble." He waved me off as he often did when he had had enough.

"Mas. You—you can't just—spit things out like that, and expect me to just *wait*!" I stammered, starting the car and heading for the freeway. I was beginning to understand Masao and recognized when he was done with his storytelling. And he was done. There was nothing I could do to get another sentence of history out of the man.

"Just tell me that you'll fill me in on the gunshot wound someday. Soon. Okay? Just tell me that."

"Heh! In time." He was looking out the window at the fall foliage as I merged onto the freeway. "Beautiful day, a-no?"

Tuesday, November 16, 2010 Masao's 94th Birthday

It was my day with Masao, but I had to share him with his family. There was a dinner planned at Pat's house. I might just as well been walking into my mom's house when everyone was there: a lot of kids running around like crazy, a lot of food, and not much quiet. Masao was sitting on the couch by himself while others were chatting in the kitchen. He seemed to be amused by the kids and their wild activities that would spill into his vicinity every few minutes.

Since everyone wanted to make this birthday special, his first birthday without Doris, he would go along even if feeling as he did, like a third wheel, a lonely half of a whole. It was something I felt coming from him, a void that couldn't be filled, only masked for bits of time. I made myself comfortable next to him.

"I guess we don't get to gamble today," I said.

"Heh! Maybe we go tomorrow," and he looked at me to see if that was possible.

"Let's do it," I assured him. He nodded, excited to have something to look forward to.

"When are we going to Vegas again? Soon, a-no?"

"In one more month," I reminded him, "December."

"Before Christmas?" He sounded like a little boy.

"The day after Christmas."

"Ohhhh. That's too long." His voice reflected the disappointment he felt. He was ready to go back to Vegas at a moment's notice. I think he secretly wished that Alan and I would quit our jobs and just play with him all the time. And it was tempting.

We seemed to be in our own little world sitting there on the couch. Masao glanced at his family gathered in the kitchen and then looked at me. "You know, my wife, she was from Hawai'i. No seasons, really, in Hawai'i. She had a hard time when we moved here."

"I believe that. It would be hard to move to Seattle from Hawai'i."

He didn't seem to hear me. He was quietly gathering his thoughts.

"After Pearl Harbor, the military was in charge," he paused as he usually did during his stories, "and, ah, they didn't know what to do with all the Japanese in Honolulu. Heh! There were too many Japanese there." He chuckled at the military's quandary. And then he relaxed and shifted so he was facing me.

I was about to hear a story.

February 1942 - Honolulu, Hawai'i

Military law had been imposed. Civilians were moved off military bases, a strict curfew had been instituted, and the blackout remained in force. Temporary military headquarters and other buildings were built on non-military sites. Not even the beautiful grounds of the Iolani Palace were spared. Schools were routinely seized by the military, forcing students to hold class in unlikely places such as churches or in parks. Long lines were still the norm at any grocery store and fuel was rationed.

Buzz about disloyal residents had been flying throughout Hawai'i. There was gossip that Japanese-Hawaiians had been in cahoots with the enemy. One rumor was that huge arrows had been carved in sugar cane fields and had pointed Japanese war planes toward military bases during the December 7th attack. Another rumor was that fishing boats floated out to where Japanese submarines waited in order to supply them with food. After a careful investigation by military officials, none of these rumors were ever substantiated.

Doris seemed immune to any of the hatred that enveloped the island, directed at those of Japanese descent. "I was born on this island, a territory of the U.S. I'm a citizen, Dad. Nobody is going to arrest me for anything," she said, attempting to ease her father's mind.

"There's still talk about sending us away, Doris. Let's not bring any attention to ourselves. It's better to play it safe and stay out of the way." But his reasoning was not going to faze Doris in the least. She was determined to be a part of civilian efforts.

"Dad. We're what – thirty percent of the total population of Hawai'i?"

"Forty."

"You think the pineapple and sugar plantations can operate without forty percent of its workforce?"

"We don't all work at plantations."

"You know what I mean, Dad. There's too many of us to take away. It's just not going to happen."

Doris's mom, who was mending a hole in a sock, looked up from the kitchen table. Her daughter made sense even though she was a bit of a hothead.

"Doris, there are rumors that there were citizens among those that General Short took away," Doris's mom injected. She rarely spoke in such a manner so Doris took note.

"What do you mean 'took away'?" Doris was unaware of such a move on the part of the military.

"He ordered almost five hundred people into custody. Mostly Japanese people, but a few Germans and Italians," her mom clarified, "just after the attack. December 10th. They live to this day behind barbed wire."

"How do you know this?" Doris wasn't convinced. She had no idea her mother was keeping up with the news at all, much less in such a detailed way.

"It was in the newspaper. You need to slow down and read. Listen. So you make sound decisions," her mother cautioned her.

"You think we're going to be sent away?" Doris asked. It was the first time she let worry enter her mind.

"No. Too many of us, like you said," her mom assured her. "One hundred forty thousand people, it's too many to move. Too many workers to lose."

Doris slumped down at a chair at the kitchen table next to her mother. "This doggone war is wrecking my life. I just want to be with my friends. They're all getting involved, and I'm stuck here at home."

Her mother looked at her father. "You are a good citizen to want to help. Just slow down, look for a proper way to help. Don't use service as a means to be with your friends. Be sincere about it," her mother advised Doris to the annoyance of her husband. And that was that. Doris had the green light to go ahead in a proper way, whatever that meant. She'd figure it out herself.

Doris had heard of hundreds of civilians, many of them Japanese-Hawaiian, helping soldiers clear the land and then lay barbed wire. Barbed wire was laid in the beaches just offshore around Oahu as well. She thought through this notion and decided laying barbed wire wasn't for her. Another civilian job she would put on her reject list was to dig trenches. In case of another attack, trenches would provide some cover for residents, as would the many shelters that were being built in the ground. People were also called on to assist in making camouflage, huge chunks of which were made to protect certain areas or buildings from being recognized from the air. While she knew how to sew, she thought that the making of camouflage net might be beyond her skill. She decided that anything physical probably wasn't for her. She kept looking.

Civilian volunteers were also helping to pack up precious items from historic sites such as the Iolani Palace. These valuable items, as well as copies of important historical and financial documents, would be sent to the mainland. Censorship of both incoming and outgoing mail had been implemented. While the military mail was handled by military officials, mail of a non-military nature was handled by a civilian office. Office work was right up her alley so this went on her list of possibilities that was growing. As it turned out, Doris would be a welcomed volunteer anywhere.

February 1942 - Masao Gets Orders

While Doris was busy finding a way to volunteer as a civil servant, Masao was patiently waiting for his orders. Shinji had packed up and left the day before. Masao was the last Nisei on base. Every time there was a mail call he would get nervous. He desperately wanted to hear from his Aunt Yukie but worried about being seen with a letter written in Japanese.

He was making his bed in quarters and getting ready for mess call when a staff sergeant marched in.

"Abe?"

"Yes, sir."

"You have orders. You leave at 0800."

"Yes, sir."

"Instructions are listed," he said, handing over the orders. "Good luck, soldier."

"Thank you, sir."

After the staff sergeant was out of the barracks, Masao reviewed the documents. A private looked on from the next row of beds.

"Where are they sending you?"

"Camp Robinson," Masao said. "Somewhere in Arkansas." He didn't waste any time. He was ready to get the heck out of Rockford and head to a warmer climate, although he was hoping for someplace closer to California so he could check on his family in person. He grabbed his duffle bag and began to pack.

February 1942 - Camp Joseph T. Robinson, Little Rock, Arkansas

Being the last Nisei to receive orders had been depressing. Once he got off the train in Little Rock, he could already feel the impact of warmer weather. He guessed that it was in the low fifties, a vast improvement over Rockford. But it still wasn't the dry warmth of the San Bernardino Valley, where temperatures, even in the winter, averaged above sixty and never went below forty.

Now on a military bus, Masao was weighed down by thoughts about his uncle. *Where has he been taken? How is his health? What about his store back home?* The bus made a turn at the main entrance to Camp Robinson where the driver stopped and checked in with one of the guards who gave him the go ahead.

The gears ground as the bus moved forward. Masao could see that this base was larger than Camp Grant and clearly a facility for military basic training. In fact, this sprawling installation boasted over forty-eight thousand square acres in 1942 with over sixty-seven hundred buildings including fifty-two hundred hutments, or soldiers' quarters.

Housed at Camp Robinson was the Medical Replacement Training Center, or MRTC. This program provided the critical training for medics who would be shipped out to battlefields. Since Masao had been through basic medic training at Camp Grant, this was his assignment. He wasn't quite as enthusiastic about being a medic as he might have been. What really excited him was the combat training that was in a heightened state at this facility.

The base was bustling with activity in every direction as far as Masao could see. Camp Robinson hosted the Branch Immaterial Replacement Training Center, or BIRTC. No matter what their specialty, soldiers would be trained at this center for basic infantry skills to prepare them for combat. At the height of war preparations, the BIRTC would continuously run at the capacity of sixteen thousand soldiers at a time. Masao was eager with anticipation; the sounds and sights of soldiers in training excited him.

The bus stopped and the soldiers exited. The benefit of being the only Asian on the bus had been that he'd had a seat all to himself; the downside, he'd had nobody to talk to. He hoped that there would be other Nisei here but as he got off the bus and looked around, he knew he would be alone.

February 25, 1942 - Terminal Island

The panic along the west coast was hitting a feverish pitch. Caucasians feared the possibility that their Japanese neighbors, people they had known for years, were actually the enemy. The media fueled hysteria and U.S. government was equally leery of Japanese residents. Many Issei men, like Tatsuo, had already been arrested and taken away to ensure security measures. But that alone didn't ease the minds of many.

Newspapers were bombarding the west coast with alarm. Headlines were laced with racist remarks that consisted of various emotional statements calling for the immediate removal of every Japanese person. There was little humanity shown. In fact, the more brazen the statement, the bigger audience it drew. The famous columnists of the time such as Westbrook Pegler and Walter Lippmann, the equivalent of today's Rush Limbaugh, fueled the fire of public frenzy with writings that suggested certain Fifth Column activity along the west coast even though government reports had emphasized there was no such activity to fear.

The decision to sign Executive Order 9066, an order that gave the War Relocation Authority and military commanders the discretion to create military areas and secure them as they saw fit, didn't come easy to President Roosevelt. He had faced enormous public and political pressure in the weeks following the Pearl Harbor attack. Powerful men opposed the notion of the relocation of Japanese from the west coast. James H. Rowe, assistant to the U.S. attorney general, wrote a message to the president urging him to consider the constitutional rights of Japanese-Americans. Indeed, the attorney general himself, Francis Biddle, addressed the president directly in an attempt to steer him away from the massive evacuation.

Reasonable voices were no match for the incendiary propaganda, though. Key military personnel were insistent that the west coast was the next target of the Japanese, and they wanted to secure the area quickly. Politicians, eager to please their constituents, jumped on the hateful bandwagon. The newspaper columnists were in heaven; they had the platform to spew abhorrence for Japanese souls far and wide and they did so, repeatedly and loudly. The language in public was becoming more vitriolic as the wrath unfolded. Some Caucasian folks who lived along the west coast recognized the additional golden opportunity of eliminating some of their competition in farming and commerce by way of evacuation, one more reason to make noise about moving the Japanese out.

On February 19, 1942, President Roosevelt made it official when he signed Order 9066. Military commanders wasted no time in establishing military areas and deciding who would be evacuated first. Six days later, on February 25, the military arrived at Terminal Island en masse. The people of Terminal Island, it had been decided, would be the first community to be moved. Signs were posted and the word got out; they had exactly forty-eight hours to take care of business and evacuate the area. Period.

The people of Terminal Island must have been absolutely bewildered, not to mention frightened. They did as they were ordered and rushed to get their affairs in order. Many had property and items they sold dirt-cheap to people who capitalized upon their vulnerabilities. Others just took what they could carry, hoping that they would soon be allowed to return and resume their lives. Most of these people left behind all their furniture, fishing boats, fishing gear, homes, and businesses, not knowing what their future held but hoping for the best. The peaceful little Furusato would never be the same again after that day.

March 18, 1942 - Western Defense Command Post, The Presidio

More officers arrived on the base that had been established as the main nerve center for the War Relocation Authority. Intense discussions took place in top-secret security clearance conferences regarding who should be evacuated from the coastal regions. The voices that carried fear about sabotage and espionage were louder than any levelheaded voice. There were many who feared any and all Japanese no matter how loyal they had proven themselves to be.

"Immediate evacuation of all persons of Japanese lineage, aliens and citizens alike." An officer was reading from an order to the Generals and Administrators who sat around a large conference table.

"Citizens, sir?" Another officer said, requesting clarification.

"A Jap's a Jap. It makes no difference whether the Jap is a citizen or not," General DeWitt snapped back.

"If they have even one drop of Japanese blood, they need to go," another administrator barked out.

"We'll have the signs ready to post in a week, sir. Assembly centers are in place and ready to house evacuees," a young officer eagerly reported. "Our vulnerable areas have already been secured."

General DeWitt nodded in approval at this. Just then, a brave officer posed a question that nobody had thought of.

"Sir, what about our guys here on base?" He was referring to the dedicated Nisei men who were, at that very moment, just down the road in Building 640 on Crissey Field studying the Japanese language, learning how to interrogate and interpret, and ready to engage in military efforts on behalf of the U.S. Army. There was an uneasy feeling in the room; possible enemies were among them on base.

"When will they complete the program?" A lieutenant asked.

"April, sir. They graduate in April."

The lieutenant looked at DeWitt and understood the look on the general's face. There was only one decision that would be acceptable.

"Move 'em out. They can't stay here. The day after graduation, they're gone."

March 1942 - Fort Missoula, Montana

Fort Missoula had been turned over to the Department of Justice and was being used as an Alien Detention Center. The Immigration and Naturalization Service operated out of this location and conducted loyalty hearings of all enemy aliens who would be detained between 1941 and 1944. Fort Missoula would be known as a separate camp from the relocation centers that would house most of the evacuated Japanese and was, in reality, a processing facility before men were sent to Department of Justice prisons.

During this period, there were some twelve hundred Italians, one thousand Japanese and twenty-three Germans who were considered resident aliens. The Italian men were mostly merchant seamen and others had been employees of an Italian luxury liner that had been seized in the Panama Canal. Most, if not all of these men, were simply in the wrong place at the wrong time.

From Tujunga, Tatsuo had been sent to Fort Missoula on a train. An armed guard was stationed on every train car and permitted little movement and less conversation. The shades were always down, day and night. The men, all considered enemies, couldn't open the shades to peek out for a moment, not even to check to see where they were or what direction they were headed. They were not allowed to ask such questions either.

At Fort Missoula, Tatsuo had endured hours of grilling at loyalty hearings in front of as many as five military and/or INS officers. These hearings were conducted to determine whether the men in custody were to be sent to relocation centers or an actual prison. Tatsuo was hoping for a relocation center.

"Do you believe the emperor is the God of Japan?" they had asked him in one of the hearings.

"No. I believe he is the emperor." Tatsuo had been told to respond in Japanese through an interpreter who happened to be Korean. He wasn't sure the interpreter was getting everything right, but understood enough English to be fairly confident. He also wondered why, if this was a loyalty hearing, these people weren't insisting on English-only answers. He certainly knew enough English to respond in English. He wasn't sure what the expectation was, but since he wanted to follow the path that would get him out of custody, he followed their instructions and spoke Japanese.

"About this war, about the attack by the Japanese that brought the U.S. into war, who do you want to win this war? The United States? Or Japan?"

"I came to the United States when I was just sixteen years old. I have lived here longer than I lived in Japan, for twenty-two years now. Most of the man I am is due to how I have been raised in the United States, not due to Japan. I am very appreciative of everything I have learned while living here."

"You haven't answered the question, Mr. Abe," one of the officers spat at him. The interpreter didn't accentuate the disdain, but Tatsuo felt it.

He didn't know how to rationalize what he was feeling. Japan was his country; his citizenship was still attached to Japan. But since he had moved to the States in 1920, he had only rarely visited Japan. He loved his life in San Bernardino and desperately wanted to return to that life as soon as possible. If he estranged himself from Japan in this hearing, which was being recorded, would he ever be allowed to return to Japan? If he estranged himself from the U.S., what would happen to him, to his family?

"Mr. Abe, please answer the question," another officer was insisting.

"I am not interested in this war. I don't care who wins. I just want peace. As soon as possible, I want peace." He thought the answer would satisfy them, but it did far from alleviate their concerns.

To make matters worse, the man he left in charge of his store, Larry Smyth, was pressuring Yukie and Tatsuo into relinquishing ownership. Yukie had been allowed to send letters to Tatsuo and had forwarded Larry's correspondence regarding the store, not wanting to make the decision by herself.

"Tatsuo, we need to decide on this quickly. Customers are dwindling. Nobody wants to buy their goods from a Japanese store. Anything Japanese is very bad. I urge you to change the store to my name as soon as possible in order to save it," Larry, a Caucasian, had written in the latest of a series of letters suggesting that Tatsuo sign the store over, legally, to him.

Tatsuo's house was in Masao's name. It would be safe. But the store, it was a different question.

"There is nothing in the store name that indicates it has Japanese owners. I don't understand how changing the ownership will help," Tatsuo had challenged, but Larry had an answer for that as well.

"Tatsuo, everyone knows that Star Cash Grocery is owned by Tatsuo Abe. Everyone knows it's owned by a Japanese man. That's why nobody is shopping here any longer. What we need to do, quickly, is change the name of the ownership, and change the name of the store. Every other merchant in Little Japan has done this in an attempt to save their property. I am trying to help you, Tatsuo. Don't be a fool."

Tatsuo had a funny feeling about it, but he succumbed to Larry and arranged to have the store put in Larry's name. He was helpless to do anything else since his future was still undetermined. And, in any case, he wouldn't be returning to San Bernardino any time soon. As he mailed the final paperwork that would solidify the deal, he wondered if Star Cash Grocery would ever again be the store it once was.

CHAPTER SEVEN

A LIFE OF LONELINESS

THIS WOULD BE THE FIRST CHRISTMAS WITHOUT DORIS. MASAO HAD assured everyone that he would attend the traditional Christmas Eve dinner, even though he hadn't joined the family for Thanksgiving. The plan was set. Pat would pick Masao up.

"He's not going to come," I said in the car as we were on our way.

"He'll be there," Alan insisted. I looked out the window at the frost along the highway. It had been a cold winter already, cold and depressing.

"I don't think so. Maybe we should come up with a plan." My suggestion only irritated Alan.

We were among the first to arrive. I nervously nibbled on vegetables while I waited for Pat to show up with Masao. Alan detected what was going on in my mind.

"He'll be here, just be patient. Jeez…you're worse than I am." With that, I switched from vegetables to the candy tray.

Eventually Pat's family showed up. They funneled into the house, all eight of them, but no Masao. I was jumping out of my skin to question everyone, but it wasn't my place. I would have to let Alan take the lead on the inquisition. He asked his niece, Katharine, what had happened.

"He was just sitting there in the dark," she reported.

"And you just left him there?" Alan asked with as much objectivity as he could muster. I could tell, though, he was immensely bothered by the vision of his father sitting alone, in the dark, on Christmas Eve.

Katharine's three little children ran around her and she needed to tend to them so Pat's wife, Stephanie, jumped in to explain. "You know, Alan, he just needs to be left alone tonight. He's pretty lonely and I think he just wants to be alone with his thoughts," she said.

"We weren't going to carry him out of his apartment. He would have been kicking and screaming if we had done that." Katharine added.

It all made sense. And it didn't.

Alan looked at me. I looked at him. He didn't have to say a word, I was already getting my shoes on and grabbing my things.

On the way to Masao's, Alan drove fast, weaving in and out of cars, a notable difference from his usual granny-like driving. I was glad, though, I wanted to get to Masao immediately.

We knocked and walked in and, sure enough, it was dark.

"Dad?" Alan called out as he flipped on the light.

Masao was surprised to see us. "Ohhh. You didn't go to Taryn's place?" he asked.

"We were there, but we were worried about you. Come on, let's go. We can go together," Alan suggested.

"Ah. No need. I don't want to go." Masao dug in his heels. I understood. It would be just another reminder that he was alone in the world. But Alan persisted.

"The whole family is there. We're all waiting for you. Come on, let's go." Masao waved him off as he picked up his TV remote.

"How about we go casino," I butted in, phrasing the question the way Masao would. That caught his attention.

"Oh, I go casino!"

Alan looked at me with wonder. I shrugged. I knew what made Masao happy—it was forgetting about his hurting heart. Although Alan hated to gamble and hated the casino in general, he was happy to be going this time; happy that his dad wouldn't be spending the night alone in the dark. As I helped him with his coat, Alan looked on, unsure how it was that I knew his dad better than he did.

"I'm glad to spend Christmas Eve with you," I said softly to Masao who smiled at me.

February 2011 - Doris's One-Year Anniversary

The three of us visited Hawai'i to honor Doris's passing. On the way from the airport, Masao looked out the window, deep in thought about his wife.

"Things sure have changed, boy," he commented occasionally as he watched things go by. He looked for places that he recognized from long ago. "Sandie..." He wanted me to be with him during those moments. "See that place over there?" He pointed to a dilapidated building.

"That building?"

"Yep. That used to be a restaurant. And they used to serve oysters. Realllly good oysters, boy." I knew he was back with Doris. "And Doris and I used to meet there for lunch, every Wednesday we would meet there."

"That's a good memory, Mas." I wanted to keep him in this frame of mind as it provided comfort for him. "What did Doris do after Pearl Harbor?"

"After the attack? Gee...that's a long time ago. The military was in charge then, a-no? They put barbed wire all over the beaches, all around the island. Can you imagine?" He looked at me and I nodded that I was listening. "But Doris, let's see now." And back to 1942 we went.

1942 – Honolulu

The United Service Organization (USO) was expanding rapidly and becoming busy due to the enormous influx of soldiers on the island. Doris found herself a job with one of the USO offices that was housed in the Japanese school she had attended as a young girl.

As a woman, it was a little easier for her to blend in. *Haoles,* Caucasians, thought she was *wahine,* native Hawaiian, and her American first name helped. While some Japanese families had actually changed their surnames to either Hawaiian surnames or European sounding names, Doris's dad refused to make such leaps. And so Doris Okada found her way to a job that suited her in a way that also helped war efforts.

Japanese-American men on the island, second- and third-generation, had a much tougher time. They were immediately considered suspect by military and civilians alike. The University of Hawai'i's ROTC program had been instantly folded into the Hawai'i Territorial Guard. The Hawai'i Territorial Guard, many of them ROTC students without full military training, proudly followed orders and stood guard in key points on the island. Close to seventy-five percent of the guardsmen were of Japanese descent and when the Pentagon realized that in January 1942, orders came down to release all territorial guardsmen who were of Japanese origin, no matter how long their families had lived in Hawai'i. Many Nisei men considered the release the most painful form of rejection from the society they had previously been an integral part of.

The former ROTC cadets, though, weren't about to give up and petitioned Lieutenant General Delos Emmons, who had been appointed as the military governor, to let the ROTC serve in some defense capacity. Emmons was benevolent toward Japanese-Americans and often brought a reasonable voice to outlandish allegations brought forth by other commanders. Emmons agreed to allow the ROTC cadets to serve in the defense effort that would become known as the Varsity Victory Volunteers. These men handled some of the most difficult manual labor the army was assigned. And they did it with pride. The same men would eventually be allowed to enlist in the military, and they did so in droves. Over ninety-five hundred Japanese-American men from Hawai'i tried to enlist in the military. Only twenty-seven hundred were accepted.

At the USO office, Doris kept busy. She worked long hours, often putting in more than the required forty-five hours per week. Men would flirt with her as they came by the office for various needs. They saw her as a demure and subservient wahine, there to fill their masculine needs, but boy, they were wrong. She was friendly, but shut them down if they went too far.

"Hey, baby doll!" one unfortunate haole soldier addressed her as he came into the office with some of his soldier buddies. She immediately bristled, but shook off her frustration and approached the counter.

"What can I do for you, soldier?" she asked politely, without even a hint of interest.

"Well, I'm here to find out about the be-bop this weekend," he said with a wide grin, eager to have an "exotic" woman to talk with. She handed him a flyer that had all the particulars.

"Here you go, all the information you'll need," she said flatly, hoping to extinguish his enthusiasm. He took the flyer without taking his eyes off of her. She was tiring quickly.

"Are you gonna be there?"

She was already heading back to her desk. "No."

"What?! Why not? What's a dish like you working in an office like this for, anyway?"

That was it.

She stood up from her desk, braced her arms on it and inhaled deeply. "Listen here, soldier, I'm not a call-girl. Why don't you get lost before I get on the horn and call your CO." Other girls in the office noticed the interaction but weren't surprised. They had seen Doris routinely shut soldiers down.

"All right, all right, no need to blow a fuse," he chuckled with arrogance. "This one's a dud, let's go fellas," he announced as he grabbed the flyer and headed for the door. Doris waved them off. These guys coming from the mainland were like toddlers in a new sandbox. They both loved being around women of color and were extremely awkward around them.

One day a handsome Nisei walked into the office. He was dressed in volunteer clothes, and she knew right away this was a guy who had done the hardest labor the army could hand out hoping to be allowed to enlist.

"May I help you?" Doris asked as she met him at the counter.

"Hi, uh, me and some of my buddies were wondering if volunteers were allowed to attend the dance this weekend."

He seemed like a guy who had been condescended to by soldiers, looked down on, even laughed at, in his attempt to prove himself loyal like so many other Nisei and Sansei men.

Doris glanced out to the front of the building and saw a group of other Nisei guys, all in the same dirty condition, waiting patiently. "Sorry. No. Those functions are strictly for military men. Volunteers can't get in." She hated to deliver the bad news to him.

"Okay, thanks. It was worth asking," his voice was low.

"What's your name?" Doris asked. It came from out of nowhere. The girls in the office almost fell off their chairs. Never had the attractive, sought-after Doris shown any interest in the men who had come through the office. The young man stopped and turned toward her.

"Oh, I beg your pardon, I should have introduced myself. I'm George." He held out his hand to shake hers then pulled it back. "Ah, sorry, I'm still grimy from work."

"It's okay, I don't mind," and she held out her hand to shake his. She liked the feel of him and she liked his eyes, they were honest.

"I'm Doris. Nice to meet you, George. You have the same name as my father." George nodded at this and smiled. "Say, George, if you're looking for a little fun, there's a gathering this weekend up in Manoa, a bunch of friends of mine are getting together for a barbeque. You interested?"

George was quick with his answer. "Sure. Can I bring some of my buddies?"

"Why not?" As Doris wrote down directions to the local hall he gazed at her. He liked the shape of her face and that she wasn't afraid to be forward. *She must be a pretty independent girl*, he thought. He liked that too.

From that moment on, George and Doris became an item. They relied on each other for strength when they felt overwhelmed by rumors or racist remarks. They spent time together and, as much as they could, traveled around Oahu discovering wonderful spots to have a picnic or neck. One of their favorite places to picnic, though, was right there in Waikiki, just adjacent to Fort DeRussy. They would sit together in the soft sand as long as they could, often watching the sunset before rushing to get home by curfew. They found ways to maintain bits of normal, Hawaiian life in the midst of confusion.

February 2011 – Hawai'i

We walked along Waikiki Beach, the same stretch that Doris and George had strolled along some seventy years earlier. Masao had been chatty all week. Being in Honolulu had sparked memories, and he was eager to share his stories. This morning, though, I was going to meet one of his war buddies. Saburo Nakamura, who went by Naki, had served in the South Pacific with Masao. I was delighted to meet someone from Masao's past.

We met at a breakfast place near Fort DeRussy in Waikiki. Fort De-Russy is an innocuous looking facility situated on a beautiful park on Waikiki Beach. It was a battery operated and manned by the 16th Coast

Artillery, one of several batteries that guarded the coast of Oahu in 1941. These forts were equipped with anti-aircraft guns, some of which had brought down enemy planes on the morning of December 7th. Now a museum, it showcases the various heroes who have emerged in wars and battles since 1924 when it was established.

We wheeled Masao to the breakfast place that was only a few blocks from the condo. Naki was waiting for us. My immediate impression of Naki was that he was a warm, congenial, gentle man, much like Masao. He was quick to smile and seemed humble in ways that I would never understand.

Watching the two men banter at breakfast was heartwarming. It was as if they had shed their elder bodies and were back in the thick of the 1940s, a couple of twenty-somethings who had survived the horrors of war. The inside jokes were rampant; Alan and I had no chance of appreciating the humor but laughed along anyway just because it was entertaining to see these guys and their youthful energy. There wasn't a lot of room in the conversation for me to insert questions, so I just enjoyed their company.

When we left the restaurant we walked Naki to his car. Masao's physique was still very trim, if not too thin, but Naki had grown some in the waistline and that seemed to make his stride a little uneven. Masao, from the wheelchair being pushed by Alan, had the audacity to give Naki shit about this.

"Goddamn, Naki, you walk like an old man!" he spouted. But Naki was also a little hard of hearing, and Masao's really great line, literally, fell on deaf ears. Or maybe that was Naki's way of being polite since Alan and I were there. It was illuminating to see Masao in this light, turning back into the soldier he had once been, reliving his younger days with one of the few men in the world who understood World War II the way he did.

Masao wanted to be sure to show me some of the places on the island that were important to him. We drove by the condo unit that he and Doris had stayed in for months at a time, we ate at Zippy's many times because they had good *saimin* and we ate at the Prince Court buffet because it was one of Doris's favorite places. And of course, we visited Doris where she was interred at the Punchbowl almost every day.

The Punchbowl boasts the most gorgeous and breathtaking views of Honolulu you can imagine. The National Memorial Cemetery of the Pacific, or the Punchbowl as most people know it, has a rich history, as do many sites on Hawai'i. The Hawaiian name for the area is Puowaina, or Hill of Sacrifice. The crater was formed by volcanic activity some seventy-five thousand years ago. Puowaina has seen evolution in full. Human sacrificials were performed there very early on. It was used as a rifle range at one point, and during WWII, tunnels were dug throughout the rim of the crater to shore up the batteries below.

The notion of placing a cemetery at this location had been considered in the 1890s but had been rejected because the island people didn't want a town of the dead situated above the living. After WWII there was public pressure to designate a cemetery in the Pacific to bury the remains of fallen soldiers, lost either through battle in the Pacific Theater or in Japanese POW camps. In July 1949, the cemetery officially opened. Ultimately over thirteen thousand military men who died during WWII would find final rest at the Punchbowl.

Names on the grave markers and on columbarium units are a testament to the melting pot the United States has become. The ethnicities of men and women who served our great country from around the world are represented there: Hawaiian, Japanese, Irish, Jewish, Italian, Latino, Pacific Islander, and others. Doris's niche was located in the columbarium. I would fix roses and arrange them at the foot. Masao would sit with his private thoughts about his beloved Doris for several moments with his head down, his hand shielding his eyes. I was never sure whether he was crying or avoiding the sun but suspected the former. After he had finished his private and silent conversation with Doris, he would come back to us.

"I think Shiro is up here somewhere," Masao said one morning while visiting Doris. I didn't know who Shiro was or how he fit into Masao's history but helped to look for his niche. We found it and paid our respects, and Masao lingered at Shiro's niche too. This Shiro was obviously important to Masao and I wondered why. The puzzle was just getting more and more complicated, but I was determined to figure it out.

Tuesday, March 29, 2011 – Our Routine

At the casino buffet, we had finished the main course, and I was onto the dessert bar. According to our routine, I would select Mas's favorite sweets:

apple pie or cobbler with a dollop of ice cream, strawberry shortcake, and strawberries dipped in chocolate — just a little bit of each. He would wave me off when I would set the assortment of goodies down in front of him, but he would always eat at least a few bites.

"You know, my uncle." Mas had a big bite of strawberry shortcake in his mouth.

I looked up from the lemon meringue pie I was devouring. "Tatsuo?"

"That's right, Tatsuo," he said, scooping a spoonful of vanilla ice cream. "He ended up in a prison."

"What? Why?" I was completely confused by this. I figured that he had been sent back to San Bernardino with Yukie and that they were both, eventually, interned together. As I was about to find out, that was far from the case.

"You see, people like him, he was considered the enemy. An enemy alien, that's what they called him. He was the president of the local Japanese Association." Mas ate another bite of shortcake. "And I think that made the FBI suspicious."

April 1942 - Fort Missoula, Montana

"Abe." The guard stood at his detention unit with papers in hand.

Tatsuo walked over to the door.

"You're being moved to a different location. Pack up."

Tatsuo packed hoping that his loyalty hearing had earned him the chance to be reunited with Yukie. With his suitcases in hand he boarded the train that would take him to yet another unknown destination.

The train ride was longer than the ride from Tujunga to Missoula. It took days and the prisoners were only allowed off once every four hours to use facilities. The shades were drawn the entire time. Prisoners had no clue where they were going or for how long.

Eventually the train slowed and the POWs were let off. Tatsuo would learn that he was in Louisiana at a military facility called Camp Livingston. He would be detained here for weeks until he would be sent to another facility, a prison, in Santa Fe, New Mexico. *That's what you do with prison-*

ers of war, he thought, *you keep them moving and mixed up so they don't have a chance to congregate.* What the U.S. military didn't understand, though, was that these particular prisoners hadn't had a reason to unite until they became prisoners of war.

Being considered an enemy wasn't what bothered Tatsuo. It was being away from his family, from his little girl that he missed, and his new little baby that Yukie might have to deliver all on her own. He missed his grocery store and his way of life in California. He thought himself a fool for turning the grocery store over to his manager. He thought himself a fool for sending all his hard earned money to Japan. From what he had heard, Japanese banks had folded. Assets had been seized and were being used by the Japanese government to further military efforts. He had nothing — less than nothing. How would he manage once he was released, *if* he were released?

As he and the other prisoners were escorted to their new detention cells behind barbed wire, he thought about Yukie. She was now four months pregnant and must be tired. He wondered what his daughter, Kathleen, looked like now and if she was close to crawling. His heart ached as he realized all the wonderful things he was missing with his little girl. He wondered if his nephew, Masao, had been shipped out to Europe yet. And he worried about Star Cash Grocery and what had become of it.

April 1942 - Terminal Island

The once cozy town of Terminal Island sat empty. Many of the fishing boats owned by the Japanese townspeople had been sold at dirt-cheap prices, those that remained had been seized by the government and would be transformed and somehow used to advance military efforts. Houses still held the belongings of their absent owners. Tuna Street, a once bustling area of commerce, was a ghost town.

The bulldozers arrived in April 1942, and went to work. When they were done not a single home would remain. One by one they were razed and the debris hauled off. The Shinto Shrine – gone. The meticulously groomed Japanese gardens – bulldozed over. The businesses that lined Tuna Street were all demolished. Nothing was spared, not even Walizer

Elementary School. The entire village of Terminal Island and everything recognizable was gone, flattened to the ground.

All that would remain after the bulldozers had done their job were the canneries. Everything else would vanish. There would be no hint of a village, no sign of the Japanese fishing life, no indication that there had been the existence of the little Furusato that over three thousand people had called home. What had once been Terminal Island had now disappeared forever without a trace.

The people of Terminal Island, unaware that their little town had vanished, had been bussed to the Santa Anita Race Track east of Pasadena where a temporary assembly center had been built in a rush. While U.S. government propaganda videos touted spacious housing with plenty of healthy and nourishing food for all, these assembly centers were actually converted horse stalls. The stench of horse manure permeated the living and eating quarters but residents made the best of it. Japanese residents would remain there for several months until their new "home" at Manzanar was ready. Since people were allowed to take only what they could carry during the abrupt evacuation, many families could occupy each hastily built barrack. Barbed wire surrounded the converted race track. Nobody was allowed out and nobody was allowed in. Rules were strict. The government wasn't taking any chances with aliens who lived among the loyal and it did a great job reminding everyone along the west coast that it was impossible to tell the difference between the two.

While the War Relocation Authority was making the signs that would announce to the Japanese-American population living along the coast where to report for evacuation, it was also churning out more propaganda ensuring the rest of Americans that they would soon be safe. They were rounding up all possible security risks. One propaganda video, narrated by the Director of the War Relocation Authority, Milton S. Eisenhower, began by reporting that the evacuation was necessary in order to protect American interests against sabotage and espionage. He spoke about how great the evacuation was for everyone, explaining what good Americans we were to be taking care of people who could very well be our enemy. The background music elicited hopefulness, optimism, and patriotism. While he acknowledged that many Japanese had made great financial sacrifices, he assured listeners that they had done so quite cheerfully, ready and willing to prove their loyalty.

He spoke of a place called Manzanar where the people of Terminal Island would end up after they had been at the Santa Anita assembly center for a few months. Manzanar was a four-hour bus ride that would take these people out to the middle of nowhere. The summers would be scorching and the winters would be frigidly cold. It was dry and dusty, as most other internment camps would also prove to be.

Manzanar was billed as a place where the land was raw but full of opportunity, ready for the Japanese to claim and turn green with their skillful and loyal hands. Of course, barbed wire surrounded this new home as well. Some of those who would be interned at Manzanar would eventually prove themselves worthy enough to work on private farms in the area as labor, but only because labor was at an all-time shortage. These laborers were paid very little and were under guard while away from their camp.

The Japanese people were taken advantage of in just about every way possible and yet still remained loyal to the U.S.

For the people of Terminal Island, the men in particular, this must have been a trying time. They were fishermen by trade. Fishermen. They had no experience in the area of farming. But the people of Terminal Island weren't afraid to get their hands dirty. In fact, they had a name for themselves, *Yogores*, meaning dirty on the outside, but pure and clean hearts within. And so the people of Terminal Island, along with many others from California, Oregon, and Washington, made places like the Manzanar their home, hoping for the day when they would be allowed to return to their real homes.

April 1942 - Star Cash Grocery, San Bernardino, CA

Tatsuo's fears were completely founded. His once tidy store with organized and well-stocked shelves had become disorderly and cluttered. His customers, who were actually very loyal to Tatsuo and continued to shop at his store even in his absence, were taken aback when they discovered they no longer had credit.

"It's not good business to extend credit," Larry pontificated to Tatsuo's favorite Latino families, "especially to a bunch of wetback migrant workers."

And to Tatsuo's American Indian customers, Larry was even more foul.

"You want to trade groceries for *this*?!" He would laugh as he waved the hand-woven baskets in the air as though they were worthless. "Take your dumb red bartering somewhere else." Humiliated and embarrassed, the local American Indians soon withdrew from Third Street altogether.

Ben Miller dared to come around the store to inquire as to when Tatsuo might be returning. "Excuse me, sir?" he asked politely from the back door of the store.

Larry approached, towering over Ben. "What do you want?"

"I was just wondering about Mr. Abe. Have you heard word on when he might return?"

Larry looked like he might haul off and clobber Ben on the chin, but instead just gave him a glare.

"He ain't comin' back. You Injuns are all the same, boy, like rats looking for any scrap of free food. Now get outta' here."

"Thank you." Ben backed away from the door, but only after he'd had a chance to look around Tatsuo's office area.

"And don't come around here again!" Larry yelled out as he slammed the door. Inside the store, Larry took stock. Business had not been good. He hated Tatsuo for having the type of personality that attracted the wrong kind of customer. Larry wanted to attract the right kind of customer: good, white, Christian folk. But he wasn't having much luck with that.

Outside the back of the store Ben made sure Larry was busy being hateful inside, then looked at the garbage can. He suspected that Larry had disposed of Tatsuo's personal and precious items now absent from the office inside. He quietly lifted the lid of the garbage can and looked inside. He dug through newspapers, bottles, and cans. He was about to give up when he spotted something at the bottom. He dug a little deeper, checking the back door to make sure Larry didn't come out, ready to run off if he did.

There it was — the picture of Tatsuo, Yasoshichi, and their father, the one that had hung on the wall in the back room. This was the picture that Ben had noticed and commented on months earlier when he and Tatsuo were sharing whiskey together. Ben carefully wiped off the grime and set it aside. He dug again. From under stained and smelly newspaper, Tatsuo's wall clock peeked out. Ben reached in with both hands and gently pulled it from the rubbish. He tucked the valuable items into an old potato sack and rushed down the alley to safety before Larry was any the wiser.

April 1942 - The Presidio

By the end of March, the Selective Service was notified to no longer accept any persons of Japanese descent for service within any branch of the armed forces, whether they were citizens or not. Not only that, the War Department also declared that any current soldier of Japanese extraction would not be sent overseas. The leaders of the Military Intelligence Service, including Captain Rasmussen, became increasingly frustrated with the mixed signals within the military. What was the point of training all the Nisei soldiers for interrogation and interpretation if they were not going to be deployed to the South Pacific because they were not allowed to leave the shores of the U.S.?

To complicate matters for the MIS, word had arrived that they were no longer welcome on the Presidio. Once the current class completed the program at the end of April, they were to vacate. The Western Defense Command was eager to proclaim the west coast completely clear of any and all Japanese, including military men. The joyful visits to the heart of San Francisco, just a street car away from the Presidio, had all but stopped for the Nisei soldiers. They had heard one too many horrible comments and decided that staying on base was safer.

This was a confusing and complicated time, a part of American history that is hard to comprehend in the mind or understand in the heart. Occurring from the very same location, the Presidio, one arm of the military was in charge of the massive ethnic evacuation along the west coast. Meanwhile, under another arm of the same military branch, Captain Rasmussen was frantically trying to recruit Nisei soldiers stationed along the west coast for his next class of the MIS. The location of the MIS Language School was yet to be determined, and it was unclear if the graduates of the program would even be utilized as intended, but Rasmussen still persevered.

Citizens along the west coast had mixed feelings about the evacuation of Japanese people. Milton Eisenhower, brother to General Eisenhower and director of the War Relocation Authority, was outwardly supportive of the massive evacuation along the west coast. Inwardly, though, he struggled with this process, stating at one point that history would prove it a mistake. He resigned within months of accepting the position of director.

The reasonable voices that questioned the constitutionality of such an act on the part of the government were quickly extinguished by the louder voices that fanned the flames of fear. Walter Lippman and Westbrook Pegler kept fear alive and fueled it with continuous newspaper columns insisting that Fifth Column Activities along the west coast were a certainty.

The vitriol for the Japanese was everywhere. "Slap the Jap" posters were sold for a mere twenty-five cents to anyone who needed a reminder that Japs were treacherous, faithless, untrustworthy, inhuman, depraved, soulless, and disloyal, among other scurrilous traits. Storefronts and public facilities were festooned with signs that told Japs to "Keep Out – You Rats." Merchants had advertisements indicating their loyalty to America by expressing hatred toward the Japanese, "We Don't Want Any Japs Back Here...EVER!." Headlines in newspapers announced the "Ouster of All Japs." In some areas, people of Chinese blood wore buttons to distinguish themselves from Japanese, not wanting to be associated. There was nothing too severe you could do to a person of Japanese descent. Every hateful act, such as spitting on them, and every vile and racist comment aimed at them, along with the anger that could be directed at them, all of it was deemed acceptable.

Young and old alike, all the Japanese in California, Oregon, and Washington were tagged and funneled through assembly centers before finally being sent to one of the relocation camps, each flanked with barbed wire and surrounded by armed guards. They were forced to leave behind many precious items and family treasures.

On the Presidio, Captain Rasmussen was busy on three points: graduating his first class of MIS interpreters, recruiting his next class, and determining a new location for the MIS Language School to appease the Western Defense Command leaders, namely Lt. General DeWitt. To find a new location, Captain Rasmussen was included in a high-ranking meeting in Salt Lake City that was attended by the governors and other representatives of eleven western states. On the agenda was the consideration of geographic areas that were appropriate for the relocation facilities as well as the location of the MIS facility. This meeting did not go well.

"If you bring Japanese into my state, I promise you they will be hanging from every tree," one governor fumed during the meeting. There was such hostility that Captain Rasmussen wondered if there was any state that would accept the MIS. None of these eleven states wanted to be burdened with any program that involved Japanese personnel, evacuees, or prisoners of war.

After the debacle of a meeting in Salt Lake City, Captain Rasmussen kept scouting for a new location for the language school. Eventually, he met with the governor of Minnesota who was willing to accommodate this military effort. There was a glitch, though. There was only one army base in Minnesota, Fort Snelling in the Minneapolis/St. Paul area, and this base was already operating at full capacity. There was simply no space to house a language school. But the governor was very eager to help and suggested using a former Civilian Conservation Corps facility that was located in Savage, a small town about ten miles away from Fort Snelling. It was currently being used to house indigent men, but the governor offered to relocate them to free up the space. Captain Rasmussen was delighted and on April 7, the move was approved by the War Department.

Rasmussen returned to the Presidio to work out his other frustrations; namely, how to get the military at large to understand and appreciate the strategic tool they had in the Nisei soldiers who had just gone through five months of interrogation/interpretation training. He had successfully located the whereabouts of 150 Nisei and had them lined up for the second class of the MIS, which would now be facilitated at Camp Savage, Minnesota. But he worried about what would come of the soldiers who were ready to deploy.

Publicly, and to the ranks of the military, the message was that no Japanese military men would leave the shores of the U.S. Among only the highest ranking officers, the top-secret missions involving American soldiers of Japanese descent were understood as necessary, and on rare occasions, accepted. With that philosophy in place, on May 1, 1942, there was a small graduation ceremony for the forty Nisei who had successfully completed the language school. Soon after, approximately twenty soldiers of the MIS Language School were shipped out to destinations unknown. The remaining soldiers and officers packed up and headed for Minnesota.

As June approached, Yukie in San Bernardino couldn't deny the evacuation signs that were posted on telephone poles all over town. Now six months pregnant, she packed what she could and boxed everything else up. She hoped that, at the very least, the house would be intact upon her return. As she packed, she wondered if Tatsuo would be with her when their second child arrived in September. She didn't care where they were, she just wanted to be with her husband again.

The defense preparations and the massive evacuation let the Western Defense Command claim success and assure the fine citizens along the west coast that the Japanese among them were no longer a threat. They had all been moved off the coast. Citizens were warned to be on the lookout and report anyone who appeared to be Japanese, even if they were wearing a military uniform. Building 640 on Crissey Field, the building that had housed the MIS since November of 1941, stood empty. The homes, farms, and businesses that had been occupied and run by Japanese had been vacated, taken over, and/or looted. The fear-mongers had won. The voices of reason had stopped trying to bring reason to an unreasonable effort.

In the still of night in early June 1942, the *SS Maui* entered through the Golden Gate Strait beneath the magnificent Golden Gate Bridge and under the watchful eye of soldiers who filled the pillboxes embedded in the bluffs on either side of the strait. The *SS Maui* docked at a port in Oakland where over fourteen hundred Nisei, members of the Hawai'i Territorial Guard, opened secret orders, learning they were now part of the 100th Infantry Battalion. These men disembarked and quickly filled one of three waiting trains, blacked-out and shades drawn, that immediately left once everyone was on board. The destination was Camp McCoy, Wisconsin. The trains would take different routes to arrive at the same destination, another ploy to keep the passengers hidden from the general public and from other military personnel.

The public was never notified. Soldiers of lesser rank were not privy. There would be many times that Nisei soldiers were transported in secrecy and only the highest ranking officers would be aware. By late June, the Nisei soldiers at Camp McCoy were training as the newly designated 100th Infantry Battalion - Separate. The "Separate" designation indicated that the battalion had no home, it would be an orphan unit until it could attach to a division many months later.

At the same time, the new MIS language school class of one hundred fifty Nisei soldiers was entering the first phase of training at Camp Savage. Meanwhile, at Camp Robinson, Masao wondered if he would ever see another Nisei. He was lonely, and he craved rice. He resigned himself to the fact that neither of these desires would be satisfied any time soon.

Tuesday, April 5, 2011 - A Trip to the Doctor

When Alan asked me to take his dad to the doctor, I thought nothing of it. I arrived at Masao's place and assumed I would be driving, but he grabbed his car keys on the way out.

"I drive today," he announced. *He must still be feeling like a kid from our visit with Naki*, I thought. I had not driven with Masao before but figured he must be a competent driver. After all, he seemed confident. We approached Masao's Honda. I walked close by him as he was a little shaky on his cane, but he insisted on using that rather than rely on a rolling walker. Those were for old people. He got in the driver's side, and I got in the passenger side noticing a new scrape along the back door.

"What happened back there?" I asked as I got in. "It looks like a new dent. Did someone back into you or something?"

Masao was busy starting up the car and chuckled at my question. "I guess I got a little too close to that cement pole thing." I looked around and saw no cement poles near his car. *How often does he go out for a spin?* As we made our way to Seattle, a city of many hills, I sat back and enjoyed the ride that quickly turned into an adventure.

We were in the left turning lane at a busy intersection at one point. It was a yield-to-oncoming-traffic left turn. Evidently, Masao didn't know that because when the light turned green he made his left turn as though he had the right of way. Cars screeched and honked as they came within inches of my side of the car. I heard myself yelp as I looked over at Masao who seemed oblivious at first, but then he gunned it to get out of the way.

"Yikes!" I said, not wanting to embarrass him.

"They must have changed that light, a-no?"

I nodded, "Maybe so." I felt myself perspire and became hyper vigilant. I noticed that he could barely see over the wheel and, all of a sudden, he looked really small in the driver's seat.

We drove around in circles for a while. *He must be looking for a parking space.* I glanced at my watch. We had twenty minutes to get to his appointment so I continued to watch the Mr. Magoo-like operation and kept the fearing-for-my-life screams inside. Just as I was about to give up hope, he turned into a parking garage and parked, but left the engine running.

"Are we here?"

He shook his head no. He seemed more than exasperated, he seemed sad. In that brief moment, I got it. He was lost. I knew it, and he knew that I knew it. He was embarrassed and disappointed.

"What's the name of the building your doctor is in?"

"It's the medical building or the dental building. Something like that."

"The medical/dental building?"

He looked over at me with hope-filled eyes. "That sounds right. Are we there?" Maybe he did drive us to the right place after all. Sadly, the medical/dental building was blocks away. I didn't have to say anything. He saw it on my face.

"You know, downtown changes so much all the time, it's easy to forget where things are. I have trouble too," I assured him, but it did no good. I could see him sink in his own doubt. He sat there assessing his next loss. "It won't be long before they take my car away."

"Who?" I couldn't take the answer.

"My boys. They think I shouldn't be driving anymore."

Here he was, a warrior, a Purple Heart recipient, a Bronze Star proudly hanging around his neck, and completely vulnerable. I didn't know how to respond.

"Losing my car…it's going to be like getting my legs chopped off," he said, almost to himself.

How does this happen? I wondered. *How does it get to the point that you don't recognize city streets that you've driven down a thousand times?* The city grows and covers up familiarity, progress eating away at history, one building at a time. This man had seen it all, every piece of the industrial revolution from wood-burning cars to hybrids. He was like a walking, breathing history book. A treasure.

While I tried to come up with a gentle way to take the wheel, he looked around the garage. I decided that taking him back to his past might be a good way to comfort him.

"Hey, Mas." He looked over. "You never told me about Camp Robinson. How long were you there?" It worked. He was going back in time, pictures were forming in his mind.

"That was, uh, Camp Joseph T. Robinson. In Arkansas, near Little Rock. Jeez. That was a long time ago, now. Let's see, I was there from February of forty-two, til, jeez, early forty-four, I guess. I don't remember. Anyway, I had medic training," he paused. The pictures in his mind were becoming clear. "The camp, it was just gearing up, a-no? Just after the attack. They had me working for a dentist, a major, a real nice guy. He treated me like a regular soldier, a-no? Major Hall. That was his name."

Summer 1942 - Camp Joseph T. Robinson

With the influx of thousands of soldiers, the clinic chairs in the waiting room were filled. The dentist, Doctor Major Hall, worked on cases as fast as he could.

"Soldier, when was the last time you brushed your teeth?" Major Hall asked a patient one day.

"I don't remember," the soldier responded with instruments in his mouth. Masao cringed and instinctively reached for a mask to put on. Major Hall nodded, indicating the mask was a good idea. They were both mortified by the tooth decay they encountered on a daily basis.

The two had a great working relationship, and Masao never felt any hint of dislike or racism coming from Major Hall. It was the one place on base and in Little Rock that Masao felt unguarded. Still, he wanted something more. He wanted to be in combat training. He regularly applied for different military positions and was regularly rejected.

"What happened to the 10th Army Division?" Major Hall asked Masao while working on a patient one day. Major Hall knew of Masao's desire to be on the battlefield and not only empathized with him but encouraged him. The 10th Army Division had a ski unit, and Masao had some experience skiing. He had been excited to apply.

"Application rejected," Masao answered flatly as he handed a different tool over. The major pondered this while he worked.

"Did they give a reason?"

"No. No reason. I can't imagine it would matter that I'm Japanese in the mountains in Italy. But..."

"It's a tough situation, Abe. Don't give up," Major Hall suggested after a few minutes. But Masao was beginning to realize that the American military didn't know what to do with him. To the U.S. Army he felt as if he was nothing more than a threat, a threat that must be watched.

❖　❖　❖

Masao's uncanny ability to find the best food in town led him to a diner in Little Rock. He would end up there whenever he was on leave or given a one-day pass. Since he was always alone, he had to figure out a way to keep the wolves at bay when it came to his heritage. There weren't many Asians in Little Rock and Japanese-Americans were almost non-existent.

The waitress, Meg, brought a T-bone steak dinner and set it in front of Masao who sat at the counter one day. He immediately cut into it and savored the warm, thick protein as he chewed.

"For a little guy, you sure do eat a lot," Meg said with a smile.

"We can't get good food like this on base," he answered with his mouth full. She brought him a cup of coffee. He had become a regular, and she knew what he wanted even before he asked.

"Thank you." Masao smiled and reached for the sugar as he stuffed another bite of steak in his mouth. Down the counter, a man stared daggers at him.

"You there. Soldier." The man said loudly. Other patrons looked over.

His mouth full, Masao motioned for him to wait a minute. But the man didn't want to wait.

"Where are you from, anyway?" he demanded. The other diners looked at Masao. They also wanted to know. He stood out. He was the only person of color in the diner.

"He's an Indian. From southern California. The Chappo tribe, right?" Meg answered for him.

Chappo. It's what all the Mexican customers called Tatsuo. Masao had capitalized on this and turned the nickname into a tribal title that saved him the agony of explaining his Japanese existence. Masao nodded to Meg, letting her know she had it right and stuffed another piece of meat into his mouth so he didn't have to talk.

"Christ Almighty. I guess they'll let anyone wear a uniform these days. At least you ain't a Jap," the man stammered and turned away.

"Good Lord, Buford. The Army ain't gonna let the Japanese join. What are you thinking?" Meg laughed as she topped off Masao's cup with hot coffee.

Masao focused on his food. He felt vindicated, and not. He was, unfortunately, getting used to routine verbal assaults on his race. Nobody liked the Japanese. Nobody. On base, he was living in isolation among the troops. Soldiers in his quarters would make small talk with him, but he always ate alone. It made him appreciate Major Hall even more. But Masao would be losing his only ally.

"Can you take me with you?" Masao pleaded in pure desperation when Major Hall announced his new orders. "As an assistant?"

"It doesn't work like that, Abe." Major Hall would be shipping out for Europe. "You'll get your orders, just be patient."

The dentist who replaced Major Hall wasn't talkative. It was all business. Masao wasn't sure if the guy was racist or just cold, but he no longer enjoyed working at the clinic and kept looking for opportunities in the army.

One morning, Masao heard a sound coming from outside. He scanned out the window diverting his attention from his job. Soldiers were marching, and in his imagination he was with them. Feet moving in perfect unison.

"Abe. Abe." The new dentist, Dr. Vance, needed a tool. Masao handed it over and returned his attention to the formation of soldiers.

"What outfit is that?" Masao asked to no one in particular. Dr. Vance glanced out the window, then looked at Masao. He could see what was going on, the longing in Masao's eyes.

"Those guys are paratroopers. They've run three miles in their boots before you get out of bed in the morning." Dr. Vance was being condescending. Translation: don't even think about trying to be a paratrooper. But that didn't stop Masao from finding out how to apply.

Masao faithfully waited for orders that never came. All he received was a rejection letter from his paratrooper application.

His military career appeared dismal at best.

❖   ❖   ❖

I heard the soft chime of my phone; a text message had arrived. This would be Alan checking to see if we'd made it to the doctor's on time. I ignored it and instead focused on Masao. If there was more to this story, the doctor could wait. Masao was still back in 1942, a young soldier eager to serve his country, despite the weight of his Japanese race impeding his progress at every turn. At the core he was a soldier, a young man, like all the other young men who were ready for battle, ready for combat.

"We should go, a-no? I just wish I could remember how to get there."

Masao was trying to muster the energy to get us to the doctor's office. I paused before I answered. "How about I drive? I know exactly where it is and I think it might be a little quicker." He looked like a man defeated. "Nobody has to know. It will be our little secret." I assured him.

He smiled and nodded.

From the doctor's office I texted Alan "of course we made it on time," even though we were twenty minutes late.

Tuesday, June 21, 2011 - Fried Egg Sandwich

I pulled into the garage and parked. As I got out, I glanced at the parking spot that used to house Masao's car. The spot sat empty. The wall sign labeled ABE had been removed as well. His parking spot now waited for a new resident to claim it until their sons or daughters decided to take that last freedom away. Masao's prediction had been correct. It wasn't long after our trip to the doctor's office that Alan and his brothers made the decision to sell the Honda. The decision was swift, and the loss was heavy for Masao. I assured him that I hadn't breathed a word of our adventure. And I hadn't.

He was just sitting down to eat. He had prepared a fried egg sandwich, one of his favorite things to eat. He toasted thick sliced bread that he and Alan bought from a Japanese bakery, made a fried egg, and added tomato and lettuce. It looked very tasty.

"I make you one if you want!" he offered.

"No, no. I had breakfast. Thanks, though." I watched him enjoy his meal and noticed that he had Doris's walker in the living room. I suspected he was relying on the walker more and more while in the privacy of his own home.

"Did I tell you about President Roosevelt?" Masao asked in between bites as he turned down the TV.

"No, you didn't." I was eager to hear about this. "What about President Roosevelt? Did you meet him?"

Masao munched on a bite of his sandwich and smiled. He was both nodding and shaking his head at the same time. *This is going to be complex,* I thought.

"President Roosevelt, he came to Camp Robinson for inspection. That was an exciting day, boy."

April 18, 1943 - Palm Sunday

President Roosevelt Makes Inspection

Anticipation filled the air at Camp Robinson. Masao was making his area perfect: bed - made, foot locker - clean, floor - swept. At 0800 they were to be lined up on either side of the road that President Roosevelt would be chauffeured along. The president would be making inspection at precisely 0830. The entire town of Little Rock had heard the news and had made signs to greet the president all along the railroad route.

"I can't believe we're actually going to meet the president," said the PFC in the bed next to Masao.

"He's not going to shake the hands of ten thousand guys, you know?" Masao tried to calm his comrade but it was no use. He was equally as excited. At last he would feel like he was a part of the military he served; he would feel like a soldier among soldiers. He felt lucky to witness such an historical event.

"Who cares! At least we'll get to see him!" the PFC was saying as he smoothed out the last wrinkle on his bed. Just then a first sergeant marched into their quarters. There were salutes all around. The first sergeant went straight to Masao and handed him a paper.

"Good news, corporal. A one-day pass. You don't have to stand for inspection."

Masao took the pass but was confused. The first sergeant was packaging the one-day pass as a gift. But this was no gift. Masao was hoping it was all a mistake.

"Go hide yourself," the first sergeant said, pounding in the final nail. Then he spun on his heel and marched out.

Masao stood with his one-day pass in his hand, stunned. The sergeant's words echoed in his ears. Nearby soldiers looked on briefly before they continued about their business. Not one of them came to the comfort of Masao. Not one of them cared if the Jap among them was left out of the magnificent presidential visit. Masao tried to conceal the humiliation he felt. He glanced at the PFC beside him who looked away sheepishly.

While President Roosevelt made inspection of the thousands of troops at Camp Joseph T. Robinson, Masao, one of the few Japanese-Americans on base at the time, sat at the counter of the diner in Little Rock.

"You're not involved in all the hoopla over at the base?" Meg asked as she poured coffee.

"Nah. No need," was all Masao could reply. There was no confidence in his voice and all that was ringing in his ears was "go hide yourself."

❖   ❖   ❖

Back in Masao's apartment, I leaned back, my hands instinctively covering my heart.

"He told you to go hide yourself." I couldn't believe my ears.

"That's right, 'Go hide yourself.' That's what he said."

Only the crust of his sandwich remained.

"What assholes," I vented.

"Heh!" Masao loved it when I got passionate about these things. "It was the time, a-no?" And there it was again, that genuine humble nature of his. He lived through deep scrutiny of his being, immense judgment of his race, and carried an enormous burden as a citizen during this trying time.

And now I had it, I had this burden in my head and it would not be forgotten. I think Masao was relieved to have someone in the world to share this injustice with, someone to help him carry the weight of it even though it had been inflicted years earlier. I looked at Masao while his thoughts made their way out of the room.

"That's just how it was." He looked at me and smiled.

Summer 2011 – Vegas

We were at dinner at Hugo's Cellar, an upscale restaurant in the Four Queens casino in downtown Vegas. We were just finishing our salads when Masao cringed a little bit.

"It's my leg," he reported.

"Did you bring your medicine?" Alan asked him. Masao nodded. His medicine, as it turned out, was Aleve. "Maybe you should soak in the bathtub tonight," Alan suggested.

I liked the sound of that. It had been years since Masao was able to soak in a tub. His apartment only had a shower, but even if he had had a bathtub, he was far too frail to try to navigate that process by himself. Baths were part of Japanese culture and a tradition that Masao missed.

"Ah. No need," Masao waved him off. I could see what this was, though. He didn't want to be trouble for anyone, not even Alan.

"That's a really good idea, Mas. A nice hot bath, it would probably make your leg feel a lot better," I encouraged him, trying to describe it in a way that would convince him. It felt like we were trying to persuade a toddler.

"Maybe," he succumbed. That meant yes in my book.

Masao resisted but eventually gave in to our demands. The bathrooms at the Golden Nugget Rush Tower are lofty; there was plenty of room for Alan to assist him in and out of the bathtub. Alan would gently wash his back for him and stay with him while he soaked, then help him dry off and get into his pajamas. Masao would sleep like a baby those nights. I couldn't think of a more loving way for one human being to care for another. It became a tradition during our stays.

The next morning at breakfast, Masao was refreshed and wanted to chat. "You know, during the war when I was still at Camp Joseph T. Robinson, in Japan, things got reallllly bad."

"How? Do you mean for your parents?"

He nodded. "For my parents, yes. For everyone, a-no?"

April 1943 - Senoue, Japan

The Japanese military was stretched thin. They had invaded countries all over the Pacific Rim and were now being challenged by the United States in the South Pacific. Japanese strongholds were falling one by one. Not only was the military running short of men to serve, they were running short of equipment. The government put on a front that Japan was winning the war, but there were plenty of signs that just the opposite was true.

In the Abe home, Yasoshichi and Tomie had only one son left at home. Jiro, their second son, had died from the same appendicitis affliction that had taken their Yuriko some seven years earlier. Only their youngest remained. He was in his early teens, and his parents already feared for his future. They hadn't heard directly from Masao since Japan had attacked Pearl Harbor. They heard about him, indirectly, through Tatsuo who was having struggles of his own. At this point, nobody knew if Masao was still in the States, in Europe, or God forbid, in the South Pacific fighting face to face against the Japanese military. If that was the case, if the U.S. had the audacity to put him there, he would surely be a target for both sides.

The loss of two children had been almost too much for Tomie to bear. She felt certain that her beloved Masao, the child she had abandoned when he was just nine, would not make it out of this horrific war alive. Her worry was only magnified by the absence of any news from him directly.

Families such as the Abe family at least had a self-sustaining source of food. They had expanded their farm and grew vegetables that they canned and stored. Other families weren't so fortunate and made a living by any means possible, sometimes resorting to scurrilous behavior. Life was bleak at best throughout Japan.

❖   ❖   ❖

"I couldn't communicate with my mom, a-no? She couldn't read English," Masao recalled as he sipped his coffee. The waitress brought our food and set it down, but Masao hardly noticed.

"And I didn't want to risk writing a letter in Japanese writing." I pushed the ketchup over to him for his Portuguese sausage. He put the ketchup on his egg instead but he didn't eat. He was still with his mother.

"It must have been hard for my mom. She lost two children, a-no?" He shook his head out of sheer empathy. "Things were bad in Japan..."

And then, he seemed to notice his food and picked up his silverware to eat. His eyes told me there was more and I wanted to hear it.

"How did you communicate with..." I couldn't think of the right words. My fruit bowl was untouched. I looked at Alan with his full plate of Hawaiian sweet bread french toast and, in that moment, hated him.

"How did you communicate with anyone in your family, Mas? Your mom, your dad, your uncle..." I ate a bite of pineapple eyeing Alan's plate, now soaked in maple syrup.

"I could only write to my Uncle Tatsuo. But I didn't want him to worry, a-no? He had enough problems of his own."

Summer 1943 - Department of Justice Detention Facility
Sante Fe, New Mexico

Tatsuo sat in his cell with the letters that had just arrived: one from Yukie, one from Masao, one from his brother. *How long have these precious letters been kept from me.* Long enough for the guys who censored all the mail to be assured there was nothing criminal or encrypted within. He first read Yukie's letter.

"I secured our house the best way I could. Mr. and Mrs. Hernandez from down the street promised me they would stop by and check on it.

My quarters here in Poston are very small. It's but one large building separated into little rooms by curtains. They let me have a room in a corner because I have little children. The wood floors are very close to the earth, and there is only dust beneath the floor. When the wind blows, which is often, dust billows up into the room and settles everywhere. It's impossible to keep clean. If I could find ample amounts of newspaper, I could use it to stuff in the cracks. But newspaper, like everything else around here, is hard to find.

"I've heard that the snakes of the desert are poisonous. There are reports that two people have died from snake bites, but I am uncertain if these reports are true. It worries me, though, that such dangers are possible, especially for Kathleen who is walking on her own.

"My hope was to be reunited with you, but my hopes are fading with each day that passes. I hope you are well, wherever you are. The camp commander assures me that this letter will find you and I can only trust. I have no other choice.

"Mrs. Yamoto is writing this for me, although I am taking classes to learn English a little better, I am still not equipped to write a letter. Maybe someday. Yours truly, Yukie."

Tatsuo set Yukie's letter down. At least she's with other Japanese, and they will look out for her and help with the new baby, he thought. He looked around his little cell, the one he shared with three other Issei guys who were considered enemies. His cellmates were either reading or writing letters of their own. One of them had been a farmer in northern California, one had been a fisherman in the Seattle area, and the other, a businessman who had become quite successful operating a produce wholesale warehouse in the Imperial Valley area not far from San Bernardino. Their livelihoods were now distant memories, occupations they had left behind, unsure of the current status of their property but suspecting that all was lost.

Tatsuo picked up Masao's letter. The postmark was from Arkansas, a place called Little Rock.

"Where is Little Rock?" he asked to those around him. One of the cellmates, the businessman, scanned his mind for the answer.

"It's east, about eight hundred miles, maybe more," he answered from his bunk.

"Past Texas, then," Tatsuo clarified.

"One state beyond Texas. Why, Abe-san?" They still used a tiny bit of Japanese culture when nobody was around.

"My nephew, the soldier, that's where he is now."

"Ah," the businessman resumed his reading. Tatsuo pulled Masao's letter from the already opened military envelope.

"Uncle. I hope this letter finds you well. I am still at Camp Joseph T. Robinson in Arkansas. I currently work as a Medic in the Dental unit and assist the dentist. There aren't too many Nisei here. The ones that come don't stay very long before they get sent somewhere else.

"One time, hundreds of Nisei came through, but that was a while ago. I'm not sure what happened to those guys – all they left behind was a bunch of cigarette butts. I heard they might be forming a Nisei only unit, but it's hard to find out information like that around here. It seems to be classified. I only want to know because I want to join a unit, and the Caucasian units don't want Niseis around. I wonder why!

"The weather in Little Rock is hot like San Bernardino, but more moisture in the air. I feel sweaty most of the time. I will write when and if I move to another base. If you can, please write to me and tell me how my parents are. I worry about them. And you. Until then, take care. Masao."

"It sounds like the Army is recruiting Nisei guys," Tatsuo informed his cell mates.

The farmer looked up from his newspaper.

"How can they do that? All the Niseis are in camps," the fisherman interjected.

"There were Nisei in other states, not just along the west coast. They must be recruiting from them, no?" Tatsuo said.

The businessman, probably the wisest among them, set down his reading glasses and closed his eyes before he answered. "The military knows where to look for resources," he said.

They all understood what he was talking about. The young male Niseis along the west coast were now conveniently located in concentrated pockets. They were there for the picking when and if the military needed more men. Tatsuo nodded slightly before picking up his third letter, the one from Yasoshichi. He was surprised it made it out of Japan. It had been dated two months prior and was mailed to Star Cash Grocery in San

Bernardino. At least Larry was forwarding the mail. It was written entirely in English, as it would have to be.

"Tatsuo, at the time of my writing, I have no idea what's become of you and your family. I thought of coming back to help out, but then I would be in the same situation as you. It would have been a useless action. Things in Japan are very dire, as you can imagine. I cannot mention details, but use your judgment to determine my meaning.

"Tomie is very worried about Masao. We have not heard word in many months. I suspect that he cannot write directly to us. The censor in the U.S. would not let such a letter out of the States, and Japan would not let such a letter in. Too many barriers between son and parents. If you know of his whereabouts and health, please write back so I can assure her of his status.

"I will keep my words brief for now. I hope the best for you and your family. Regards, Yasoshichi."

"Things are dire in Japan," Tatsuo shared. His cell mates perked up at this. They often had debates about the goings on inside Japan and with the Japanese military. They all shared the vision that Japan was successful in its military efforts in the South Pacific and China. The only holdout was the businessman who often chimed into these debates with doubtful thoughts about Japan's success. He would be the first to comment.

"The Japanese military – they bit off more than they could chew." And he closed his eyes for a nap. "And now they will choke on their own arrogance."

Summer 1943 – Honolulu

Doris had left the USO and found a civil servant job with the quartermaster. She liked this better, if only because she didn't have to fend off overly zealous sailors and soldiers. She and George had dated for several months. While they'd had a good thing, she had not heard from him since he'd shipped out over a year before. He had done it — he had been accepted into the ranks of the Hawaiian Provisional Infantry Battalion, and she was happy for him. But she knew he wasn't the one for her, so when he finally stopped writing to her from the mainland, it wasn't a disappointment.

She had a good group of friends with whom she socialized, and they had several favorite clubs that they frequented: Club Pago Pago that was not too far from the fated McCully and King Street intersection that had been ravaged on December 7th, and La Hula Rhumba as well as Kewalo Inn. The attractive Doris had no trouble finding a date and had many suitors. Her current beau was with a young man named Stanley Namashima, and she was absolutely crazy about him. He didn't fawn over her like other men had and that made it interesting for her. But Doris wondered if maybe Stanley wasn't as interested as she was.

One night the group went out to Pago Pago. At their table the conversation had darkened. Doris had kept apprised of the goings on regarding Japanese internment, while most of her friends were ignorant to the plight. Stanley would sometimes lose his patience with Doris and her serious outlook on life. Doris would sometimes get frustrated that she knew more about worldly issues than anyone else did.

"Of course we'll be fine. We're Americans just like anyone else." Stanley's boisterous laugh followed his claim. He wanted Doris to leave the subject of internment altogether.

"So are all the Nisei along the west coast," Doris stated with a smile.

David, another friend, chimed in. "There were too many Niseis and Sanseis here. The economy would have collapsed," David offered. Stanley gazed out at the dance floor without a care in the world.

"Who cares! Let's not waste the night talking about depressing stuff," June blurted out, hoping to get people looser and out on the dance floor.

Doris wouldn't have it, though. She loved a good time like anyone else, but wanted her peers to be a part of the solution of the bleak situation that plagued her people. "It's not depressing, it's reality. June, honey, read the news every once in awhile, would you?" June shrugged and took David by the hand onto the dance floor. Doris smiled at June's innocent ways.

"My serious Doris. A true American girl," Stanley commented as he sipped from his singapore sling.

Doris didn't know if Stanley's remark was a compliment – or an insult. He abruptly took the hand of another girl and led her out to the dance floor, leaving Doris sitting at the table alone. She hated the way he treated her, yet couldn't get the man out of her system. As much as he frustrated her, she really believed he was the one.

Summer 1943 - Camp Joseph T. Robinson

Little Rock, Arkansas

Masao had succumbed to the notion that he might begin and end his military career at the Camp Robinson dental clinic. The current appointed dentist was a guy named Major Duncan. He originated from the San Francisco area and seemed to have an unusual empathy for Japanese people. He talked with fondness about the Japantown in the Bay Area and had developed a liking for Japanese food. As such, he sympathized with Masao's rice cravings as well as Masao's desire to move up in the ranks and find a place in action.

"What is Kibei?" Dr. Duncan asked Masao while working on a cavity-ridden mouth of yet another private who didn't brush his teeth.

"It's a term used to describe people like me. American born, but educated in Japan."

"Ehhh??" The private with a mouthful of instruments jerked when he heard the word Japan.

"Relax, private," Dr. Duncan insisted and pushed him back down in the dental chair. His patient tried to relax but kept an eye on Masao as though the enemy himself were in the room and loaded with grenades. Masao felt it and wished he had cloaked his answer with coded words that Dr. Duncan would have understood.

"Why?" Masao handed a different tool to the doctor noticing the heavy, gross plaque that needed to be chipped off. "And we might need a chain saw to get this mortar off."

Duncan chuckled at Masao's humor. "I saw a posting at HQ. Some language school in Minnesota looking for Kibei. Have you seen that?"

"Never. And I check that board all the time." Masao was floored.

"Thanks." Dr. Duncan took another tool that Masao anticipated he might need. "Well, you might want to check it out. It looks like it's been there a while."

Immediately after work, Masao was at the bulletin board filled with announcements and opportunities. He hadn't been there in weeks; he had tired of all the rejection notices and needed a break from it. He scanned the board for the notice Dr. Duncan talked about but couldn't find it. He was about ready to give up when he spotted it on a small piece of paper that had yellowed over time. *How did I miss that?* But this posting was intended to be inconspicuous, almost hidden, so it didn't attract the wrong kind of attention.

The next day, on a one-day pass, Masao sat at Meg's counter eating a steak. He pulled the notice from his pocket and read it again. He wasn't sure what the position was or what the language school was all about, but he knew he had to pursue it. He wanted to be with others like himself; he needed it. When he got back to base, he submitted his application for the fourth class of the Military Intelligence Service Language School at Camp Savage Minnesota.

CHAPTER EIGHT

FINDING HIS WAY

"Mas?" I called out as I went in his apartment. He was sitting in his recliner watching the Japanese channel. He was in sweats, a sure sign that he wasn't feeling well, either physically or emotionally.

"Hey, Sandie." He turned down the TV a little bit.

"Are you feeling okay?"

"Oh. So-so."

He didn't look okay. I noticed some newspapers had been knocked off his dining room table. I was almost afraid to ask. "What happened here?" I said in a light-hearted tone as I picked up the mess. He looked over and shook his head.

"I took a little tumble this morning," he said casually. This was a man who did not want any sympathy and further, he trusted that I wouldn't go that direction.

"Are you okay?" I asked as objectively as I could.

"Oh, yeah. Just feel like an old fool. Can't even trust myself to get around a small apartment. Sad case."

I looked behind the table in the corner and there it was - his cane. It had been out of reach for him. In one morning, it had become a tool he could no longer trust. Then I noticed Doris's walker was closer to his chair than usual. I carefully picked up the cane and placed it by the table, within his reach. *It's got to be so hard*, I thought, *getting to the point that falling down is the scariest thing you can think of.* He must have dragged himself up; it probably took several minutes and utterly exhausted him. I sat down and watched TV with him. There were no subtitles, but I didn't care. I was figuring out how to approach this situation with him.

"You want to go casino?" I asked.

"Nah. No need." Translation: I'm scared I will fall and it will be embarrassing more than anything.

"How about dinner somewhere?"

"Nah. It's okay." Again, he wasn't going to risk going out in public feeling like a complete invalid.

"I'll go get something, then."

"Nah. I have a-food here." He motioned to the refrigerator. I got up and strolled around his apartment while I figured things out. I stopped at his wall of pictures and looked at the one of his war buddies, all dressed in their finest, cleaned up and shaven, posing as a team for the photographer. I noticed Naki and how young they were. Their whole lives in front of them, if they could survive the war.

"Is this Naki?" I asked him, pointing to Naki in the photo. My strategy worked, he perked up and took interest.

"Yep, Naki. Which one am I?" He was testing me. I could pick Mas out in any picture.

"That's easy, this one," and I pointed to a guy I knew wasn't him.

"No. I'm – I'm the one sitting." He was getting up to show me, wheeling over with the walker. "This one," he pointed himself out.

"I know. I'm teasing you." He chuckled as we both admired the young men in the photo. "Where was that taken?"

"New Caledonia. After Peleliu."

I looked at the photo again. "Who are the other guys?"

"We were a ten-man team, attached to the 81st. That was a long time ago, boy."

"There are only nine guys in this picture," I pointed out.

"Yep. A guy named a-Frank, he wasn't there. He didn't like to socialize with the rest of us," he said as he rolled himself back to his recliner and sat down with a sigh. He suddenly looked bored and restless.

"I'd love to hear about this team."

He glanced at me and pondered my request. "How about we go casino? I tell you on the way." Two minutes ago, the casino had been out of the question.

"Of course, but one condition." I looked at him the way a mother would look at her child.

"What's that?" He was curious.

"We take the walker," I said, patting Doris's walker.

"Nah. It's too big for the car," he argued.

"It is *not* too big for the car. But nice try."

He looked dejected, not really wanting to admit that it had come to this – that he needed the walker, that the cane was no longer strong enough to support his progressively weak legs.

"Come on, let's not take any chances. If you take a spill on my watch, I'll never hear the end of it from Alan." This made him chuckle. I waited while he changed his clothes. When we left, we took the walker. The cane was left behind. The transfer had been a lot easier than I imagined it would be.

"We were ten guys who were on the same IIT team," he started out before we even got out of the garage. IIT meant, I knew from before, Interpretation/Interrogation Team.

"Was this at Camp Savage?"

"That's right. Camp Savage." My recorder was catching every word, thankfully, because the information was pouring out of Masao swiftly. This was a period of his life he was eager to share.

1942 – 1943 - Military Intelligence Service, MIS

The Military Intelligence Service Language School graduates were scattered throughout the Pacific Rim in one of two capacities. First, they would be assigned to groups that would serve at one of the large intelligence centers located around the Pacific Rim. This was by far the most common route for MIS graduates. The three main intelligence centers were in Hawai'i, Australia, and New Delhi. These intelligence centers would be manned by the Nisei linguists who would listen to Japanese radio chatter and news channels for intelligence-related information and would also scour Japanese documents pertaining to military strategies and strongholds.

The second course was for graduates to be a part of a small team and attach to combat units, working either on the front lines embedded in units, or for division headquarters behind the lines, available for the detailed interrogation that could not occur on the front line. This facet of the MIS operation took many months before it became effective.

The first graduates of the Presidio MIS Language School had been split up. About half went to Camp Savage to continue the efforts of the school. The other half were dispersed throughout the Pacific Rim. Five were sent to Alaska; eight to Australia; three to Fiji; and six to New Caledonia.

Things hadn't gone as intended for this first round of graduates; the notion of this type of intelligence work was dramatically under appreciated. The MIS Nisei were often given tasks that were menial and well beneath their skill level. To make matters more complicated, the MIS operation was still top secret. On the battlefield, hatred toward Japanese continued to rise.

One Nisei was sent to the South Pacific attached to an infantry battalion. This Nisei spoke and read perfect Japanese, having spent years in Japan. There was little intelligence work to do at his location on Bora Bora, however. There were no captured prisoners to interrogate or any documents to translate. He was eventually assigned to drive a truck.

The Nisei soldiers who had been deployed to New Caledonia arrived at the dock and were immediately told to cover themselves, cloaked in secrecy, while en route to the base. Their presence in New Caledonia, a colony of France and a hub of U.S. military activity, had to remain top secret. At first, these Nisei were assigned guard duty around division headquarters and sometimes had innocuous documents to translate. In the coming months, though, they would interrogate downed Japanese pilots. In one case, the Japanese pilots were so badly burned that all they could utter was, "Kill me." When the Nisei reported the limited interrogation they were admonished by commanding admirals.

"Goddamn you. What in the hell did you go to school for anyway? You damn bastards," one admiral was reported to have said in a public berating of the Nisei soldiers.

In the case of other MIS graduates, three had been attached to the 37th Division that was shipping out for Fiji. The MIS Nisei were sent to join the 37th Division in Pennsylvania. They arrived only to find that the 37th Division had already left for the west coast, the very place they had just traveled from. Adding insult to injury, once the Nisei arrived on base they were arrested for being absent without leave. They eventually convinced the military police of their identities and were allowed to return to San Francisco just in time to catch up with the 37th before they shipped out to Fiji.

There were two Caucasian graduates of the Military Intelligence Service Language School from that first class on the Presidio: Captain John A. Burden and Captain David W. Swift. Both had lived in Japan and spoke excellent Japanese. The first round of trained MIS linguists, including Captain Burden, was only allowed to support the marines on Guadalcanal and elsewhere from a distance. They were not included in battle strategies. They were never sent to the front lines. The founders of the MIS and the captains on the field became increasingly frustrated that the skilled and trained MIS soldiers, who were waiting for orders and eager to serve, were simply being overlooked. The MIS operation was not working as it had been intended.

The second class of MIS linguists graduated from Camp Savage, and they were also sent to various places along the Pacific Rim. It was much the same for them. Eventually it became evident that communication between the front lines and the MIS soldiers who possessed a wealth of interpretation expertise had been faulty. Commanders on the field didn't know who to contact or how to arrange for linguists. Finally Captain Burden was summoned to attach to a marine division on Guadalcanal.

When the marines raided Guadalcanal they had interpreters in the way of Japanese-speaking officers who were Caucasian. But the prisoners they had in custody spoke too fast for these Caucasian officers to garner any information. Not only that, Japanese prisoners were few and far between, most of them never had a chance of making it back to headquarters (HQ) alive. There was simply too much anger that had swelled toward the Japanese. The story went that imperial soldiers had ambushed and then executed wounded and helpless marines in horrific ways. This story spread like wild fire and as a result it became common for Japanese prisoners to somehow "die" on the way to HQ.

Upon arrival on Guadalcanal, Burden discovered that the culture had been to take no prisoners. "The only good Jap is a dead Jap" was a phrase he heard often. Burden heard one commander issuing orders to "Kill the sons-of-bitches." Not only that, documents found in enemy camps were often overlooked or just destroyed; soldiers were more interested in gathering souvenirs than they were in securing documents. There seemed to be no understanding on the front lines that Japanese prisoners might contain valuable intelligence that could assist the Allied Forces with strategies to secure islands currently held by the Japanese.

Captain Burden continually addressed his concerns. Eventually Burden convinced the commanders to offer incentives to marines to bring prisoners back alive. The tactic worked. The linguists, all Caucasian, worked around the clock as prisoners and documents were escorted back to division headquarters. To the surprise of the commanders and marines, Japanese prisoners were cooperative, sometimes even asking fellow prisoners the answer to questions they themselves did not know. The intelligence the Japanese prisoners revealed was astounding, including position of troops, casualties, locations of command posts, the morale of soldiers, and other bits of intelligence that proved extremely useful.

Burden's experience on Guadalcanal convinced him of two things: the MIS operation was crucial to effective military strategy in the Pacific and positioning interpreter/translators far to the rear was not effective. He wanted the Nisei linguists on the battlefield where they could produce the quickest results. He wanted the Nisei on the front lines.

Meanwhile the Nisei linguists stationed on various island posts were still performing menial tasks. Burden arranged for two Nisei to join the offensive on Guadalcanal. When the Nisei first arrived they were mistaken for Chinese-Americans. But after they produced noteworthy intelligence they were accepted as part of the war effort by the small circle of military personnel who were involved with the interrogation process. The Nisei, and the presence of them on Guadalcanal, was never made known to the ranks.

It was the same situation in other campaigns in the South Pacific. Commanders were reluctant, at best, to bring the likes of Nisei linguists to the front and preferred to keep them at a distance. Eventually, the Nisei were brought forward, a few at a time, and embedded closer to the action where the immediate interpretation led to swift results on the battlefield.

In January 1943 President Roosevelt made the official announcement that all citizens would be considered for military recruitment. Considering that Nisei soldiers were already on the ground around the South Pacific, and that the 100th Infantry Battalion had been activated and was in its seventh month of training, this was just a formality.

There had been several homogenous battalions formed with other ethnicities: Philippino, African American, Chinese, American Indian, and others. In April 1943 the 442nd Regimental Combat Unit was formed at Camp Shelby, Mississippi, and was designated as an all Nisei unit.

While the one hand of the government was clearing all Japanese out of the west coast, the other hand of the government was quietly and efficiently using Nisei men in various branches of the military and shipping them out to strategic, if not highly sensitive, locations. President Roosevelt was a genius in this sense. Seemingly benevolent to the needs of his voters, he cleansed the west coast of any Japanese while, at the very same time, he was shrewdly capitalizing on the loyalty and honor of the many Nisei and Sansei who wanted to prove their worth. While the Nisei linguists were not yet fully embedded on the front lines, the operation was gaining steam and heading in that direction.

It was because of the character and perseverance of the men in that first MIS Language School class from the Presidio that other operations were allowed to develop, including subsequent MIS classes, as well as the 100th Battalion and the 442nd. The graduates of the second and third MIS Language School would follow in the footsteps of their alumni and scatter throughout the Pacific Rim, while the 100th Battalion would eventually attach to the 442nd and head to Italy where they would prove themselves more than valiant.

July 1943 - Camp Savage MIS – Fourth Class

Masao stepped off the train at Camp Savage in July 1943. The first thing he noticed was that the camp was small but filled with Nisei. It felt good to be around others like himself. He had been so isolated at Camp Robinson.

Class began almost immediately. His instructor was none other than Captain Burden, fresh from the battlefield. Masao sat at a desk along with the other thirty Nisei assigned to this particular classroom. Captain Burden rolled out a map. He stood with a pointer in hand.

"Good morning," he greeted the Nisei after the formal salutes. "I'll be your instructor at the outset. I was a part of the first graduating class from the Presidio. I've been stationed in various places in the South Pacific, trying like heck to figure out the best way to utilize the brave men of the MIS."

He looked around at the Nisei who were paying full attention to his every word.

"We learned a lot from Guadalcanal," Burden continued. "Point one. How many of you think that you'll be involved in the torture of prisoners?"

The Nisei soldiers looked confused. A few raised their hands.

"Compassionate and humane treatment is the better approach. Japanese prisoners open up and reveal information and intelligence when they are treated with humanity. At first we had only Caucasian officers fielding intelligence on the line, but we've also learned that Japanese prisoners feel more at ease when they see faces like their own."

Masao nodded slightly and took some notes on this point. He was relieved that he wouldn't have to torture anyone.

"Point two," Burden continued. "Before Guadalcanal, the military had Nisei soldiers driving trucks around for Christ's sake, and manning interpretation far at the rear. Not anymore, though. Some of you will be on the front." He let his words resonate with that last statement.

Masao felt a surge of energy shoot through him. At last he would be able to utilize his training from both the Japanese and the U.S. military. It would all be useful in the line of active duty.

"Other soldiers don't know about the MIS operation nor will they," Captain Burden continued, matter-of-factly. This caught Masao's attention. He wondered how the operation all fit together if the American soldiers were unaware. *This could get ugly.* "A lot of them will think you are all Chinese who speak Japanese." This drew soft laughter.

"One general — this is a true story now. One general asked a Nisei if he was Chinese. The Nisei told him, 'No, sir.' The general asked if he was Philippino. The Nisei said, 'No, sir.' The general asked if he was one of the code-talkers. The Nisei said, 'No, sir.' The general said, 'Well you can't be—.' And the Nisei said, 'Yes, sir.' And the general had the Nisei taken off the line, back to the rear, and eventually out of the sensitive zone."

The reality of Captain Burden's story settled on the soldiers. A couple of them glanced at each other. Masao didn't know anyone just yet, so he just looked down and pretended to scribble more notes. *What the hell am I getting myself into,* he thought as he adjusted his glasses.

"The mentality out there is this: the only good Jap is a dead Jap. It's only been recently that our higher-ranking officers saw the benefit of taking prisoners. We've uncovered a lot of intelligence at the hands of the MIS - guys like you who are out there, risking their lives, as we speak. We need you to do the same. And we know you will."

Masao felt better. This Captain Burden seemed like a good fellow, the kind of guy you could trust. *I'll probably die out there trying to get intelligence, likely at the hands of some radical like Kunio, but at least a few people will appreciate why.*

There was little time to develop close ties with anyone at Camp Savage. The daily routine of the MIS Language School was the study of Japanese kanji — all day long. Wednesdays were reserved for military training and tactics. Oftentimes soldiers would march for five to ten miles as a mere warm up. Exams were given every Saturday. These exams would place students in a level system that had been established by the school. Soldiers would banter about what class they had been assigned to — smart or stupid.

Saturday nights and Sundays were the only blocks of free time. Poker games would break out in various barracks. Masao was always around for poker games and soon had buddies that had formed a coalition, a type of brotherhood Masao had longed for.

As Masao endured the routine, week after week, he started noticing soldiers who were Japanese-American, but seemed to be standoffish. It became almost unnerving the way these guys would just hover and watch the others, especially during poker nights.

"Hey, George," Masao said in a low voice one evening just before the poker club gathered. His buddy, George Inagaki, had become a trusted friend. George leaned in to hear Masao. "Those guys, like David over there. What's he doing? He never joins us, he just watches. I've seen others, too," Masao whispered gesturing toward David who was loitering nearby.

"Maybe he's CIC. Counter Intelligence Corps. Those guys are here to keep an eye on us, I've heard," George explained.

Masao's eyes widened, then squinted. "Well that's a bunch of shit."

❖ ❖ ❖

The MIS operation was gaining more and more steam and making direct contributions to the progression of American and Allied troops in the south, southwest, and now the Central Pacific regions. Masao and his friends understood that they might end up face to face with the Japanese enemy. They also understood that they would be seen as the enemy, not just by Japanese Imperial soldiers, but by Allied soldiers. Some of the missions the MIS soldiers would embark upon would be the most dangerous in all of World War II, simply because of their ethnicity and where they would inevitably serve.

In the spring of 1944 the Nisei were in class as usual when in marched a new face. Everyone stood at attention. Once at ease, the new instructor gave surprising information.

"Soldiers, you're near completion of the course. The next stage of your training will be infantry. At Camp Blanding."

While the instructor rambled on, Masao wrote a note to George. "Where the hell is Camp Blanding?" George shrugged.

Camp Blanding had been established as a military training facility in 1939. Located about fifty miles southwest of Jacksonville, Florida, Camp Blanding had housed two complete infantry divisions. By 1943 it had become an Infantry Replacement Center, or IRC, and as such, routed through thousands of soldiers who would be trained in infantry, tank destroyer missions, field artillery, engineering, calvary, and more.

The trains were waiting for the soldiers as they packed up. Once again, the cars would have the shades drawn and soldiers on board would be warned about the dangers of alerting the public at large to their presence.

At Camp Blanding the MIS soldiers were trained in the necessary combat and infantry skills, but they were trained in separate locations from the other GIs. Masao wasn't sure if their presence on base was ever even noticed, much less acknowledged. Whatever the case, the infantry training that he and other MIS soldiers had endured meant one thing: they were heading to the battlefield.

May 19, 1944 - Graduation Day

The graduation was uneventful. The Nisei had gone through a nine-month rigorous training, had succeeded in passing the courses, the physical and combat training, and had passed a loyalty screening. Masao had also been promoted to staff sergeant, now wearing a new uniform that carried the stripes of his new rank.

"You have two weeks leave. Report back here at 0800 on June 2nd. Your orders will be waiting for you at that time," the commanding officer stated at the end of the ceremony.

Back in the barracks, Masao hastily packed a duffle bag.

"Where are you off to?" George asked him.

Masao desperately wanted to see his Uncle Tatsuo, who had now been moved to a Department of Justice prison in Santa Fe, New Mexico. "I've got to get to my uncle out west."

Without saying a word, George dug in his foot locker for some hidden cash. He handed a wad of it to Masao. It was over a hundred dollars.

"Here. Take it, Masao," George insisted.

Masao was astonished, but waved him off. "Thanks, George, but no. I have no way of paying you back."

George continued to hold the money out for Masao and looked into his eyes. He saw that Masao was a very proud man, someone who had the utmost integrity. It would be hard for him to accept any help at all. "Masao, consider this a gift. Your family is scattered around, at the hands of the very government that has put us through the loyalty wringer and embeds CIC to spy on us. We have to stick together, guys like us."

Masao was unsure.

"Please," George pleaded with him. "Besides, this is really just money I've won off you over the last six months. Look at it that way."

Masao smiled, accepted the money in one hand, and shook his good friend George's hand with the other.

"Thank you." Masao's voice was sincere and honest. The train whistled in the distance.

"You gotta go." George picked up Masao's duffle bag and handed it to him. Masao sprinted for the door, then stopped and turned.

"Thank you, George."

❖   ❖   ❖

He took the train to the city of Santa Fe then hitchhiked the rest of the way. The truck he had ridden in from Sante Fe pulled up across the street from the prison. Masao got out and thanked the driver, a Mexican guy.

"Gracias," Masao obliged. Masao stood there in awe as he stared at the prison surrounded by high cement walls. Guards in towers were stationed at all four corners, thirty-caliber machine guns pointed down and in. He was horrified. This was a place that looked like it housed the most ruthless murderers and rapists. Inside, though, were nothing more than farmers, businessmen, and fisherman who had been deemed as dangerous enemies.

Two teenagers from across the street noticed Masao and their words snapped him out of his stunned gaze.

"Traitor!!!" One of the teenagers shouted. Before Masao could comprehend this little punk's words, the other one sounded off.

"You should be in there too!!"

"Go back to Japan, you ugly Jap!" The first one yelled before they ran off feeling vindicated and having a whopper of a story to tell their family and friends, how they faced the enemy himself and let him have it.

Masao shook this off and approached the guard station. The guard looked up. At first he was shocked to see a Japanese man in front of him, but then he noticed the uniform, the stripes.

"Sir. Can I help you?"

"I'm here to visit my uncle."

"Your uncle, sir?"

"Yes. Tatsuo Abe. I believe he is being held here."

The guard looked through papers while Masao fixated on the machine guns in the towers.

"Sign here," the guard was saying. His voice had changed. A minute before, he was talking to a soldier of the U.S. military. Now he was talking to the relative of an inmate. Masao felt it.

"There's a visiting shed over there. Go outside and wait," the guard directed.

"Thank you." Masao stepped away and waited. Another guard came over and opened the shed. But for two chairs, this makeshift visiting room was empty. He was never allowed inside the prison itself. Thirty minutes later, Tatsuo was escorted in. He was a shell of the man he had once been, weak and pale. Masao immediately stood up and went to his uncle, who smiled when he saw Masao.

"Uncle."

"Masao. Boy, you look swell in that uniform."

They shook hands warmly. Tatsuo motioned that they should sit. The escorting guard was suspicious; he looked at Masao in his uniform with disdain. Masao focused on Tatsuo.

"You don't look so good, uncle. They aren't feeding you in here?"

"They feed us. But the food is horrible. No rice," Tatsuo looked at the guard to make his point.

"I can't believe you are a prisoner." Masao was scanning Tatsuo up and down, noticing the bones sticking out on every limb.

"I guess I'm the enemy," he chuckled. "So, you finally going to Europe?"

"No. South Pacific. To fight Japan."

"Japan! You'll die for sure. Better for you to go fight the Germans." The guard took delight in Tatsuo's assessment of Masao's fate. This didn't go unnoticed by Masao.

"Japan, Germany. It's no difference."

"Japan is winning the war, Masao. You have less chance of survival against Japan."

"Where do you hear that?"

"Well, in here. Everybody says so." Tatsuo insisted.

"In here? Uncle, these Issei guys just want Japan to win. Japan's not winning." Masao laughed at his uncle's lack of information. "Japan is getting pushed back into itself."

The guard smiled at this, as though he, himself, was responsible for the success of the American and Allied Forces.

"Japan wins. U.S. wins. I guess it doesn't matter. Me and my family, we've already lost. The store - gone. All the money I sent to Japan – gone," Tatsuo resigned himself to the worst possible scenario.

"What happened to the store?"

"I put it in my manager's name. Foolish, I think. No?"

"Probably so. Larry's a scoundrel. He won't give it back."

The guard took note of this. He had not heard this angle of the Japanese internment/imprisonment before.

"I'm sorry about all of this." Masao looked at Tatsuo, his beloved uncle and the rock of a man he had depended on.

"Not your fault, no?" Tatsuo glanced at the guard before he continued. "So - what if you face one of your cousins or schoolmates in battle? You gonna shoot?"

"Heck yeah, I'm gonna shoot! If someone's shooting at me, I'm going to shoot back!"

"I guess you have to, no?" Tatsuo nodded. He understood. It was kill or be killed. There was a moment of anguish before Tatsuo spoke about what truly ailed his heart. "They tell me the only way I can ever see Yukie and my daughters is to return to Japan. I haven't even met my new daughter." He was becoming emotional. Masao didn't want the guard to have the satisfaction of seeing a strong man, like Tatsuo, broken.

"What name did you give your new daughter?"

"Anna. Her name is Anna."

"Pretty name. That's a pretty name, uncle," Masao reassured Tatsuo. "Uncle. Stay here, in America. I have a feeling it will get better."

"They don't want us here, Masao. I just can't bear to think of my little girls living like this." Tatsuo was near his breaking point, but he refused to give in to the looming tears.

Masao needed to say something to pull him back from the brink. "Uncle, I will check on them. Poston, a-no?"

"Poston, yes. Thank you, Masao."

"One more thing, I have taken out life insurance on myself. Ten thousand dollars. You are the beneficiary. It's in my will and it's final." Tatsuo was flabbergasted and speechless. "If I don't make it back, you have a way to start over again in San Bernardino."

"I don't know what to say. You honor your family in every possible way."

They visited for the full hour they were allowed before Masao began his journey west, to Poston, Arizona. On the train, he was hoping that Yukie had it better than Tatsuo. He couldn't shake how his uncle had changed. He couldn't let go of the injustice of it all. The glares from white folks were becoming more and more noticeable and irritating. They had no idea the turmoil that he and other Japanese-Americans had churning inside of them at all hours of the day. Had they no empathy? The answer, sadly, was usually no.

Masao hitchhiked his way to Poston from the train station in Blythe. He was tempted to go the two hundred miles to San Bernardino to give that Larry, the son-of-a-bitch store manager, a piece of his mind and a knuckle sandwich. But he was short on time and wanted to get to Yukie.

As he walked toward the Poston Internment Camp, his heart ached even more. Rows and rows of barracks out in the desert; it was literally out in the middle of nowhere. Barbed wire surrounded the facility and guards were posted at strategic points. He approached the main entrance that was flanked with guard stations. These guards were different from the ones at the Santa Fe prison; these had come to know and even liked the thousands of Japanese-Americans who lived there. Even more, they had grown used to seeing military Nisei come for visits.

"Good morning, sir. Are you here to visit a relative?" The guard asked in a cheery voice. It was music to Masao's ears. At least they were pleasant here.

"I am. Yukie Abe, my aunt. I believe she is here."

Within minutes Masao was escorted to Yukie's "home", her cordoned-off section of a barracks.

"Ahhh. Masao!" She put her toddler down and went to Masao to hug him. Then she stood back and took him in, how handsome he looked in his uniform. The two little girls, Kathleen and Anna, sat shyly behind their mother.

"You wear that uniform well!" she admired as she picked up little Anna. "This is your cousin, Masao!" Little Anna pointed a finger at Masao, and he gently took it and wiggled it between two of his fingers.

"How are you doing here, Yukie?" Masao looked around, noticing the newspapers that were stuffed in the cracks on the floor and in the walls. Her little area was the size of a bedroom.

"We make do. Did you see Tatsuo?" She asked with a great sense of hope in her voice. "They are pressuring him to go back Japan. They say it only way he can see us again. Is this true?"

Masao sat his aunt down on the bed as a means of calming her. He picked up a toy and handed it to Kathleen who was still clinging to Yukie's dress.

"I have no way of knowing, Yukie. But they can't keep you here forever. Encourage him to stay in the States. I think it's best. Don't you?"

Yukie nodded and held little Anna close. The sound and voices of other families in their rooms was ever present. Nobody was overly loud, it was more like a low murmur that never went away.

Yukie pressed her lips together biting her inner mouth to stop the tears from coming. "It's not good place to raise children. And it's not good they don't know father."

Masao nodded. He agreed with everything she said. It was hard for him to have two worlds on this clear collision course inside his heart and mind. Nothing made sense and everything made sense.

"They have you. And you are strong. You'll be back with Tatsuo in San Bernardino before you know it."

Yukie tried to be strong and smile but instead leaned into Masao and wept.

June 1944 - Shipping Out

"Christ almighty, why'd they want us back here so soon? I could have spent more time with my aunt, or gone to San Bernardino to check on my uncle's affairs," Masao said one night while resting in his bunk, frustrated with the slow pace of the military and the issue of orders.

"I could have spent more time with my wife," George added with a sigh.

"I need a girl," Masao said, sharing his private thoughts. "A nice Japanese girl who is smart, independent, and knows how to make great sashimi." His thoughts drifted back to Japan, to Miyoko. "I had a girl in Japan, before I came back to the U.S. I wonder what's become of her."

"Ah. If she's in Japan, she's aged twenty years in ten, Abe. Both resources and hope are scarce commodities. Only the strongest are living well," George speculated.

"By now she's met someone else, a-no? Maybe she ended up with my classmate, Kunio, the radical. Kunio. Hmm," thoughts drifted through his mind and out his mouth. He knew they were safe with George. "He must be an officer by now. I wonder where he is."

"Maybe you'll meet him on the battlefield. What's he made of?"

Masao thought about this as a breeze came through the open window and wafted across his face. "He's made of anger. The most dangerous kind of soldier."

"Nah. The most dangerous kind of soldier is one who has been trained well and acts with honor."

Masao rolled over onto his side, propping his head on his hand so he could look at George in the next bed over. George rested with his eyes closed, probably thinking about his wife.

"It won't matter anyway," Masao lit up a cigarette, "our own guys will be aiming for us first." George opened his eyes wide. This thought had not occurred to him before.

❖   ❖   ❖

It would be days before they would receive orders. Masao would get his first. "They want me on the train tonight. 2100." Masao read from the paper he had been issued.

"Does it say where?"

Masao shook his head. "Nope."

They waited a while longer to see if George would receive similar orders, but nothing came. At 2030 they shook hands. Masao picked up his duffle bag and looked at George.

"I'll never forget you, George. Thanks again, for everything."

"You bet. And good luck out there."

Masao nodded. "Same to you."

With that, Masao left the barracks. George and Masao would never see each other again and Masao never forgot George and his kindness.

Masao was on his assigned train car early, along with a dozen other Nisei who were all in the same mental state as Masao — excited and anxious at the same time. Masao had seen all of these guys on base but didn't know any of them. A younger soldier with a fresh face boarded and Masao recognized him as Saburo Nakamura.

"Abe, right?"

Masao nodded and they shook hands. Saburo sat beside him after he hurled his duffle bag on the shelf above.

"Saburo?" Masao was trying to remember his name.

"I go by Naki. I don't know how I got that name, but it sure has stuck with me." Naki smiled as he talked. Masao noticed his sincere presence and almost sweet face. *He's going to be a weapon on the battlefield*, Masao thought, *no enemy in the world could feel threatened by this guy. They'll tell this interrogator anything he wants to hear.*

"Long trip ahead of us, don't you think?" Naki asked as he looked around to take inventory of the other passengers.

"Probably so," Masao agreed as he watched more soldiers get on.

Just then, a Caucasian soldier boarded with a clipboard. "At ease, soldiers. Wave good-bye to the good life you're leaving behind, then close your shades for the duration. This will be a long journey. There will be stops along the way, don't worry. The USO has been generous with all our troops, including our guys from Savage. You have eight minutes if you need to use the facilities before departing. One last thing, the shades are drawn for a reason. Leave them down the entire journey. Nobody sees in, nobody sees out. Godspeed."

And then he saluted and jumped off the train to head to the next car. Masao and Naki looked at each other.

"We can't even look at the scenery," Masao commented. Naki shrugged.

The train chugged through the flat land of Minnesota and into North Dakota. Just before sunrise, it stopped. A Caucasian soldier boarded their car.

"Soldiers, listen up. You will de-board here for forty-five minutes. Use the facilities, the wonderful USO ladies have coffee and snacks for you. Wash up if you want. It's 0545. We depart at 0630."

Off the train Masao looked around. The countryside was flat and deserted. The USO had a tent set up and tables were lined up with various food items and hot coffee. He helped himself to coffee and a breakfast roll, then glanced at the lady behind the table.

"Do we pay somewhere?"

"No, soldier. We're here to support our troops!" She was delighted to report.

"Well, thank you." Masao tipped his hat to her.

"You're welcome! Take some for the road if you want." That sounded like a good idea to Masao and he helped himself to another.

"Where are we, anyway?"

"You're in Bismarck, North Dakota!" Her enthusiasm was annoying for a soldier on little sleep who knew not his destiny.

"North Dakota." Masao looked around. *This must be a sad place to live,* he pondered to himself. *Dry and desolate.*

"The town is over that-a-way," the lady pointed off in the distance as though she could sense what Masao was thinking. "We're the capital of North Dakota!" She had far too much energy for him.

"Thank you for supporting us," he nodded as he headed over to where other soldiers were smoking. The soldiers in the group were having a debate about where they were going and when they would arrive.

"We've got to be in Wyoming or Utah, somewhere like that," one of the soldiers was saying.

"Wyoming and Utah are states that have trees and mountains. Do you see any trees around here?"

Another soldier chimed in. "I think we're in Nebraska."

Masao, forever the gambler, decided to capitalize on this and ratchet it up a notch.

"Let's get a little pool going," he proposed to the group at large.

"Okay, Abe. I say we're headed for Los Angeles." A guy that went by Jack, even though his name was Masaru, threw out the first bet.

Masao nodded and looked around. "Okay, Jack's in. Anyone else?"

"I'm in. I say the Bay area, maybe Oakland," another soldier added.

"Bay area."

"I say Portland," said another soldier, switching it up.

"I'm going with Jack on this one. Los Angeles." The last soldier besides Masao and Naki made his bet.

Naki studied Masao, he knew Masao was up to something. "What's your bet, Abe?" Naki asked shrewdly. Masao knew that Naki knew he had the inside scoop. It was a brilliant move on Naki's part.

"Ah. You should put your bet in first. You're smarter. You were in the smart class at Savage. I was in the stupid class." Masao wasn't going to take the bait and it was true. Masao hadn't been in the top tier for whatever reason; it had been a mystery to him. But the match was on. No matter what other soldiers would bet, this was really between Masao and Naki.

"All the more reason to allow you the first wager," Naki came back in a quiet voice that carried great weight. "After all, we all know that Abe should have been in the top class. You were robbed of that, so I wouldn't dream of robbing you of the first wager."

Boy, he's good, Masao thought. Naki just waited patiently to see what Masao's next move would be.

"I think we're still in the north. It's dry like Nebraska, but not humid," he bullshitted. He had no idea about humidity in Nebraska. "I'm going to say we're headed more north. Seattle. Tomorrow night at the earliest."

The other soldiers laughed their asses off at this and gave him shit about his lousy bet.

"Two more days on this goddamn train? I don't think so, Masao," Jack lobbied, "we'll be in some port by tomorrow morning."

"Seattle isn't even on the radar for the army." another soldier claimed.

But Naki knew Masao was on to something. And after the shit-talking stopped, he made his wager. "I'll go with Abe's theory. Seattle. As for the time, I think it will also be tomorrow night. Abe, let's pick times. I say between 2200 and midnight."

Holy Shit. This Naki has just beat me at my own goddamn game, thought Masao. His cigarette nearly fell out of his mouth. Naki saw this and the slightest smile appeared on his face. Then Masao grinned. He liked this Naki.

"I'll say this," Masao started out, "I hope to have you at my side on the line." Naki smiled at the compliment, probably the greatest compliment you could ever give a fellow soldier. "Okay, Naki. I say tomorrow night between 2000 and 2200."

"Five minutes!!" A soldier called out from the train. The gamblers agreed on five dollars each for the pool as they headed for the train.

Back in their seats, Masao eyed Naki. "Goddamn, Naki. Those other guys can't gamble for shit. But I could lose my ass if I don't keep my eye on you!"

Naki just smiled and closed his eyes for a nap.

The next morning Masao woke up before anyone else. From the feel of the train, they were either on a decline or on flat terrain. He dared to open the window shade enough to see out. The sun was about to come up and provided just enough light for him to see that they were crossing land that looked like wheat fields. *We could be anywhere.*

After another hour the train slowed and stopped. A soldier soon hopped onto their car and made the usual instructional announcement, with one exception.

"You'll have over three hours at this stop, soldiers. Do not leave the USO designated area. This facility has showers. However, there are only two shower stalls for over forty men. Be swift in there. The USO has generously provided towels and toiletries. It's 0840. Be back on board at 1200."

It was a long three hours. This stop, like all the other stops, was far away from any city, town, or civilization. Only the kind USO workers were privy to the Nisei soldiers en route to the coast. On the train, a deck of cards made its way out. Masao was thrilled to join, but lost half his money to Naki. After a few hours they felt the train start to move and soon after that, the unmistakable grind of the train crawling up a steep grade.

The soldiers looked at each other, trying to figure out what mountain range stood between them and the coast.

"Sierra Nevadas?" Jack posed the first question.

"Could be." Naki threw down an ace that gave him a royal flush. He cleaned up again. And now, Masao figured, Naki was baiting Jack. His concurrence with Jack's prediction about the mountains only beefed up Jack's confidence. As the train pulled itself up the grade, it jolted, making it hard to shuffle the cards. Naki was the new dealer and dealt cards to the remaining players.

"Want to double down, Jack? On the pool?" And there it was. Naki was going in for the kill. *Boy, is he good*, Masao thought. Masao folded his hand immediately and waited to see if the fish would bite on Naki's well-placed bait. They would. Everyone doubled their bet. Everyone sure they had picked right. Everyone but Masao; he was beginning to doubt himself and wished he had paid more attention to his third grade teacher in San Bernardino when she talked about mountain ranges.

This one thought took him back there, to San Bernardino. He longed for the days when things weren't complicated, when things made sense. When it wasn't a crime to be Japanese and when he didn't have to hide himself. He started to think about his Uncle Tatsuo, his Aunt Yukie, his parents in Japan, the house in San Bernardino. The wonder turned into worry, and he wished he could just gaze out the window if only to take his mind off his concerns.

"Abe." Naki nudged him.

"You in or out, Abe?" Jack was like a shark circling prey. Masao was annoyed by this Nisei hiding behind a white name.

"I'm in."

Naki studied Masao. He knew what had just happened. He knew that Masao had gone down the vortex of Japanese-American strain and distress.

"Good. We're all in then," Naki said out loud then nudged Masao ever so lightly. "Thought I lost you there...," he said so nobody else could hear.

Hours passed before the train started to descend. This would be it. It wouldn't be long before a winner would be declared and claim the pot of money. Surely, they were close to the port. Then the train slowed and stopped. They all thought they must have reached their final destination but something was wrong. There were no sounds of a train station, of other trains. They waited. The train huffed and spewed steam as it stood still on the tracks. Masao checked his watch. It was seven p.m.

"Why are they waiting?" Naki asked.

"Waiting until dark," Masao said, clearing up the mystery, "so nobody sees us get off the train." The severity of that thought seemed to bother Naki. It was incomprehensible to realize that the military would go that far to keep soldiers, American citizens, a secret. But he knew that Masao was right. Naki looked down.

"Nothing to be ashamed of, Naki, it's just the way it is." Masao, a few years older than Naki, may not have had the academic smarts of his new buddy, but he had more wisdom. He had overcome more challenges and could frame this unfair military approach in objective terms.

"The air is cool." He nudged Naki with his elbow. "We're in the north. There's an outside chance it's the Bay area, but more than likely, you and I are right. Seattle."

Naki looked over at Masao and finally smiled. "Now it's just between you and me, old boy."

"That's right," Masao affirmed. "Thought I lost you there…"

After a long while, a Caucasian soldier boarded their car and walked down the aisle checking each shade and making sure it was shut.

"Final approach, gentlemen," he called out.

When the train was underway it moved along more slowly than its regular speed, as though cautious in its approach to wherever it was going. The soldiers on board were quiet, straining to hear anything that would give them a clue as to their whereabouts. It wasn't because of the bet, it had become nerve-wracking trying to figure out where they were going. Finally, the train slowed then crept along before coming to a halt.

"We're here," Masao assessed.

Naki nodded in agreement, glancing at his watch. "It's 10:00 sharp. If we're in Seattle, looks like we're splitting the pot." Naki showed him his watch as proof.

All Masao could do was chuckle.

It was a stealth-like operation in the darkness. The Nisei soldiers quietly disembarked the train and loaded a nearby bus. There were Caucasian soldiers lined up like traffic cones to direct the Nisei soldiers where to go. Busses were waiting for them not more than fifty feet from the train platform. There were no detours, not even for the bathroom. The entire operation was shrouded in secrecy.

As Masao stepped off the train he spotted the Smith Tower just a few blocks to the north and knew right away — they were in Seattle. Soldiers weren't permitted to talk at all during the short walk to the bus, but he and Naki exchanged glances and Masao nodded over what was unmistakable: they had won the bet.

On the bus windows were covered. Naki and Masao sat together silently. A soldier stepped on the bus with a clipboard. He walked down the aisle and checked off names.

"Listen up soldiers. You're en route to Fort Lawton. It's approximately a forty-minute ride. From there, you'll be assigned to barracks. Some of you ship out as early as tomorrow morning so be prepared." He saluted and left. The door closed, the gears ground, and the bus started its trek to Fort Lawton.

Fort Lawton, located on a bluff just north of downtown Seattle, was the closest military facility on which to harbor the Nisei soldiers until they were shipped out. The next morning Masao woke up early, well before reveille. He just had a feeling that he would be getting orders to ship out, and he was right. Some of the Nisei had been at Fort Lawton for several days while others, like Masao, had been plucked the morning after they arrived. He and nine other Nisei, including Naki, were ordered to report to the pick-up location on base where a bus was waiting.

The bus took them to a pier down the bluff from Fort Lawton where they were loaded onto a military transport vessel that already held a thousand soldiers. They were quickly ushered below deck before any of the other soldiers noticed their presence.

These ten men would form an Interrogation/Interpretation Team, or IIT, and would be attached to the 81st Infantry Division, known as the Wildcats. The team would be split up. Four men would remain attached to division headquarters, two men would attach to the 321st Regimental Combat Team, two to the 322nd, and two to the 323rd.

All of this was still unknown to Masao and his comrades who had been escorted to the belly of the vessel, undetected.

❖ ❖ ❖

"There were ten of us. Four were attached to division headquarters. That was Jimmy Kai, Bob Sakai, Shiuso Chojin, and one other, geeee, now, why can't I remember his name. He's still living somewhere in California, I think, gee, what's his name now…" he was thinking hard. I could tell that it bugged him that the names weren't just rolling off his tongue. At the same time, I was so impressed that his memory of events seventy years before was so sharp.

"Ah. Hiro, Hiroki Takahashi, that's it. Four guys, attached to Division Headquarters. Then, a guy named Frank Kubota and I, we were attached to the 321st. The 322nd had, uh, let's see now, Tomio Ichikawa and Saburo Nakamura, and the 323rd had Shiro Sakaki and Kei Kitahara. James Kai was our team leader. He was a realllllly sharp guy."

"Shiro. Is that the Shiro we visited? At the Punchbowl?" I was trying to hang on while all of his history came pouring out.

"Yep, that's right. And Bob Sakai, he was attached to division headquarters. He was a smart guy too, boy. He went to, ah, what's the name now, Harvard. He went to Harvard after the war." Masao always admired those who had gone to college, an opportunity that had escaped him. He was so smart in so many ways but didn't appreciate that about himself.

"You're just as smart as Bob Saki, or whatever his name is."

"Sakai. He died, though, some years ago."

"Okay, okay, Sakai. But you knew all about Japan. Did any of those other guys know about Japan like you did?"

"I think three of us had lived in Japan. Me. A guy name Hiro Takahashi, and Chojin, Shiuso Chojin. Funny story about Chojin." He grinned as he remembered this story. "The Caucasian army guys, they were always trying to give us names they could remember. So they came up with Jonesy for Chojin. Heh! Jonesy!" He chuckled.

"Did you call him Jonesy?"

"Nope. Never. His name was Shiuso. We all called him by his last name, Chojin." And he chuckled again. Masao's name would have been easy to whitewash, I thought. Abe, with a short, accented A, and a short E, Ahbay, could easily be turned into Abe with a long A – Aaabe.

Names. They were probably the least of the worries of the men on this team. During the trip from Seattle to their next destination, the ten guys formed camaraderie unlike any other during World War II. These ten, the only ten Nisei in an Infantry Division comprised of twenty-five thousand soldiers, would also become beacons for each other.

Once they landed in the battle zone, they would be isolated targets.

July 10, 1944 - The 81st "Wildcat" Infantry Division

While Masao and his new comrades sailed, their future was being planned in San Francisco. On shore and ready to board a military transport vessel in San Francisco Bay was a young Counter Intelligence Communications (CIC) officer by the name of William Aimone. He was recently married, fresh, and considered a shave-tail, a non-commissioned officer.

Captain Aimone had earned his gold bars as a second lieutenant by coming through the ranks. He was drafted in August 1941 and after Pearl Harbor was offered the opportunity to be interviewed to become one of the first of 150 special agents of the army's CIC. He jumped at the chance. As part of the CIC training, he was instructed, in part, by top former FBI, CIA and other "super-snoopers" as to the tricks of the spy trade. Special agents, like Aimone, had even undergone covert surveillance of rabbit spies, trailing them around cities such as Chicago and reporting their whereabouts and activities. The mission of the CIC was specific: catch enemy spies or saboteurs who were after the nation's weapons, plans, and/or codes.

Aimone was eventually assigned to Central Command Headquarters in specific states where he would conduct extensive background checks on army personnel who had access to top secret activities. This meant questioning family, friends, employers, schools, and any social connections to be sure that there was no questionable character traits of the army personnel who had access to national security information.

In September 1943, Aimone learned he would be transferred to the South Pacific. He would be attached to an infantry division and would be the commanding officer of the divisions CIC detachment that consisted of fifteen special agents. That infantry division would be the 81st.

On board the transport vessel in San Francisco Bay, he was summoned to the private cabin of the commanding general of the 81st "Wildcat" Division. Aimone entered the private cabin/suite office and was directed to wait. Moments later, in walked Major General Paul Mueller, the general in charge of the entire 81st. General Mueller was in his early forties and was a no-bullshit kind of a guy, one who got things handled efficiently and effectively. Captain Aimone stood at attention and almost broke out into a sweat when the Major General himself walked in.

"At ease, captain," Mueller said, wanting to get down to business. "Have a seat."

Anxiety filled Aimone's body. *Focus, focus,* he tried to calm himself.

"You're the only officer in the 81st with an intelligence classification," Mueller stated firmly assessing Aimone head to toe. Aimone was glad he had given his uniform a fresh press early that morning. Mueller continued as he methodically paced the small room, "I have an important job for you."

"Yes, sir."

"The War Department has sent us a team of Jap soldiers. I don't know why we got stuck with 'em but I don't trust 'em. Not a one."

"American, sir?"

"Supposedly. The War Department says they're going to be our secret weapon. Top secret, they say. It's a *goddamn quagmire* if you ask me. I don't know how the hell are we supposed to run things in the South Pacific when we have to watch these guys. But who am I to question those War Department assholes."

Aimone's eyes were wide. He was trying to digest everything that was coming at him. *He wants me to put these guys under surveillance.*

Mueller continued to sputter out his thoughts, forming his plan almost on the spot. "They're all sergeants, like your CIC men, but they came without a CO, of course. They're attached to the G-2 Intelligence Division, same as your detachment." Mueller paused before delivering the punch line. "I want you to take them under your command. You're their CO, effective immediately."

A hundred questions cluttered Aimone's brain. "According to the War Department, what is their assignment, sir?"

"Good question, captain. I'll tell you this much," Mueller walked to a map detailing military strategy — what island would be hit first and by what units. He studied the map as he completed his thought. "We're going into enemy territory. An enemy that those American Japs can communicate with easily. It's your head if those soldiers are spies and give us any trouble. So get on the job and find out what they're here for because I don't have a *goddamn* clue." Mueller glanced over at Aimone who was now standing near the map. "On the other hand," Aimone met Mueller's glance, "if the War Department has their head on straight, which I doubt, but if they do, and these guys happen to be clean, find out what they can do to help us with this war."

Aimone nodded. "Yes, sir."

General Mueller looked him in the eye and deliberately paused before he spoke again. "One more thing."

"Sir?"

"They're going to have the biggest goddamn target on their chest of anyone out there. Spies or not, I figure we need to keep 'em safe." Mueller pointed to the map he stood by. "Our guys are trained to kill. I'd hate to see them take out a useful weapon." Mueller's eyes gave him away; he wanted to believe that these Japs weren't trustworthy. It would have made everything a lot more manageable for him. But there was something inside the general that knew how useful Japanese speaking soldiers could be on the battlefield.

Mueller nodded then left as swiftly as he had arrived. Aimone, a sweaty mess beneath his pressed and starched uniform, exhaled deeply and wiped his forehead. After he collected himself, he wandered over to the porthole where he could see the long lines of soldiers, almost all of them Caucasian, loading the ship. *Holy shit…*was all he could think.

❖   ❖   ❖

Aimone's ten-man team, on a different vessel, soon learned that they were headed for Hawai'i. The seven-day voyage was grueling for the soldiers who didn't fare well on the sea. For Masao, the only grueling part of the voyage was losing every last dime in poker and having to borrow from Naki who had won loads. The Nisei soldiers interacted with the other soldiers, most of whom took them for Chinese. But the trip wasn't without problems. Soldiers of lesser rank would sometimes treat the Nisei as though they were nothing. On one occasion in the galley, the mess sergeant challenged Masao.

"You there. You need to pick up the dishes from the table," the mess sergeant blurted out. It was unheard of for a staff sergeant to pick up after privates or PFCs.

"Excuse me?" Masao asked. He couldn't believe his ears, and yet he could. Nothing surprised him when it came to Caucasians and their feelings about Japanese. He tried to remain neutral about this, even though inside he started to fume.

"You heard me. You can't leave the table in shambles." He was referring to other soldiers' food splatter and utensils that had been left behind.

"I'll tell you what," Masao chose his words carefully. "When I see other staff sergeants picking up after soldiers, then I will too. But until then, I'll just pick up after myself."

The mess sergeant glared at Masao. How dare some Jap stand up for himself, he didn't care what rank he was. But Naki, who had noticed and had been lingering to see if Masao needed backup, came close to Masao. The mess sergeant sneered at them both, then disappeared to the back of the galley. Masao and Naki looked at each other.

"I hope this isn't a sign of times to come," Naki commented. They both knew, though, that the times ahead were going to be tough.

With the exception of the few soldiers who felt the need to pick on the Nisei soldiers, the voyage to Hawai'i was smooth sailing. Within miles of the Hawaiian coastline, the warmth of the Central Pacific called men to the deck where they soaked up sun on their leave time. When the transport vessel approached the shores of Hawai'i, excitement on the ship grew. As it came through Mamala Bay heading toward Pearl Harbor, the waters turned from a deep, sparkly azure to a beautiful glittery turquoise. The soldiers couldn't wait to hit those beaches covered with white sands and beach babes.

When the ship entered the channel between Ewa Beach and Hickam Air Force Base the mood shifted dramatically. The men knew they were about to witness for themselves the massive destruction of the famous December 7th attack that had occurred two-and-a-half years earlier. The captain deliberately took the vessel down battleship row where the soldiers could see remnants of the gigantic battleships that had been sunk on that fateful day. Salvage crews had been working for two solid years, yet masts still reached out from the depths of the harbor and hulls were still visible, marking the graves of hundreds of men still encased below.

Seeing the evidence of the terrible bloodshed by the enemy they would soon face fueled the anger of the soldiers on board. Testosterone flared as the men, who moments before could think about nothing more than finding a woman to screw, now wanted more than ever to move into the battle zone and reap their vengeance.

Masao felt the same; a big part of him wanting to settle the score. There was a part of him, though, that wondered where he might be right now had he stayed in Japan. Could he have been one of the fighter pilots picked for the very mission that left this swath of destruction he was looking at, or would he have already been killed in the war with China? Fate had dealt him a gentler hand. He was part of a more cautious, more calculating, and more humane military. Of that, he was proud and content. He was happy to be on the American side, even though it had its complications.

On shore, soldiers were bussed to Schofield Barracks. The Nisei were on a bus with the other soldiers but were kept on board while all the Caucasian soldiers were exited on Schofield.

"Gentlemen, remain on the bus. You'll be taken to your location momentarily," the young corporal directed them politely. Masao looked out the bus window at the hustle and bustle of Schofield. On perimeter of the base, Masao noticed a thick thatch of trees that seemed to go on for acres. Huge banyan trees grew limbs that spanned out far and wide, the roots draped down and anchored to the earth. Palm trees and ferns that were the size of army tanks added to the density of the tropical forest.

The bus door closed after the last of the soldiers disembarked leaving only the Nisei, the bus driver, and a corporal, who happened to be Hawaiian.

"Sirs. Welcome to Oahu. My name is Corporal Waimea, and I will be assisting you with your quarters. Your assignment, as you know, is sensitive. It's best that you have separate quarters than the general population for obvious reasons. We're traveling just one mile to the northwest where you will be stationed for ten days. After that you'll head to Fort Hase, the marine base. I saw you admiring our jungle out yonder. Soldiers stationed on Schofield use our jungle here but you'll have your own jungle. You'll receive the same training plus more." The bus slowed and turned.

"We're approaching your quarters. Thank you and godspeed."

The facility sat right along the Wahiawa Reservoir in the midst of a jungle that grew around a small building converted into a barracks specifically for MIS personnel. The soldiers endured jungle training along the reservoir. They played poker, smoked, joked, and worried together. And they waited. They waited for their leave time when they could get away from each other and enjoy the sights, sounds, and wahine of Honolulu.

While still on Schofield and before the transfer to Fort Hase on the east coast of Oahu, the Nisei were given a short leave. They enthusiastically primped themselves for a night on the town and headed for Honolulu. Naki suggested Club Pago Pago as their first stop.

Meanwhile in Manoa, Doris was getting ready for a night out with Stanley. They had been together for a couple of years, now, dating on and off. They would break up every few months because they couldn't seem to strike a rhythm but then get back together because they had a hard time being without one another. Doris had just bought a new dress with her most recent paycheck. She looked absolutely stunning in it and couldn't wait to tantalize Stanley.

He was picking her up at seven and they would be hanging out with their old gang at Club Pago Pago.

❖   ❖   ❖

"Wait, you were in Honolulu? Did you see Doris there?" I asked as I brought Masao his apple crisp from the dessert table at the casino buffet. *Maybe this is where they met, it makes perfect sense. She lived on Hawai'i and he was stationed there for a couple of weeks.*

"No. Never saw her there," he said dashing my hopes of these two young people, who were destined for each other, having a chance meeting on a balmy evening while walking along a deserted beach. "I saw lots of other women there, though!" He sounded like a teenager and evidently wanted to set the record straight: he had gotten some action during his stay on Oahu. I looked at him and smiled. No matter how old men are, many are the same. Always worried about their manliness as measured by how many women they've taken to the sack.

"Okay, settle down. Let's get back to Hawai'i. What happened at Club Pago Pago?"

July 1944 - Fort Hase

The bus made various stops, the most popular being the one on Beretania. The thirty or so soldiers on the bus, including the Nisei, unloaded and walked the few blocks to Club Pago Pago. A line already formed out the door of the nightclub. The women were all dolled up and seemed to notice the new crop of soldiers approaching.

Once inside the club, the Nisei were seated at a table on the dance floor. There was no shortage of dance partners. The soldiers had a spectacular time and hated for the night to end. And even though they were in the same club, dancing on the same floor and, at one point, dancing just next to each other, Masao and Doris would only cross paths that evening. They would never actually meet.

After two nights of heavy partying and dancing, the tired and hungover soldiers were loaded up for Fort Hase. Captain Aimone was already stationed on Hase and had a plan prepared for the Nisei upon their arrival. He had studied the mission of the ten Japanese-American soldiers now assigned to him. He learned about the MIS operation, about how MIS soldiers had been utilized around the South Pacific, and he was sure he could make better use of this well-trained resource.

He had a tough decision, though; he wanted to get as many Nisei interpreters on the front line as possible but had been ordered to assure loyalty. He also had to keep them all safe. He wasn't sure it was even possible to accomplish all that but had worked day and night to figure out how it might work. After weeks of research that included an extensive review of the family of each soldier, a careful examination of their military histories as well as schooling, Aimone was convinced that the MIS soldiers were, indeed, loyal to the U.S., even the three who had been educated in Japan. He looked forward to the day when he could hand a favorable report to General Mueller, a report that would reveal the honor of the ten-man MIS team.

❖ ❖ ❖

Aimone waited in his temporary office at the officer's headquarters. He had sent for three soldiers, two privates and one private first class. He had carefully chosen these men.

In came three young men: Jack O'Malley, a big, tall, red-headed guy: Edward, "Eddie" Garcia, a shorter Latino with soft eyes: and Ruben Escola, your average all-American.

"At ease. Men, I have a special assignment for you. I can't share many of the details of this operation, but what I can tell you is that it's sensitive."

The soldiers' faces revealed the excitement they felt; they were being included in some secret military operation.

"Once we're out there," he pointed to a map in the general area of the South Pacific, "there's a good chance we'll have Japanese prisoners to interrogate. We have the trained man-power to do just that. The problem is, our guys are also Japanese. They are Americans, but their ancestry is Japanese. I'm concerned for their safety. Very concerned."

The excitement faded. Were they actually going to be babysitting some Japanese guys? Or were they going to be involved in the torture of prisoners? Neither prospect appealed to any of them.

"Questions so far?" Aimone felt their anxiety.

"Sir," Garcia started out, "when you say interrogation…"

"I mean interrogation, questioning. Nothing more. Our methods are humane, I assure you." He saw the soldiers relax. "Your assignment will be to protect one soldier. Staff Sergeant Masao Abe. He's on his way to Hase now. He's part of a ten-man team, each team member has three guys assigned. You are bodyguards. I don't want anything to happen to your interpreter. Not a scratch."

"Sir." O'Malley raised his hand slightly. Aimone nodded for him to proceed. "Are we being pulled out of our unit?" O'Malley wanted to be in the middle of the action. The only thing going through his mind was that some little Jap was now ruining all the training, all the anticipation, everything he had been working for. It was gone. Because of some guy whose name he couldn't begin to pronounce.

"No. You're all still with your unit, the 321st. Sergeant Abe will be attached to your unit as well. Don't worry, boys, you'll see the action. We want these interpreters embedded right on the front line. That's why we need the protection. And I mean twenty-four hours a day, seven days a week."

The soldiers smiled at the thought of being real soldiers, out on the front line, taking no prisoners – wait – dammit, taking prisoners.

"Sir." O'Malley wasn't done. Aimone nodded, wondering if this man had been a bad pick. "What do we do if we get a prisoner? Take him to the rear?"

This guy needs the whole picture painted, Aimone thought. "We'll have military police assigned to each platoon. They will bring any prisoner back to division headquarters. Your job is to protect Sergeant Abe. He knows his job, he's been in training for months. You worry about watching him. Like I said, not a scratch."

❖   ❖   ❖

When the Nisei soldiers arrived at Fort Hase, the entire team, the ten Nisei and thirty bodyguards, were brought to a special conference room for orders. Captain Aimone was at the front. This would be the first time the Nisei would hear of the bodyguard plan.

"You all know me, and this is Second Lieutenant Bufoy." He motioned to a young, fresh faced man who had the hands of a woman, soft, and had never seen labor. The young man beamed at the introduction. This guy had not come through the ranks and it showed.

"You'll be here until we ship out on August 12th," Aimone continued. "Lieutenant Bufoy will be available in battle. He's a trained interpreter as well."

"Sir, I thought I would be assigned to division headquarters." Bufoy looked worried as hell that he would be plopped on the front lines. Aimone noticed his concern, as did most of the soldiers in the room.

What a dumb shit, Masao thought.

"That's right, lieutenant. Division headquarters will be secured but won't be far from the line." Aimone put him in his place as much as he could without humiliating him. He turned his attention back to the soldiers.

"Work hard over the next two weeks, gentlemen. The training will pay off."

❖   ❖   ❖

Grueling didn't even begin to describe jungle training. They had guys scaling trees, crawling through mud, digging holes in the clay, creeping on their bellies into dark caves, and running every day.

"Is he really a Jap? He looks kind of like you. Is he a spic?" O'Malley whispered to Garcia while they were trudging knee deep in mud.

Garcia scowled at him. "Are you really that ignorant?"

"I've been thinking," O'Malley continued, ignoring Garcia altogether. "If he is a Jap, do they want us to protect him? Or do they want us to make sure he's not a spy or something?"

Garcia stopped in his tracks. He hadn't thought of that angle. O'Malley had planted a seed. He knew there were other bodyguards who were equally as skeptical of this operation. They kept their suspicions from Captain Aimone, though, knowing that he was a strong supporter of these Japanese-American guys.

The ten-man team of Nisei, loyal Americans, would be heading into battle under the pretense of protection.

August 12, 1944 - Headed for Battle

On a transport vessel heading west, Masao was assigned to quarters with his bodyguards. By night three, there had been so much vomiting that Masao had had enough. The bunks were four high, one stacked right on the other, and when soldiers on the top bunk got sick it spilled down to the bottom bunks. It was hot and that made the sour stink even more unbearable. Masao couldn't stand the stench for another minute. Not only that, the constant sound of gut-wrenching puking made it impossible to get any sleep. He grabbed his pillow and blanket and headed out of his quarters.

In the cargo hold, Masao found a place under one of the Jeeps and made himself a little bed all by himself. He slept like a baby.

When O'Malley woke up and saw Masao's bunk empty, he flung himself out of bed to find Garcia. "Where's Abe?" He whispered.

"He's not in his bunk?"

O'Malley pointed to Masao's empty bunk and gave Garcia a "See, I told you so" look.

"Shit. We've gotta find him. Get Escola."

"I'm going to kill that little son-of-a-bitch for making me lose sleep," O'Malley huffed as he found Escola and woke him up. The three searched the decks for Masao to no avail. Not in the latrine, not in the galley, not on deck anywhere.

"Jesus, where could he be?" Garcia asked. "I hope he didn't go overboard." The thought made the three nervous. It would be their asses if he did.

"Maybe he's in the cargo hold," O'Malley said.

"Why would he be down there?" Escola said but O'Malley persisted.

"Because he's sabotaging gear, that's why. I'm telling you - he's a spy."

"Let's not jump to conclusions, Jack. Jesus Christ." Garcia reasoned.

The search intensified as the three made their way down to the cargo hold. They traversed the area, darting in between landing craft, trucks, and Jeeps.

"Abe. Abe - you in here?" O'Malley called out, not giving thought to address Masao as sergeant, not a single concern to address him as "sir", as a private first class should.

"Over here," Masao called out. The three followed his voice but it took them a few minutes to spot him. He was peeking out from under his Jeep/bedroom.

"What in the hell are you doing down here?" O'Malley barked.

"The stench from all the vomit is killing me. Three nights is enough. I'm not spending another thirty up there. This is my new bunk. Like it or not." O'Malley, Garcia, and Escola looked at each other, then more closely examined Masao's "bunk."

"There are other Jeeps, you know," Masao pointed out.

A short while later, each of the four had established their own bunk area in the cargo hold. They had carefully chosen a vehicle to call their own knowing that it wouldn't be long before other soldiers, who were disgusted by all the vomit in quarters, would seek out a vomit-free zone.

❖   ❖   ❖

Weeks passed before they spotted Guadalcanal in the distance. It had been taken back from the Japanese months earlier. Charged with a blend of excitement and anxiety, soldiers stood on deck watching the island become bigger and feeling their freedom and worry free nights slip away.

"All hands. All hands. Now hear this. We anchor at Guadalcanal at 1300 for a dry run. All hands. All hands. We anchor at 1300," announced a voice over the loudspeaker. They knew what to do and sprang into action.

As they neared the shore, the Jacobs ladders were tightened for soldiers to scale down.

Landing craft deployed from the cargo hold through huge doors at the mouth of the ship. When the orders came they scrambled down the rope ladders and jumped into the nearest landing craft to head for shore. Masao, surrounded by his reluctant bodyguards, felt self-assured. He glanced around and took pride in his military. All the men, many younger than he was and a few, older, radiated confidence. The ride to shore was bumpy, and eventually they felt the craft come to a sliding halt. The doors of the craft opened with a crash, and the soldiers piled off heading through the shallow water for shore as ordered.

On shore the seasoned and fatigued marines, battle scarring their faces, looked at the army soldiers in their clean uniforms, their shaved faces, and full bellies, with detestation. Every U.S. Army soldier felt it. It sank in and the enthusiasm vanished. This was real. In a matter of weeks, if not days, and if they were still alive, they would have the same expressions, the same loathing for inexperienced soldiers who came on shore clean and smiling.

There was a dramatically different mood on board after the dry run. Soldiers, at the very least, were apprehensive. Most were afraid. Lieutenant Bufoy, who had been making annoying appearances mostly just to garner salutes from men of lesser rank, approached the table of Nisei in the galley. After the formalities that only buffed Bufoy's ego, he sat down next to Masao.

"Nervous?" he asked in the most condescending tone imaginable. After all, Bufoy would be attached to division headquarters. His station would be established after an area had been secured and they could set up CIC, well behind the front line. This guy had nothing to worry about. His uniform probably wouldn't even get dirty. *What an idiot*, Masao thought to himself.

"Yes, sir. Of course I'm nervous."

Bufoy, who touted his expertise of the Japanese language, which is how he had maneuvered his way into his nice, cushy position, rattled off, "Don't worry," in Japanese.

Every soldier at the table wanted to get in on a group beating. This guy was a piece of work. Did he think he was alleviating any anxiety with his visit? Because he only added to it. If the guys in charge were dumb shits like this one, the 81st was in trouble. But, instead of punching him in the face, Masao nodded politely.

"Okay, sir. Thank you," Masao managed to utter as he glanced at Naki.

CHAPTER 9

BATTLE

ALAN AND I HAD MADE THE DECISION TO TAKE MASAO TO VEGAS FOR Thanksgiving. Once there, we followed our usual routine and sat at Grotto one evening. I was, as usual, devouring the strawberry cassata that I had been fantasizing about all day. Masao would have a bite of mine every so often, but I made Alan get his own dessert. I was turning into my own worst nightmare, blowing money like I had it to spend and eating huge dessert as though my body could afford it. Rather than focus on what a gluttonous gambler I had become, I remembered where Masao had left off when we last talked about the war.

"Hey, Mas," I said in between bites. He looked up as he sipped his coffee. "Last time we talked you guys had just completed your dry run on Guadalcanal."

"That's right. Dry run. Yep."

"What happened after that?" Alan waited to hear his dad's war story too. We both loved it when Masao went back to the 1940s and pulled up history for us to hear.

"Heh! After that, we went into *battle*!" He looked at me to see if I was focused. I nodded that I was. "On Angaur. An island."

"Find out where that is," I motioned for Alan to get out his phone and look it up.

"And, gee. Things got tough after that," Masao reflected.

"Were you scared?" I asked, then realized what a really stupid question it was. Alan looked at me like I was an idiot.

"Heck yeah! I was scared shitless!!"

0830 Sunday, September 17, 1944

FOX DAY

Angaur, Palau Islands

Masao, in full battle gear, looked off the bow as he waited, packed in with all the other soldiers. They watched navy destroyers pummel the island with shell fire, bombarding it heavily before sending in ground troops. Fighter planes attacked from overhead. Masao wondered if the Japanese had a chance against all this firepower, then he thought about Kunio and that radical will of his. Surely, there would be many soldiers who had that same sense of superiority, even in the face of certain doom.

"Move out!" The soldiers, in rows eight wide, hurled themselves onto Jacob's ladders and climbed down to hovering landing craft. Masao climbed down the rope fixture with ease, glancing at smoke rising from the tiny island.

"Shit, whose idea was this?" he said, his private thoughts erupting from his lips. Garcia, who was just next to him, heard.

"I don't know, amigo."

They both jumped into the landing craft followed by O'Malley and Escola. In a flurry, the landing craft deployed along with several others, forming a ring at sea and awaiting orders to go ashore. On board it was a choppy ride; soldiers struggled to keep their balance. One soldier got sick, likely more from nerves than the motion. Relentless explosions continued in the distance. The craft rolled and rocked in the swells. Tension was mounting with every passing second.

"Maybe they'll all be dead by the time we get there," Garcia hoped. Masao nodded, looking at the soldier who was puking again.

"Wave 3 - commence to Blue Beach," a voice on the commander's radio announced. The landing craft broke from the ring and headed to a beach in the distance. Fear escalated rapidly. Masao's heart was pounding faster and harder than ever before. To make matters worse, somehow he and Garcia had been shuffled to the very front of the craft.

"How'd we end up in the front?" Garcia said. Masao thought that Garcia must be the type of guy who talks when he's nervous.

The tempo of the naval gunfire intensified. Fires burned all over the island. Black smoke billowed into the clear sky, debris and chunks of trees fell with a splash in the surf. A beautiful paradise was quickly being demolished. The landing craft was a thousand yards from shore now. LCI, Landing Craft Infantry, gun boats and mortar boats took position in front of the craft. As landing crafts neared the beach, naval air fire concentrated on the shore, clearing the way for ground troops.

On the beach army tanks now dragged themselves out of the surf onto land, taking position to protect the dismounting men. The landing craft approached the beach facing relentless rapid fire and mortar rounds by the enemy. With a loud bang, the ramp of the craft released, making way for the men to jump off. The radioman was just to the side of Masao and leaped, immediately sinking to his neck. Masao abruptly stopped.

"Christ, the water's too deep!" Masao shouted.

The radioman stood up, and Masao could see that he had fallen. The water was only a couple feet deep. The radioman called back, "My knees buckled. I'm so damn scared." Masao noticed that his face looked like a little boy.

"Shit," Masao jumped off the craft in unison with Garcia. He looked around for O'Malley and Escola, they were right behind them.

"*Let's go let's go let's go!*" O'Malley was shouting out of sheer fear. The four of them ran as fast as the surf would let them. Fifteen feet from the beach now, Masao heard the unmistakable whistle of a mortar just above their heads.

"Christ almighty — *run!*" He shouted to nobody in particular. A grenade landed twenty feet in back of the four, thrusting them forward. Masao looked back to see the faces of men as their bodies exploded. His first inclination was to go back to see if any were alive, but Garcia grabbed his arm.

"*Mi Dios, mi Dios!*"

On the beach, code-named Blue Beach, the four slammed their bodies down against a sandy ridge, cutting their hands on the sharp coral.

Other soldiers lined up beside them. Machine gun fire hit all around. Shards of coral scattered in all directions spraying the men with razor-like fragments.

Masao looked back to the surf as the landing craft's ramp went up and it retreated back to the sea, leaving the men to fend for themselves. Bodies littered the beach. *This can't be real*, he thought. He looked at Garcia who was terrified. To his other side, O'Malley had his eyes closed. *Maybe he's praying*, Masao thought. Escola, on the other side of O'Malley, clutched his gun, his eyes squinting to avoid fragmented coral from injuring them.

Navy fighter planes screeched overhead. Tanks advanced off the beach from all directions. Masao watched Tech Sergeant Dan Cooper, the leader in charge of the company he was assigned to, scurry down the coral ridge. He grabbed the radio and tried to communicate in the midst of the explosions. Masao waited and watched, his hands glued in a firing position on his rifle.

After what seemed like an hour, the incoming machine gun fire ceased. The grenades stopped. Masao looked around and saw several amtraks advance off the beach, armored bulldozers forging the way through the dense foliage. Sergeant Cooper crawled over to his squad. They huddled around him.

"We got lucky," he yelled over the gun fire and the tanks menacing grinding. "Our planes knocked out most of their mortars. There's still dozens buried in, we don't know how deep. We're going to push our way inland as far as we can until we meet up with the 322nd. It could be a while. They're having a hell of a time on Red Beach. They haven't even made it on shore yet."

Masao thought about Naki attached to the 322nd as he watched Cooper pull out his map to check coordinates then scan his unit. "Where's my radioman?"

"Over there, sir," Garcia pointed down the ridge.

"Don't call me sir," Cooper stated as he motioned for the radioman, "unless it's your intention to get me shot. Not sir. Not serge. Not commander. Call me Coope."

"Sorry, Si—Coope."

Cooper rolled over and scanned the terrain with his binoculars, "That way," he pointed. "Stay close by the amtraks. *Let's move!*"

The soldiers hauled ass over the ridge and hovered behind an amtrak. Twenty yards in sniper fire took down a soldier at the front. They heard the yell as he went down. They all instinctively dropped for cover.

"Man down!" someone called out. Soldiers scrambled to move the wounded soldier to the rear. A trail of blood followed as he was dragged by Masao.

"He's not going to make it," Masao heard himself say. *Fifty feet into battle and he's gone.* The enormity of the thought weighed heavy on him.

"Over there! *Let's get the little ape!*" another soldier hollered, eager for revenge. The racial slur pierced Masao's ears, he watched the soldiers go in for the kill. They threw a grenade at a cave opening where the sniper had shot from.

"Don't let the little weasel come out alive!" another soldier shouted. A soldier armed with a flame thrower went out first, shooting liquid fire directly into the cave. The Japanese soldier ran out on fire, screaming and writhing in pain. Machine gun fire immediately put him out of his misery. His lifeless body continued to burn. It was a horrific sight for any human to witness. Masao knew it would get worse. Much worse. He looked around at his unit. But for Garcia—all of his U.S. Army comrades were white.

"Yeah! Take that you little nip," the flame throwing soldier bellowed as though he had just scored a touchdown in a high school football game. While the soldiers celebrated their first kill, medics ran by Masao with yet another wounded U.S. soldier from the front, from a different squad entirely. Masao gripped his rifle a little tighter. Soldiers who drew back to the Amtrak gave Masao a steely look. *I'm never going to make it out of here,* he thought. *It will only be a question of what side will take me down.*

The platoon inched forward. It wasn't long before a routine developed, find caves, employ the flame thrower, and gun down the burning soldiers who ran out on fire. The 110-degree heat was oppressive, and guys were soon shedding their shirts. The constant satchel charge explosions were unnerving at first, but became normal. Enemy bodies started to clutter their path, they were burned beyond recognition and still smoldering.

Now two hundred yards from the beach, a narrow swath had been etched in the tropical landscape. It was barely enough for tanks and troops to maneuver, but it sufficed. Sergeant Cooper dropped back to the middle of the platoon to meet up with Masao and his bodyguards. Acutely aware of Masao's mission, the safety of this Nisei Interpreter on his shoulders, and the realization that the other soldiers in his platoon were out for blood, he couldn't help but be uneasy.

"Abe. I'm inclined to have you fall back to combat intelligence. We can bring POWs back for you to interrogate, at least until division headquarters gets set up."

"It might be better if I keep pushing the line with the squad. These guys aren't coming out alive anyway," Masao suggested. He thought about division headquarters and that idiot Bufoy. He'd rather take his chances on the line than spend more time with him. From the front of the line, heavy incoming machine gun fire followed by another satchel charge shook the ground. A mortar shell landed fifty yards behind them killing medics and a wounded soldier.

"Shit, they're everywhere. *You two*!!" Cooper shouted and pointed at O'Malley and Garcia who were ducking behind an amtrak. "*Cover his ass!*"

September 18, 1944

Fox Day Plus One

Angaur

Dawn was barely breaking when Masao opened his eyes. He vaguely remembered trying to dig a foxhole but the ground was made of hard clay. No soldier had success with digging so they'd barricaded themselves with small boulders instead. He'd maybe slept an hour, the sounds of constant artillery and brilliance of the continuous flares making it impossible to get rest. Plus, he was still scared shitless. He thought that if he fell asleep, O'Malley would find a way for him to have some sort of fatal accident. The only reason he allowed himself to nod off at all was that O'Malley had fallen asleep and was snoring, thus taking away one less threat.

He heard the sound of tractors that had been working through the night, it must have been a hundred yards up from their location. Just then, O'Malley jerked awake.

"Shit. How long was I out?"

"Two hours, asshole," Garcia informed him.

"Wake up, sleeping beauties!" shouted Sergeant Cooper. "General Mueller landed at division HQ pissed that we're behind schedule. Grab your gear, let's move out." Moments later, Masao and his bodyguards took their positions behind an amtrak. Soldiers armed with flame throwers and mortar gear ran by them heading for the front of the squadron.

"It's time for another nip barbeque," the flame thrower said as he looked right into Masao's eyes when he trotted by. The word *nip* hung in the air. Masao didn't have time to react, though, because suddenly, there was an enormous explosion, shaking the ground in all directions. Soldiers crouched as the amtrak halted and the driver popped out of the top. Masao looked a half-mile to the north where billows of black smoke rose up, darkening the sunrise.

"Holy shit! What kind of bombs do they have?" Garcia sputtered as he hovered next to Escola.

O'Malley nodded toward Masao. "Maybe he knows," he insinuated loud enough for Masao to hear. Masao was reaching his limit. He and O'Malley locked eyes; neither backed down.

"Guys. *Guys!* Knock it off. We're moving," Garcia said, interrupting their standoff. They fell in behind the amtrak as it crawled along the narrow path.

"They hit the ammo dump on Red Beach!" A soldier called out.

"The little rats aren't going to back down without a fight," O'Malley said.

"Of course not, Jack. Neither would our guys. Do you think these things through before you say them?" Garcia said as he wondered if the real battle would be in their group of four.

❖   ❖   ❖

It was hours of plodding through the jungle in the sweltering heat. Suddenly there was excitement from the front.

"*Enemy spotted! He's surrendering!*" An exuberant soldier called back. A Japanese soldier waving a makeshift white flag, barely emerged from his foxhole at fifty yards. The expression on his face was clear: he was terrified.

"*Abe!*" Cooper shouted. Masao, O'Malley, Garcia, and Escola ran to the front of the platoon. Other soldiers took position around them.

"Let's get a little closer," Cooper motioned. They warily walked as a huddle toward the Japanese soldier.

"Tell him to come out with his hands up," Cooper ordered.

"Come out with your hands up!" Masao shouted to the prisoner in Japanese. His white flag still waving, the soldier slowly came out. He was skin and bones, his ribs protruded from his chest. Sergeant Cooper motioned for the group of six to close in on the foxhole, vigilantly. The Japanese soldier looked at Masao, they nodded, ever so slightly, to each other. O'Malley noticed.

"Abe, tell him to—" Before he could finish, sniper fire hit the Japanese soldier in the back of his head—exploding it. Brain matter sprayed the soldiers. They automatically hit the ground.

"*Cover us!*" Cooper yelled back to the platoon as he scanned the area. "Where'd it come from?"

"We're never going to get prisoners at this rate. Their own guys aren't going to let them surrender," Garcia whispered to O'Malley on the ground.

"That wasn't Jap fire," O'Malley stated. "Otherwise, why didn't they shoot more of us?"

Garcia glanced at Masao. "Then we'd better stick close to Abe."

"Why? Haven't you heard? The only good Jap is a dead Jap."

"Jesus, Jack. He's American."

"Yeah? Then why'd he look at that Jap soldier like he knew him? They've got some sort of code."

"Man. You're imagining things. He's one of us."

"He weaseled his way into one of our uniforms. But he's not one of us."

Still on their bellies, Cooper thought through his next move. "Shit. We've gotta go in there."

"In where?" O'Malley asked, not believing what he was about to hear.

"*There!*" Cooper motioned to the foxhole, "*We're on orders, goddammit.* Okay, *Abe*, get ready, we're going in. O'Malley!" he quickly assessed O'Malley and decided he was too much of a hothead. "You stay here. Garcia, you're with us."

Masao thought he was going to shit all over himself. He looked at Garcia and could tell—he felt exactly the same way. Cooper, Masao, and

Garcia shimmied on their bellies toward the foxhole passing the dead soldier on the way. The opening of the hole had remnants of camouflage netting, and it was dark inside. They hovered on the edge in squatting positions, guns drawn. Masao felt his legs shake and thought that his pounding heart was a sure giveaway to Cooper that he was scared to death.

"Holler in there, Abe. Tell 'em their comrade is dead. To come out with their hands up," Cooper ordered.

Masao cupped his hands around his mouth. "Come out with your hands up. Your comrade is dead!" *Goddamn my voice sounds weak.*

It was silent.

"It could be a trap," Garcia cautioned. Masao understood what Garcia was getting at. But Cooper had his orders: gain intelligence. That couldn't happen if everything was blown to pieces.

"I don't think so. I think the guy was solo here." Cooper stood. "I'll go in first." Cooper, gun still drawn, dropped inside the dim hole. Masao followed with his sidearm ready to shoot. Garcia was close behind Masao.

Inside, the soldier's meager existence spoke volumes about the shape of the Japanese military on Angaur. Empty cans of rations that had been licked clean, water bottle, drained. There were two rifles and no ammo. Masao noticed some papers and books and collected those. Cooper explored the back of the hole to see if there were tunnels leading to other locations but it was walled in.

"Anything useful, Abe?" Cooper asked, motioning to the books.

"I don't think so, sir. But I'll have a look outside."

Garcia took the rifles and Cooper led the way out. Outside, Masao scanned the papers while Cooper waited.

"Letters to his wife," he reported. "He had two little girls." He looked at Cooper. "One was learning the piano, he wondered if they still had the piano." He continued to flip through pages of letters, then switched to the books. "These are just novels," he said, leafing through to make sure he wasn't missing anything on the inside. "Just novels."

"Okay, let's take it back to headquarters. It'll give those assholes something to do," Cooper stated.

Back at Blue Beach where division headquarters was set up, Cooper's platoon emerged from the jungle to report in. As Cooper conferred with his commanding officer, Lt. Bufoy approached Masao.

"Sounds like you boys aren't making very good progress. Not one prisoner yet?" Bufoy sounded condescending and pious as usual, as though he could do a much better job on the line.

"No, sir. They aren't surrendering." Masao thought it was better to be brief so left out the part about the one guy who had.

"Well, they'll come out eventually. Once you guys soften them up. But at the rate you're going, that could be days." Bufoy looked at Masao with a sheepish grin. Masao really disliked him.

"Don't worry," Bufoy said in Japanese, figuring that would impress Masao somehow.

❖　❖　❖

I was so enthralled by Masao's vivid description of the battle zone that I had stopped eating my cassata.

"That second lieutenant, Bufoy, I didn't like him," Masao recalled. "He wasn't a soldier. He was more like a desk man. But he was a ranking officer so we had to call him sir." He shook his head at this.

"Do you really think that it was American fire that killed the prisoner?"

Masao nodded affirmatively, "Oh, yeah."

I sat back in my chair, taking it all in. I gazed at Masao with intense admiration. He felt my emotions, my interest.

"We were scared shitless for two or three days. Then we just got used to it. But the nights, they were the worst. There was no way to dig a small foxhole to sleep in, you know? The ground was too hard. So we just found-a small rocks and tried to surround ourselves with those. But... it was useless. It wasn't any protection. We all had diarrhea. We were all hungry." He paused for a moment, lost in though. "Tough times."

❖　❖　❖

The nights were only slightly less hot than the days. Cooper's platoon hunkered down on the line taking turns getting shut eye. Flares went up every few minutes to light up the area. Any movement would be shot at so when a flare went up, soldiers kept still. Machine gun fire and mortar shells exploded from distances in all directions. Sergeant Cooper walked through the line. His soldiers littered the area with their tired bodies.

"Stay alert. They'll be trying to infiltrate the line," he warned in a whisper as he waded through. Soldiers who were on lookout, worn from the hyper vigilance it took to constantly scan the surrounding jungle, struggled to stay awake. Masao sat next to Garcia while O'Malley and Escola slept. He watched another flare go up. Garcia nudged him.

"Shit. See that?" Garcia whispered.

"What?" Masao tensed up and looked around thinking the enemy was approaching.

"Alacran. Muy pelegroso. Scorpion. Very dangerous." Garcia pointed to a black scorpion crawling along.

"I'm going to kill it. If it stings you, it's going to hurt like hell."

"Okay," Masao nodded. Garcia grabbed a rock and was ready to go in when a shot went off. The scorpion was obliterated by O'Malley, who had woken up and noticed the crustacean.

"*Jesus, Jack*!!" Garcia shouted in a whisper. But the charge from the bullet had made them a direct target in the darkness of the night. Suddenly, there was rapid machine gun fire coming at them from fifty yards out, spraying bullets all around them. The four hugged the ground. Realizing his grave error, O'Malley grabbed his Browing Automatic Rifle (BAR), stood up, and ran toward where the shots were coming from, shooting his weapon and spraying the area. Garcia, Escola, and Masao followed, the three shooting relentlessly with whatever weapon they had. The incoming fire stopped and the four hit the ground together, now well outside line camp.

"Do you think we got 'em?" O'Malley whispered.

"I don't know. Shut up so we can listen," Masao whispered back. On the ground, they searched the darkness for any movement, listening with intense concentration.

"Dammit, between the enemy and these damn scorpions, this is going to be a long night," Garcia said in a low voice to Masao who nodded in agreement. Another flare went up. They spotted no movement but didn't stop their intense scrutiny of the area.

The next morning, all four were still alert, hugging the ground. They slowly felt safe enough to stand. They looked at each other not sure what to do next—fall back to line camp or go in to see if they were successful in defending their line camp. Meanwhile soldiers had branched out to search the perimeter for the four who had gone missing in the night.

"Come on," Masao motioned for them to go forward.

"You're a crazy son-of-a-bitch. Let's get back, they'll be looking for us," Escola reasoned.

"Escola's right," Garcia urged. Masao looked at O'Malley. His eyes asked the question "What's your stand?" O'Malley wasn't about to chicken out. He nodded at Masao. They didn't have to speak; they both knew they were made of the same cloth and neither of them liked that thought.

"I'll lead." O'Malley started to cut through the brush.

"He's right," Garcia said as he held Masao's arm so he couldn't take the lead. "We have our orders too, Abe." The four lumbered through the thick brush until they came upon two dead imperial soldiers, their bodies ripped apart by the overly executed barrage. They stood there for a few minutes feeling the weight of the moment, of taking lives in the true spirit of war. The enemy shot first, after all.

Masao perused the bloody sight, noticing a pack on one of the dead soldiers. He went in to take a closer look.

"What are you doing?" O'Malley's question was more like an accusation.

"I'm supposed to find intelligence, but I also want to see what kind of rations they have." He opened the soldier's pack and pulled out a tin can. He wiped the blood off and read the Japanese writing.

"What is it? A bomb?" Escola asked.

Masao shook his head, "No. Teriyaki beef. My favorite." He tucked it in his uniform and took the pack of Japanese cigarettes too. He was looking through their uniforms for any papers of significance when Sergeant Cooper marched up.

"I don't know which one of you imbeciles attracted the fire last night, but I don't *ever* want to see a stunt like that again. *Understand?*"

"Yes, sir," the four answered together, standing at attention.

"Abe, you are here on a unique mission, goddammit. Your orders are to stay embedded in the platoon until you're called for interrogation. Don't make me regret the decision to pull you along. I'll have your ass back at CIC before you know it."

"Yes, sir, uh, Coope."

"If I might—," O'Malley started to speak, but Cooper cut him off.

"No, you might not. Abe—stay in the middle. You three—your orders are to cover him. *Do I make myself clear?*"

The soldiers nodded and Cooper marched off in a huff.

"We got 'em good, though," Escola congratulated the group. The four followed Cooper at a distance, their voices low so Cooper couldn't detect their giddiness.

"I'm pretty sure I had the kill shots," Garcia claimed.

"Shut up, asshole. We all know it was me who killed the bastards so let's just leave it at that," O'Malley said.

"What are you talking about. You were shooting up in the air. My grandma has better aim," Garcia shot back.

And while Masao enjoyed the banter among his team of four, he didn't feel quite part of the team, he didn't feel the camaraderie. He wasn't sure he ever would.

❖   ❖   ❖

Back in Vegas, it was midnight and Masao was going strong. Alan had given up and gone to the room an hour earlier.

"Those guys, heh! They would congratulate themselves after something like that." He remembered the incident like it was yesterday. "I didn't feel so good about it. No need to celebrate when someone dies." His voice had changed with his afterthought. I glanced over and noticed that he was making ten dollar bets. *Holy shit*, I thought.

In between button pushes he looked over at me noticing my tired, red eyes. "You want a-coffee?"

"No, I'm fine. Keep playing! You're doing good!" I pointed to his winnings on the machine, it was approaching the thousand-dollar mark.

"Heh! I finally found a good one." He was right. His luck came and went, but mostly went. After a few pushes, a thought occurred to him.

"You know, we took Angaur in just a few days, maybe a week or so." I nodded that I was listening. "We went in one way, and, ah, the 322nd, they went in a different way. And then we met up at a point. That was a good day."

❖ ❖ ❖

Cooper's platoon moved along with the amtraks, following tractors as they cleared the way. Suddenly, voices called out from the distance, American voices.

"*Hold your fire!* 322nd approaching! Hold your fire!"

The 321st and 322nd Regimental Combat Units had successfully completed their assignment. Soldiers were allowed to relax for a brief time. Masao and Naki sat together under a tree.

"Have you taken any prisoners?" Naki asked Masao in between drags off a Japanese cigarette.

"Just killing everyone we see," Masao answered as he watched Garcia and Escola use palm leaves to fan themselves.

Naki looked off in the distance. Masao felt a heaviness coming from his friend. He examined Naki noticing that his face looked strained. He nudged him.

"You okay?"

Naki looked at Masao. There was a long anguished pause before he spoke. "I've seen..." his voice trailed off. He was unable to put words to the horror his mind had been replaying over and over, scenes that had permeated his mind, destined to remain there forever. Naki didn't have to complete his sentence. Masao looked into his friend's eyes. He understood the essence of the situation, as well as the scar it had left on Naki's psyche and heart.

"I wonder if we're going to make it out of here alive." Naki's voice was faint. Masao looked over at O'Malley who was bullshitting with other white soldiers. They appeared over-confident and borderline obnoxious. O'Malley spotted Masao's glance and gave him a glare.

"The odds aren't too good." Masao succumbed to that reality as he put his cigarette out in the sand.

❖　❖　❖

After a few hours, the 322nd was ordered back out. Masao and Naki bid farewell, wondering if they would ever see each other again. Masao, still attached to Cooper's squad, waited for orders. He found a nice spot in the shade with Garcia and Escola. O'Malley came from out of nowhere and joined them. Masao lit up.

"Did you hear about the guy in the 322nd?" Masao asked to nobody in particular. Garcia glanced over. O'Malley was disinterested.

"What happened?"

"Stung by a scorpion. Right on the balls," Masao announced. O'Malley took note.

"Shit. I knew the scorpions were going to be trouble," Garcia said.

"His nuts, they swelled up to the size of melons," Masao was going for the shock factor. It worked. O'Malley cringed.

"Jesus. That's just—Jesus," O'Malley uttered. The four sat there thinking of the poor guy with aching balls.

"Is that one of those Japanese cigarettes, Abe?" Garcia asked. Masao nodded, offered one to Garcia, then to Escola, who declined, then to O'Malley, who reluctantly took one.

They sat in silence smoking the strong tobacco.

"So, Abe. What are you anyway—a Jap or a Chink or what?" O'Malley blurted. Garcia looked like he was going to punch him.

Masao took long, thoughtful drag from his cigarette. "I'm Irish."

O'Malley softened ever so slightly.

"Round up, fellas!" Cooper hollered. They grabbed their gear and joined the company. "We're being shipped out to an island six miles north. Peleliu. We'll be attached to the 1st Marine Division. Four thousand marines already downed in just one week. They estimate over eleven thousand Jap soldiers still occupy the island. It sounds like a goddamn hell hole. Red Beach – 1700." He looked around at his guys. "Soldiers, brace yourselves. Angaur—was a cakewalk."

September 1944 - Peleliu, Palau Islands

Orange Beach

Soldiers stood on deck as the landing ship approached Peleliu. They were alarmed by the destruction. Not a tree stood on the beach and surrounding hills, all had been torched, leaving only charred stumps in the wake.

On shore the sickly sweet smell of death was immediately noticeable. Marine 1st Division Gunnery Sergeant Rae, his face reflecting utter hell, saluted Cooper and the other tech sergeants as they approached followed by their soldiers.

"Get used to the stench. Over here." Rae waved them over to a makeshift headquarters. A map was laid out on a crude version of a table.

"What's left of the 1st Marines are up in this area here - near what we call the Five Brothers. The 7th Marines are here. Your men will fan out and meet up here, at the base of these hills throughout this area here." He spoke quickly as he pointed at different areas. Masao lingered on the beach nearby with the rest of Cooper's outfit. The sound of a bulldozer a hundred yards away caught his attention. He strained to see what it was doing and realized it was scooping up swollen bodies and dumping them into a mass grave. Back in the huddle where the map was being studied the army sergeants heard the bulldozer as well.

"Get used to that too. Enemy bodies. We figure they had over ten thousand when we got here, and we've taken out at least half, but they keep pouring in from somewhere. No telling how many are here now." Rae pointed to the map again. "Recon says East Road on the way to Five Brothers is secured along here. But we're finding out that recon is full of shit. Either that or these Japs have one hell of a labyrinth of tunnels throughout these hills. They're still locked in heavy on this mountain, Umurbrogol. They own it. But not for long. At any rate, you'll encounter pockets of resistance at every turn. Sometimes it's just a lone guy, sometimes it's a whole shit load. Watch yourselves."

"What kind of artillery are we dealing with?" a sergeant asked.

"Everything. You name it, they've got it. They seem to have an endless *goddamn* supply," Rae spewed out as he glanced around. Then he noticed Masao.

"*What's this shit?*" He motioned toward Masao as he demanded an answer.

"Sir, he's with intelligence. Interpreter," Cooper spoke up.

"You've got to be kidding me. What the *hell* do we need to interpret? I hope you ain't planning to take any of these pricks alive after what they've done to my guys out there. Hell, what they've done to all our guys on every *goddamn* island we've taken back."

"Sometimes there are documents." Cooper again voiced reason.

"Documents my ass. Just like the army to cavort with the enemy. Jesus Christ."

"Sir, uh - where, exactly, is headquarters?" Tech Sergeant Thompson asked.

"You're standing in it—exactly," Rae responded with a grimace, waiting for any of these army pricks to challenge what the marines had accomplished. "Welcome to purgatory."

February 2012 – Hawai'i

The holidays had been tough for Masao. He hadn't gone to any events with his family, and he seemed more depressed than usual. When he became depressed and lonely, he would sink deeper than normal and stay there longer. I kept my routine with Masao sacred. Nothing interfered with our Tuesdays and Saturdays. It was a relief when we went to Hawai'i with him; the trip seemed to lift his spirits.

Our first day in Honolulu, we spent the day visiting Doris at the Punchbowl and eating a lot of food. It was a beautiful evening, and we were tired from traveling. The next day we would see Naki, something I was looking forward to. Masao was sitting on the balcony, taking in the activity of the tourists below on Lewers Street, a great little area in Waikiki. I spotted him out there watching the sun set and decided to join him. I brought two sweet iced teas and handed one to him as I sat down.

"Thank you," he said as he sipped. "Beautiful night, a-no?"

"It sure is." There was wonderful Hawaiian street music playing in the distance, the sultry voices drifting up to our balcony and soothing the air around us. It was perfect and relaxing. I tried to let my body unwind and settle into Hawaiian mode. That was until I heard the clang of the washing machine lid opening.

"Do you have any darks you want washed?" Alan barked out from the kitchen. *Good God, does the man ever settle down?*

"Come on, Alan! We're trying to relax out here!" I heard him laugh and continue with his noisy and intrusive laundry operation.

"Heh!" Masao seemed amused by the banter between Alan and me. After Alan finished making all the racket, he went into the bedroom to watch TV. The calm returned to the balcony, the sun completely set, and dusk fell upon Waikiki.

"One time, during the war, we caught a prisoner. Our first prisoner, in fact." Masao said, pausing for a moment as he formulated his thoughts.

I shifted my body and turned toward him.

"I was with an outfit, and the tech sergeant was a guy named, ah, Cooper I think. He was a good guy, a great soldier. Anyway, it had been days in that jungle. It was hot, reallllly hot, boy. Jeez. And we were already tired and hungry. But nothing like those Japanese guys… They really had it bad."

Masao looked at me to see if I was awake and listening. I felt flustered because I didn't have my tape recorder or anything to take notes on. I nodded and squelched the urge to run for paper and a pen and, instead, just listened.

September 1944 - Peleliu, South Pacific

Cooper's squad navigated the dense brush in the sweltering jungle in an area known as the Badlands. Suddenly sniper fire came at them from a cave at close range. The soldiers dropped to the ground and returned machine-gun fire in the direction of the sniper bullets. Masao was on his belly along with Garcia and O'Malley. The sniper fire stopped just as abruptly as it started.

"*Hold your fire!*" Sergeant Cooper commanded. They all waited. Nothing. They shimmied closer to the cave opening.

"*O'Malley*. Fire a round." O'Malley sprayed the cave opening with his BAR. No fire returned. Cooper motioned for Masao to come forward. Masao shimmied up to the front.

"Okay, do your thing," Cooper ordered. Masao nodded.

Masao called out in Japanese, "Come out. You will not be harmed."

A voice from inside the cave called back in Japanese, "I'm out of ammunition. I am unarmed. Don't shoot. Please."

"What's he say?" Cooper inquired.

"He says he has no more ammo."

Cooper surveyed the area. He was suspicious. "What do you think?"

Masao shrugged. "He would probably still be firing at us if he could."

"Okay, get him out here."

"Come out! You won't be harmed! Keep your hands up!" Masao called out loudly in Japanese.

Out came the terrified Japanese soldier. The American soldiers almost gasped at the sight. He was skin and bones, his ribs visible. His uniform was tattered and dirty. Two soldiers quickly ran in and patted him down while two others went into the cave.

"Poor devil. All right, ask him where his CP is." Cooper motioned to Masao as he took in the pitiful sight.

Masao looked at the soldier wondering whether he knew him. Maybe they went to school together in Japan, maybe he was a distant relative. It would be hard to tell with the guy's body so emaciated.

"Where is your command post?" Masao asked in Japanese.

He still had his hands up, nervous about his fate with these American soldiers. "It used to be over that ridge. But you guys got too close so they moved it." His voice was weak.

"It used to be over that ridge, but they moved it." Masao reported to Cooper, who was still examining the soldier's withered body.

"When?" Cooper wanted to know.

"When?" Masao asked the soldier.

"Maybe eight days ago. I'm not sure. Time has been lost to me." The Japanese soldier reported.

"Eight days ago, he's not sure. He's lost track of time."

Sergeant Cooper examined the soldier. His face softened, and he sounded almost empathetic. "The guy's been without supplies for a week. Left here to die." The U.S. soldiers came out of the cave with books and papers. Sergeant Cooper looked through them and handed them to Masao. "Look through this stuff, see if there's anything useful. Okay, let's get him back to camp."

Back at line camp, which wasn't much of a camp but more like a few holes and a makeshift galley, Masao instructed the prisoner to sit.

"Sit here. Don't move from this area. Some of these guys are trigger happy," Masao told the prisoner. Masao sat and read through the prisoner's books and papers. A mess sergeant by the name of McCoy walked over with a plate of hot food and a cup of water and handed it to the Japanese prisoner. Masao couldn't believe his eyes.

"Hey. Hey, McCoy. Wait just a darn minute. What gives? What about me? How come this guy gets hot meals and we don't?" Masao asked as he watched the prisoner scarf his food. McCoy refilled the prisoner's water cup as he looked at Masao. Clearly, McCoy was a humane guy. It didn't matter what uniform a soldier was wearing; starving was starving.

"Don't bitch. You guys eat three meals a day - this guy here hasn't eaten a full meal in days, weeks maybe." Masao looked at the Japanese prisoner. He took out his K-ration and bit off a chunk of the dry biscuit.

"This is bullshit if you ask me," Masao scoffed.

"Well, no one's asking you." McCoy huffed off. Masao was figuring out how to steal some of the prisoner's meal. The prisoner felt it, he turned away and hovered over his plate to eat in private.

Sergeant Cooper came to the area with a crumpled map. "I'd like to get a closer look at their CP, or what's left of it. Ask him if he remembers how to get there."

Masao nodded, tapped the prisoner. "We want to go to your CP. Do you remember where it was?" Masao asked. The prisoner, with his mouth full, nodded. Cooper laid out the map on the ground. The Japanese soldier scanned the map and pointed to an area.

"Way over there, huh. Okay. It'll be easier to get to it by road. We'll have to get back to HQ so we can pick up a Jeep. Shit." Cooper said.

Soldiers in general hated to go back to HQ but squad sergeants hated it most. The only military that hung out at HQ were a bunch of higher ups who didn't know the first thing about ground combat but who made most of the decisions for guys on the line. Cooper probably hated HQ more than anyone but he wanted to check out the CP. It was the first one they'd heard of and he didn't want to let anything go untouched.

Back at HQ it was evident how much better officers had life. Hot coffee was brewing, heartier food was abundant, and fresh water was plentiful. Lieutenant Bufoy, lingering about sipping on coffee, stood erect as he spotted Cooper's squad escorting a prisoner back to camp. He was excited to finally have an enemy to interrogate.

"So we got our first prisoner. Well, well. You boys did a swell job out there," Bufoy preened as he met the outfit at the edge of HQ, not daring to step a foot beyond what was considered safe.

Sergeant Cooper, eager to get away from HQ, tried to cut to the chase. "Thank you, sir. We did some interrogation up on the line, sir. If we could get a Jeep, we could-", but Bufoy interrupted. He wasn't about to let some high school dropout take charge of *his* prisoner.

"Hold your horses, sergeant. We need to do some interrogating here. I want to make sure we're getting quality intelligence, not some willy-nilly intelligence from the line," Bufoy said. He looked at Masao, "Abe, let's get started."

Bufoy moved the prisoner away from the others and motioned for Masao to follow. Masao looked at Cooper and reluctantly went with Bufoy. The prisoner looked nervous as he watched Masao for instructions.

"Okay, let's ask him where the command post is. Or - wait, let's ask him about their supply line." Bufoy's chest was all puffed up. This is what he had been waiting for, dreaming of. Bufoy had been bragging for weeks about his perfect Japanese so Masao waited for Bufoy to take the lead. Bufoy looked at Masao.

"Well, go ahead, Abe. What are you waiting for?"

"I was waiting for you, sir. I thought you'd want to handle the interrogation directly."

"My Japanese is mostly business lingo, sophisticated stuff. What matters here is that we get some good intelligence that I can pass up to *my* commanding officers. So you just interpret what I ask. Now, ask him where their command post is."

What bullshit, Masao thought. *He doesn't speak any Japanese.* He looked at the prisoner who was confused by the conversation between the two Americans. "I'm going to ask you the same questions I asked you before."

"Okay," the prisoner responded, eager to cooperate.

"What's he say?" Bufoy was almost foaming at the mouth to get information.

"He's trying to remember where the CP is," Masao assured him. Then, to feed Bufoy's narcissism, Masao said the Japanese words that Bufoy always said to him, evidently the only two Japanese words Bufoy knew: "Don't worry." Bufoy nodded, his eyes lit up, ecstatic to recognize some Japanese, then motioned for Masao to carry on.

Masao looked at the prisoner. *This Japanese guy is just a pawn. Ordered to hold his post but ... left to die.* A little thought-of casualty of war. Bufoy had Masao pepper him with question after question. Finally, after forty-five minutes of useless interrogation, Bufoy succumbed to Cooper's request to hand over a Jeep for the afternoon.

Jeeps were built for this terrain. They were rugged, sturdy, and could navigate anything. Sergeant Cooper was in the passenger seat alongside the driver that Bufoy had hand-picked so "Nothing" could happen "to the military equipment."

A short distance from HQ, Cooper muttered, "Dealing with goddamn HQ. What a snafu."

Garcia looked at O'Malley and mouthed "snafu?" O'Malley answered, "Situation Normal, All Fouled Up."

"When it's headquarters you're dealing with, it's all *fucked* up," Cooper corrected O'Malley. The soldiers look at each other and grinned, they liked Cooper's style.

The first part of the route had been easy to travel. Cooper had the map open, and the prisoner would point to different roads they needed to follow. Eventually, they ended up at the foot of a steep hill. The road looked more like a trail with huge gouges cut every which way. It seemed like an impossible climb. Cooper looked at Masao.

"Where to?"

"Which way do we go?" Masao asked the prisoner.

"Up that hill. It's on the other side."

"It's on the other side of this hill," Masao reported.

"Okay, let's take 'er up," Cooper ordered the driver, who put the Jeep in first gear. Up the Jeep started, gears grinding as the driver shifted up and down. Wrrrrr...wrrrrr. The drive shaft groaned and the tires dropped in and out of the deep groves. But slowly and steadily the Jeep climbed. Then, at one point the hill took a steeper grade, and the prisoner waved his arms frantically. Cooper noticed.

"Whoa. Stop!" Cooper ordered the driver. "What's his deal, Abe? Are there land mines?"

"What's going on? Are there mines?" Masao asked the prisoner.

"No. No land mines. We-" the Japanese prisoner began to answer, but Masao interrupted to ease Cooper's mind.

"No land mines," he said, and to the prisoner, "Continue."

"We must get out of the car and push it over the top. It won't make it up this steep part." The prisoner was making all sorts of hand gestures as he spoke. The soldiers in the Jeep looked on, bewildered. Masao listened, but was confused. "The car, it will tip over," the prisoner insisted, concerned about their fate.

"What's he say?" Cooper wanted to know. The Jeep hung there in limbo on the hill while the interpretation ensued. Masao was timid to give the interpretation for fear of being laughed at.

"He says that the Jeep won't make it. That we should get out and push."

"Get out and push!? Is the guy nuts? Let's go." The Jeep made more wrrrr-ing noises but easily made it to the top after tossing the guys around and passing the swollen bodies of several dead Japanese soldiers. At the top of the hill, the Japanese prisoner was astonished. He looked around in amazement at the feat of the Jeep and was awestuck by the four-wheel drive ability. He said something in Japanese and Masao chuckled.

"What's he say?" Cooper asked.

"He said, 'No wonder we're losing this war.'" Masao responded with more chuckling. The entire Jeep enjoyed the remark as they rolled down the other side of the hill toward the abandoned Japanese command post.

❖　❖　❖

"They didn't have anything like a-Jeeps, so that guy, he was realllly impressed, boy!" Masao chuckled at the memory. I laughed along with him, waiting to see if there was more to the story. Alan emerged from the bedroom and joined us on the balcony.

"What's so funny out here?"

"You're missing some good war stories," I told him. "Sit out here with us."

"That's okay, this is just you and dad's time together. Besides, there's a good show on TV."

I looked at Masao. I liked the idea that he and I had private time. Then I looked at Alan, Masao's son and my love. I was content. "What show?" I asked, thinking it would be some fascinating show on the Discovery or History channel.

"*Magnum P.I.*," he answered sheepishly. I sucked my lips in and shook my head, showing him that I could not believe my ears, but would refrain from giving him any shit.

"What?" he laughed. But he knew.

"Go watch your show. I want to hear more about World War II." Alan noticed our iced tea glasses were getting low, so he filled them up. After he was back in the bedroom and I was sure we had our quiet time back, I looked at Masao.

"Did you find anything at the command post?"

He strained to think about this, trying hard to bring the memory back in focus. "Gee, now, let me think." He searched his mind once again. "I think that was the time," his eyes squinted as he thought through the memory, scouring his mind for the correct details, "it might have been the time we found the payroll."

I cocked my head, "What's a payroll doing out in the middle of the ocean on a little island?"

"I don't know," he answered sounding like a child would.

"So what happened?"

❖   ❖   ❖

There was an unnerving feel to the deserted CP. The Jeep rolled in slowly. They all got out and looked around. The Japanese prisoner motioned to a weathered, makeshift hut. "That used to be the ammo hold," he told Masao.

Masao nodded to Cooper: "Ammo hold." Cooper motioned to Garcia to check it out.

Garcia went in with his gun drawn and came out within seconds. "Nothing."

After searching around a few minutes more, Cooper ordered them back in the Jeep. "They cleaned up before they moved. There's nothing here. Let's get back to HQ." The Japanese prisoner said something to Masao. Masao stopped and looked off in the distance.

"What's going on?" Cooper asked.

"He says there was a pond, over there. The payroll was buried there. Maybe they left it behind. He wants us to take a look."

"Could be a trap. I don't trust the guy," O'Malley spouted off before Cooper could.

"Will you help us dig?" Masao asked the prisoner who nodded eagerly.

"Don't think so," Masao reported. "He's happy to help us dig."

The soldiers dug with their helmets as makeshift shovels. The prisoner was right in there with them, chatting away in Japanese. Masao kept interpreting to ease Cooper's mind.

"He doesn't know why they kept money for army payroll. They were supposed to die here. He's got a point. Who's the payroll for? Soldiers have been ordered to fight to the death, not to let the Allied Forces advance through the island, even if they have to die defending it."

"Probably for their officers," Cooper figured. "It's always about the goddamn officers. Doesn't matter what side you're on."

O'Malley hit something with the stick he was using for a shovel. "We've got something here," he announced. Sure enough, out came a box, heavy and muddy. They struggled to get it on land. Inside were thousands of yen and documents. The prisoner looked vindicated.

Back at headquarters, Lieutenant Bufoy saw the Jeep approach and walked toward the edge of HQ. "What do we have here? Any good intelligence?" He was eager to score a victory.

"It's their payroll, sir, and a few documents that may be of use." Cooper wanted to get this over with so he could get away from headquarters but Bufoy wouldn't have it.

"Payroll, huh? Let's take a look!" His eyes lit up as the soldiers heaved the box out and opened it. "Anything in the documents, Abe?"

"Probably, sir. They're military." *What a dumb shit this guy is to even ask. They're documents. Hidden in a secure box. Buried. In a pond, underwater. Yes, they're important.* But Bufoy was so preoccupied by all the yen, he didn't even hear Masao's sarcasm.

"I'll have one of the CIC guys take a look." Bufoy was entranced by the money. "Go get Sakai for me, will ya?" He motioned for Masao to get one of the Nisei interpreters assigned to headquarters. Masao did as ordered by the idiot, then he sat down next to the prisoner.

"What will happen to me now?" the prisoner asked, terrified. They both watched Bufoy as he handed one Japanese yen to each of the soldiers who had retrieved the payroll from the pond, careful not to dispense more than just one to each.

"You will be taken to one of the POW camps. But probably more interrogation here first."

The prisoner's eyes widened. "Torture, no? Or worse?" He asked afraid of the answer.

Masao watched Bufoy stuff his pockets with yen. The other soldiers gathered their gear.

"No. No torture. The guys who will interrogate you are Nisei, like me. They won't hurt you." Masao assured him. The Japanese soldier looked over and saw Bufoy's greed and self-indulgence.

"Officers. They're all the same, no?" The prisoner assessed. Masao nodded and moved his attention from Bufoy to the prisoner. Their eyes connected for just the briefest of moments, but in that instant – a thousand thoughts. Masao wondered how it was that fate had dealt him a better hand than this guy. Had one variable in his life been different, he could have very well been sitting on the other side, starving and scared to death. Had his father not sent him back to the States when he did, had the Japanese military changed the age of conscription, had the Japanese government not let him out of the country, had his little sister not died…

The prisoner looked at Masao and thought that this American soldier must have had the best of parents to keep him away from the Japanese military. He thought about how he had hated the military from the time he was little. He hated the military drills while at grammar school, he hated the uncomfortable uniforms, he hated swords, and he loathed violence. But he was just a farm boy. His parents were illiterate and unable to maneuver the path that would have kept their sons from entering the military as some of the wealthier families had done. It was his fate to be a soldier, and a bad soldier at that. Now he would either die a slow and painful death, or, even worse, be sent back to Japan as a failure.

Bufoy looked over and saw that he was being watched by the two Japanese men. He felt uncomfortable. Bufoy was unable to admit to himself that he was useless on the battlefield and equally as useless as an interpreter for which he had been recruited. He was the product of the upper class; this military stint would add to his resume as he pursued politics. He just didn't want to get harmed in any way. He didn't really care about the soldiers who were out on the line, they didn't have a future anyway. Part of their job was to protect him, he was going places after all. He mulled over his next action and decided to be philanthropic. He walked over to Masao. "You deserve a little something." He handed Masao a bill, worth about a dime. "Good work today. I think this is worth a Silver Star."

"Thank you, sir," Masao said as he looked up, completely astonished by Bufoy's generosity at recommending a Silver Star for him. Maybe he'd been wrong about Bufoy, maybe this guy was a decent man after all.

Lieutenant Bufoy was confused for a moment, then realized that Masao misunderstood.

"Not for you, Abe. The army doesn't want to decorate Japs, for Christ sake. I meant for me."

❖ ❖ ❖

"Those Japanese guys were just left behind on that island. Nobody cared what happened to them. They were just regular guys, a-no? Just doing their job." Masao's empathy for the Japanese soldier permeated the balmy evening air on the balcony, and it was contagious. I had seen pictures of Japanese prisoners and their wasted bodies, but to witness it in real time must have been more than poignant.

I looked at Masao, as I often did, and admired this man who had fought like a soldier with the heart of a saint throughout the war and beyond. Even now his memories focused on the frightened Japanese prisoner instead of the self-absorbed second lieutenant.

"Just following orders..." His words floated out into the evening Hawaiian breeze.

❖ ❖ ❖

After spending the morning taking fresh roses to Doris, we met Naki at Zippy's. The two war heroes nibbled on their saimin while chatting about this and that and giving each other shit whenever the opportunity presented itself. The current topic was how Naki qualified for one hundred percent disability while Masao did not.

"It's my hearing, though, Abe, my hearing is bad," Naki was explaining.

"What?" Masao strained to hear, but did not.

"*His hearing is bad*," Alan nearly shouted so his dad could hear.

"So is mine, heh! And I have a *bullet* in me!" Masao shot back. Naki just shrugged. I was about to ask about this bullet he'd mentioned before when the conversation went in a different direction.

"Did you tell her about the nights?" Naki asked Masao.

"What nights?"

"You know, the nights. On the islands."

"Honolulu?"

"Noooo...not Honolulu," Naki chortled. "The nights during the war! In the jungle, *those nights*!"

"What about them?" I wasn't sure if Masao was really confused or just being cantankerous with his old war buddy.

"Well, you know, how bad they were, with the Japanese making all the sounds and calling out things to us," Naki turned his attention toward me. "In the beginning, it was especially bad. It was kind of scary to sleep at night, you know?" Then he looked back at Masao, "Wasn't it?" Masao nodded, remembering.

"At night," Masao said, "those Japanese soldiers would try to scare us by yelling things. They spoke English, a-no? Bad English, but English. And-ah, in the beginning, it did scare us, boy..."

❖ ❖ ❖

"Get yourselves dug in," Cooper ordered as he walked along the primitive line camp that had been assembled. Masao and his three body-guards had found a natural indentation in the ground and used it for their dugout. At the first sign of darkness, the flares started. Masao was just about to doze off when he heard something.

"Heeey—yeww!" someone called out from a distance. The voice had a distinct accent.

O'Malley jerked his head up. "*What was that?*" he whispered.

"*Shhh...*" Masao cautioned him. "Be quiet, don't move." Their bodies clenched up, their ears strained to listen, their eyes scanned the darkness. Finally another flare went up. O'Malley slowly reached for his BAR. The weapon weighed thirty pounds so it was a struggle for him to maneuver it quietly.

"*Shhhh!*" Garcia motioned for him to halt.

"*Hey Yann-kee* - you go-ing to *die* tonight Yann-kee!!!" the voice hollered out.

"Shit. Where's it coming from?" Garcia was wildly surveying the dense foliage. O'Malley steadied his rifle in firing position. It seemed like years before another flare went up. Masao shifted his position so he could examine a different perimeter. His heart was pounding; sweat trickled down his cheek.

"I *see* you Yann-kee!!" the voice shouted.

"I don't know," O'Malley answered Garcia in a hushed whisper. "It seems to be, what, a hundred yards away? What do you think?"

"Maybe. He could be up in that hill, over yonder." Escola pointed to a small hill jutting up from the forest.

"Yann-kee's gonna *diiiiie*!" the voice taunted, followed by an evil-sounding laugh.

"It's not getting any closer," Masao assessed.

"*What?*" O'Malley whispered.

"The voice. It's the same voice over and over, and it's not getting any closer to us. It's one guy, and he's staying in his cave."

O'Malley nodded. "You could be right," Everyone was hyper alert for several minutes, watching flares go up, straining their eyes to see any hint of the enemy approaching. It was eerily quiet for several moments.

"Now I'm nervous," Masao whispered. He readied his sidearm and motioned for Escola to do the same. Another flare went up.

❖   ❖   ❖

"Some of them must have been very confident, a-no? To do that," Masao thought as he remembered those horrible and frightening nights.

"Yeah, because we were losing a lot of guys on that island, a lot of marines died there. Right, Abe?" Naki added.

"That's right. And the Japanese soldiers just kept coming in from somewhere, thousands of them. Nobody could ever figure out how their military was getting so many guys, a-no? Replacement soldiers. They just kept coming."

"And those bodies." Naki appeared physically sick. His face cringed and contorted as he looked at Masao, who immediately understood what he was talking about. Naki couldn't finish his thought so Masao finished it for him.

"There were bodies all over that island, enemy bodies. We picked up our guys, a-no? We took our guys to a special place to be buried. But enemy bodies, you saw them everywhere. Hundreds."

This is going to get gross, I thought. *Thank God we're done eating.* I looked at Alan, he was oblivious to what was coming.

"And sometimes," Masao continued, his eyes wide as he remembered this thought, "their bodies would swell up, you know, because of the heat."

I swallowed. *The challenge, here, is going to be how to keep my food from coming up.* I wanted him to stop.

"And, sometimes, a soldier would go by and stick them with a knife, or bayonet and their bodies would explode." He used his hands to illustrate what an exploding body looked like.

"That's right." Naki had hand motions going too. Alan and I looked at each other, it was a visual we wanted to rid ourselves of. Unfortunately, it was also one of those visuals that impacts your psyche forever.

"And sometimes—" Masao was going again. I put my hand up, palm out, to shield myself from his words, but it did no use. "Sometimes, their bodies would just explode on their own. Guts and bodily fluids would spray for feet." There was no amusement in Masao's voice, this was just part of the hell that was Peleliu. I felt myself swallow and instinctively dried my mouth so I wouldn't gag. Alan was doing the same.

"That stench. It would get into your, uh, uniform. It would get into your, your nostrils and it would just stay there for days." Naki's face was that of a young man, reliving just one of the horrible aspects of the war.

Then the two soldiers at the table went silent, lost in their thoughts back in 1944 on that island out in the middle of the ocean. An island that had turned from a paradise into a hellhole and had become a graveyard for thousands. Masao made a "tsch" sound with his mouth as he often did when he told stories or considered unthinkable situations.

"One time," Naki began. He had the look on his face, the same look Masao had when a memory was crystal clear in his mind. The same look he wore when I knew a memory had to come out, had to be heard, maybe even recorded somehow. "I was—just landed on the island. What was that island, Abe?"

"Uh, a-Angaur? The first island?"

"No, no. The other one, what's the name, now?"

"Peleliu, no?"

"Yeah, Peleliu. And, uh, your team—you were already there. But we just arrived. And, ah, I was attached to the 322nd. Regimental Combat Team."

"322nd, that's right," Masao nodded.

The mood at the table was serious. "And, uh, there was this one lieutenant. He wasn't supposed to be with us, you know? But he knew we had a live cave. He knew there was some action and he, you know, wanted to be a part of it, I think."

Early October 1944 - Peleliu

Naki, with his bodyguards close by, huddled around a cave nestled in the side of a hill. The rest of the outfit stood at the perimeter, scanning the brush for movement. An hour or more had passed while Naki spoke with this enemy soldier, persuading him to surrender. But now, it seemed, there was a glitch of some sort with headquarters. Their tech sergeant was on the radio some distance away in an ongoing negotiation about what to do with this enemy prisoner.

One of Naki's bodyguards nudged him and pointed toward the cave. "Do you think he's alone?"

Naki nodded. "And out of ammo. I think we'd all be dead if he had any grenades left."

The bodyguard nodded in agreement, then nodded toward the tech sergeant who had hung up the radio and was on his way to the cave site with a scowl on his face. "Looks like trouble."

The tech sergeant stomped over. "We gotta wait, boys. The son-of-a-bitch lieutenant wants to 'oversee' the operation." He used air quotes to make the point that he was beyond annoyed.

Twenty minutes later, a lieutenant in a clean uniform arrived, sur-rounded by an entourage of protection, and carrying a rifle with a dark wood butt. "Okay, what do we got?" the lieutenant spouted.

"Sir, Nakamura, here, has been in contact. We think he's alone and without ammunition."

"Very well. Nakkiworra, is it? Go ahead and do your thing. Let's get him out here."

Naki nodded as he inched forward to the cave opening. "Soldier, are you still there?" he called out in Japanese.

"Yes," the Japanese soldier answered back, his voice was laced with fear.

"Okay, here's what I want you to do. Take off your uniform except for your loin cloth. Tell me when you have that done." Naki looked at the lieutenant. "I'm telling him to take off his uniform."

The lieutenant nodded. He looked at Naki as though Naki, himself, were from the Imperial Army and had somehow manage to slip into an American uniform.

Naki felt it and suddenly an uncomfortable feeling swept over him. He looked at his bodyguards, guys he had come to trust. They felt it too; he could see it in their eyes. The presence of this lieutenant poisoned the air around them. But one small nod from the bodyguard standing next to Naki eased his heart.

"Okay, I'm in my loin cloth," the Japanese soldier called from inside the cave.

"Okay. Now I want you to come out with your hands above your head. Nobody will hurt you. Just come out slowly and with your hands above your head. Okay?"

"Okay," the weak and petrified voice answered back.

Naki nodded toward his tech sergeant, "He's coming out."

As soon as Naki could see the enemy come into the light, he continued coaxing him out, "Just stop there for a moment and let your eyes adjust," he said when he noticed the soldier squinting in the sun. "It's okay, we're not going to hurt you. Keep coming out."

Inch by inch, the enemy soldier made his way out of the cave. He stood there in his loin cloth, with his hands up, his skeletal body trembled.

Naki looked at his tech sergeant for instructions when, out of nowhere, the lieutenant raised his rifle and shot the prisoner in the head at almost point-blank range. The blast of his rifle reverberated throughout the area. Blood-spatter landed on the shocked faces of Naki and his bodyguards. Naki watched with disbelief as the prisoner's limp body fell backward onto the jagged rocks. He felt his bodyguard step back and wondered if this was the end.

Am I next?

"Jesus," the tech sergeant said under his breath and then bit his tongue. The look on the faces of guys in the outfit were all the same: astonished and mortified. Naki looked down at the Japanese soldier and watched blood ooze onto the rocks. His neck looked broken by the fall.

The lieutenant didn't seem fazed in the least by the disturbed reaction of the platoon. He lowered his rifle, looked around for anyone to dare him, glanced a steely glare at Naki, and then gave a slight nod of self-approval at a job well done. As if it were part of his routine, he searched the ground for a stone, spun his rifle around and carved a notch in the butt using the sharp stone as a carving tool. Naki noticed that this was his seventeenth notch. *He's keeping track of all the enemies he's killing.* The lieutenant gave one last look at the man he had just killed, the trophy he'd just scored, and marched off.

Naki found himself alone at the cave opening, looking down at the soldier who had followed his instructions, who had trusted that he wouldn't be harmed, who wasn't armed, who wasn't even dressed in his uniform. He felt a tap on his arm.

"Let's go, Naki," his bodyguard said as he pulled Naki to the safety of the platoon.

❖ ❖ ❖

Back at Zippy's, we were in a world of our own at the table. Naki's memory was heart-rending; its heaviness lingered at the table, even while busy waitresses bustled by.

"It was just—murder, you know?" Naki looked around the table. The feeling of injustice was intense, the responsibility Naki had carried for almost seventy years was palpable. "He only came out of that cave, you know, because I persuaded him to come out. I felt like I was part of it, you know. But I didn't know that was going to happen that way. He wasn't killed in a battle or anything like that. It was just - murder."

It was quiet while we all digested this ugly piece of history.

"Not your fault, Naki. There were guys like that, a-no?" Masao comforted Naki. "Did you tell me that before?"

"No, I never told anybody about this. Nobody, not even my wife. It's too…" Naki didn't have words to describe what he felt, but the look on his face was pure shame. "Besides, I don't have anyone to corroborate my story, you know? Who would have believed me?"

Masao nodded. "I would have believed you."

I looked back and forth at Naki and Masao. These men were warriors of the bravest kind. And yet, at the height of the war when their bravery was the most necessary, their word counted for nothing. They were soldiers of a discounted variety, treated less than second-class citizens. Even seven decades later, they felt their word couldn't stand on its own. *How could this happen?* I thought as I sat there admiring these two great men. *How many others in our great nation feel like they don't have a voice?*

May 8, 2012, Tuesday - A Little Excitement

It was already quarter to three and I was supposed to be at Masao's by three fifteen. I got in my car and dialed his number.

"Hello?"

"Masao?"

"Hello?" he repeated.

"This is Sandie." I felt the need to identify myself. Something wasn't right on the other end of the phone.

"Hey, Sandie."

"You want to go to casino today?"

He chuckled. "Heh! I don't know. There was a little excitement around here today!"

Oh my God, I thought. *Another resident has died. How depressing.* "What happened?"

"I don't know. I was just a-making my lunch when all these firefighters busted into my place."

"What??" Now I was concerned.

❖　❖　❖

He had slept until eleven, then turned on the TV to the Japanese channel. After watching a while, he had decided to make himself a fried egg sandwich. A decent cook, he always had the thick sliced Japanese bread on hand, eggs, tomato, and lettuce. A fried egg sandwich was something he enjoyed often. He started the toast while he fried his egg, scrambled style. When his egg was done and the toast not, he'd put the egg aside and gone back to his recliner to watch TV.

But the toast was set on dark and was burning. Smoke billowed into his room and set off the fire alarm. Masao, a little hard of hearing, was enjoying a show that really captured his attention—obviously, because he didn't notice the smoke or hear the alarm. Meanwhile the facility management was notified of the fire alarm, as was the local fire department.

Masao watched TV, having forgotten about his toast by then and oblivious to the impending intrusion.

"Huh?!" Masao uttered when four firemen bolted into his apartment.

"Sir, are you okay?" one of the firemen asked. The others searched the apartment, and the problem in the kitchen was quickly discovered.

"What's going on?" Masao asked, confused and feeling embarrassed — another old codger who could no longer be trusted to live on his own.

"Your toast, sir, it set off the alarm."

"Ohhhhh, my toast." Masao smiled. "It was for my fried egg sandwich." He was now up and rolling himself into the kitchen to make his own inspection. It was true. His popped toast was black and smoldering. He glanced at the firemen surrounding him. "You guys sure did respond — a-quickly!"

The firemen smiled at him.

Masao wanted to offer something for their trouble. "I make you a fried egg sandwich. You want-a one?"

❖　❖　❖

Back on the phone with me, Masao described their entrance, "And they came in with their *axes* and their big *jackets.*" He accentuated the axes and jackets.

"Are you okay?" I asked him, thinking about how impressed he'd been by their appearances.

"Oh yeah. It was just a lot of excitement, that's all."

"Well, do you want to just stay home today? Or do you want me to come get you to take you to casino?"

"Oh, I go casino!" he answered quickly.

When I walked into his apartment, I smelled the burnt toast. The remnants of his fried egg sandwich remained on his plate. Masao was brushing his teeth while I made sure all the burners were off. *No need to set off another alarm.*

"Those guys sure reacted quickly," he commented as he rolled himself out of the bathroom. I nodded and smiled as he sat down in his recliner with a sigh. The day had really taken a lot of energy from him.

"Are you sure you want to go?"

"Oh yeah, I go," he leaned down to get his shoes on, using a long-handled shoe horn to get the job done. I resisted the urge to help him — he wouldn't want to be treated like an old man, especially now.

"You know, there was a guy during the war. A really nice guy. What's his name, now?" He looked down and closed his eyes to bring the memory into focus, calling up the man's face, bringing his name forward from 1944.

"Galligan. His name was Galligan. Or something like that. He was a-realllly nice to me, boy."

I leaned forward, interested to hear about this newest addition to the cast of characters in Masao's history.

Early October 1944 - Peleliu

Cooper's squad had been pushing hard toward Umurbrogol Mountain, a peak on the island that was actually a conglomeration of coral hills. The Japanese navy had dominated this part of the island and had held it fiercely, new troops coming in from somewhere to continue fighting off Allied Forces. Recon had been working day and night to try to identify where the supply line for the Japanese military was, but they had come up empty-handed. The dead bodies from both sides continued to pile up.

Dusk was closing in and Cooper wanted his guys back at line camp where flares would be going up. "Hold your fire! Coming through!" Cooper shouted as they approached the primitive camp that was supposed to provide some sort of secure shelter and food for the tired soldiers.

"Grab a bite and get yourselves dug in," Cooper ordered. Masao attempted to dig through the tough clay with his helmet. He finally gave up and found rocks to protect himself. A medic approached him, a soldier Masao had never seen before.

"Hey, sarge. John Galligan." He held out his hand to shake. Masao took it, confused by the hospitality. "Here." Galligan handed Masao a tin cup full of steaming-hot water.

What's all the hospitality about? Masao held the tin cup.

"For coffee or something. You got one of those little packets of instant coffee from your rations? Or just let it cool and drink it. It's safe. It's been boiled." Galligan nodded and then disappeared as quickly as he had arrived in Masao's space.

Masao searched his pockets for an instant coffee packet and finally found one in a beaten-up package. He ripped it open with his teeth, careful not to spill a drop of the precious, clean water, then sprinkled it into the tin cup. He swirled the mixture, then took it in, closing his eyes to get the full effect.

He imagined that he was back in San Bernardino on a crisp, autumn morning, when coffee tasted its best, or in that wonderful diner in Chicago before Pearl Harbor had ever been a blip on the radar. He imagined that he was anywhere but the South Pacific, where he was dirty and hadn't seen a shower in weeks, hot and exhausted, and most of the time scared for his life. He sipped the coffee that, in any of those other scenarios, would have tasted horrible. But in this moment, it tasted like the finest coffee in the world.

❖　　❖　　❖

"Every time I was at-a a line camp, that guy, Galligan, would bring me hot water. He was really nice to me, boy," Masao remembered with fondness and gratitude.

"How often were you at line camp? Every night?" I was struggling to understand how the battlefield worked.

"Nooo, not every night. Sometimes we would advance on the line, a-no? And then just have to set up camp when it got a-dark. Those were tough nights, boy. Reallly tough." He sat back in his recliner and stared off in the distance. It was as if he was watching himself in his mind's eye, replaying history, one frame at a time.

"Heh! My bodyguards and I, we used to pass the time whispering back and forth on those nights. We should have been watching for the enemy, a-no? But we would get bored. Heh!"

❖　　❖　　❖

Cooper's squad was ordered to stay out for the night, it was too far for them to fall back. They had stopped advancing at the foot of a hill that had supposedly been secured. There was a high degree of likelihood that intricate caves had been tunneled throughout the hill, even though recon had assured them the caves were clear. Cooper was a shrewd soldier, though, and knew how to protect his squad in even the most risky situations.

Masao and his bodyguards found a tree to lean against, ordered to get some shut-eye before taking over perimeter watch. It rained all day and the men were soggy and hot at the same time. Still, they tried, lowering their heads with helmets on, weapons readied. The rain stopped and the jungle became eerily quiet.

"Apple pie," O'Malley whispered in the darkness out of nowhere.

"Are you sleep-talking again, old boy?" Garcia nudged him.

"It's funny what you miss. Right now, I miss my grandma's apple pie. She makes it every Thanksgiving and Christmas." O'Malley's face revealed his longing for the sweet taste of his grandmother's apple pie.

There was only the sound of raindrops falling from palm leaves. The skies opened up and the moon shone through clouds that had been so relentlessly pouring rain.

"I miss my girl, Lupe. But now that you mention it, I sure wish I had some of my mom's tamales. She takes days to make her tamales, all wrapped in banana leaves. God, those are good. When I get home, I'm going to have her make me a batch. Maybe two batches." Garcia could smell his mom's fresh tamales baking on the open wood fire stove they had in the backyard. He breathed in through his nose, imagining he was there with his family.

Masao listened as he scanned the terrain.

After a few moments, Escola contributed. "I have a little girl. She's three. She has curly red hair and a beautiful smile." Escola smiled as he thought about his daughter's face. "I have no idea where she got the red hair. There's no red hair on my side. But I know my wife didn't cheat. So it's got to be in the gene pool somewhere. But my little girl, Sarah is her name. Her smile…that smile…makes me melt. I miss that. I miss melting when I see her smile." The other guys looked at Escola and realized he had it the worst. Escola was a man of few words but, evidently, had the most to say. His eyes filled with tears. The men looked away to give him his privacy.

"What about you, sarge? What's the first thing you're going to do when you get home?" Garcia asked Masao.

"Huh. You know, I don't think I have a home any more" he said.

"What are you talking about?" O'Malley blurted. *That crazy Jap, he doesn't even know what he misses.*

"I was living with my uncle in California. But he was sent away. The whole family was." There wasn't a hint of self-pity in his voice. Garcia and Escola, both from California, understood right away. They both nodded with genuine empathy. But O'Malley, the Irishman from Illinois, didn't have a clue.

"What? Where'd they go?"

"Jesus, Jack. You are a stupid shit. His family was sent *away*. To a camp. An *internment* camp. Everything was taken from them. Everything. Get it?" Garcia was annoyed with O'Malley. Masao smiled at this and nodded in agreement. Garcia had it right. Except for the part about his uncle being sent to prison, he had it right. Except for the part about the grocery store being swindled from his family, he had it right. Except for the part that he had a little cousin who had been born in a dusty barrack out in the desert, he had it right. It was close enough.

"Okay, settle down, Eddie. Jesus." O'Malley thought for a few minutes, trying to understand. "So, I don't get it. Where are you going to go when you are discharged?"

Garcia had just about had it with O'Malley and hit him on the arm, giving him a "shut the hell up" look.

"What did I say?"

"It's okay, Eddie," Masao gently eased Garcia's heart. "Jack, I honestly don't know where I'm going to go when I get discharged. I have no idea." He paused for a moment. "If I make it out, I'll find a new home."

❖   ❖   ❖

"When we had nights on the line, away from line camp, none of us got any sleep. It made the next day realllly hard, boy," Masao recalled.

"Were you guys allowed to sleep during the day?"

"Nah. If you didn't sleep, you didn't sleep. That's just the way it was." He paused. "You know, sometimes, guys developed *battle fatigue.*" He looked at me. "And some guys would get that, a-no? I remember one guy, a major. A marine. He had it bad."

❖   ❖   ❖

Cooper's squad had spent days on the line. The constant sound of mortar explosions indicated they were very close to the action. They were finally falling back to line camp to replenish their ammo and catch a quick break. The marines were close by and a few lingered in the area.

"Coming through! Coming through! Hold your fire!" Cooper announced as they came within forty yards, waiting for the signal to move forward. The exhausted soldiers hiked into the primal-looking line camp, eager to get their hands on K-rations. Out of nowhere, a major named Irving jumped in front of them. The squad sprang into action surrounding Masao, who was startled and stepped back into the loose huddle.

"Hey - Hey! There's a *Jap!*" Major Irving shouted as he wildly pointed his sidearm directly at Masao. Things got tense in a hurry. The major took aim directly at Masao ready to fire. Garcia quickly stepped in front of Masao as a human shield.

"Major, he's with us, sir. Hold your fire!"

"He's a *Jap!* Don't you see?! *Move out of the way or I'll kill you both*!!" His eyes were jittery and unfocused as he motioned for Garcia to move.

"You shut up, major. You're not going to touch him." Cooper secured the major's sidearm with little struggle. Major Irving looked confused and unstable, unable to digest that his own soldiers would turn against him.

"Sir. He's U.S. He's an American soldier," Cooper wanted to avoid further escalation.

"They can't be trusted. He might be a spy," he protested, realizing he was outnumbered.

Cooper assessed the camp and spotted the commanding officer.

"Major, sir, let's check in with the CO." He took the major by the arm and escorted him. Garcia relaxed and looked at Masao.

"That was a close one," Masao uttered.

Cooper saluted the commanding officer while keeping an eye on the major who was watching Masao's every movement.

"Sir. We encountered several pockets of enemy along East Road. The ridges in that area are full of Japanese soldiers. They keep coming in from somewhere." Cooper pointed to the map.

"Those goddamn little gnats. Keep your eye on him. He shouldn't be here," Major Irving spat out as he paced back and forth. The commanding officer glanced at Irving, then at Cooper.

"Have your guys grab supplies and move out. We'll have you go along the back, this way," he pointed to the map. "See what you can find. It's frustrating as hell out there, I know that. But let's have you move out sooner than later," the CO nodded toward Major Irving. Cooper nodded back that he understood. Masao wouldn't make it through the night in the same camp with Irving.

"We can't afford to let these little monkeys destroy what progress we've made. You've got to get that prisoner back to HQ for interrogation," Major Irving mumbled to himself.

Cooper looked at the CO and nodded. "Yes, sir." He glanced over at his tired soldiers and sighed. This would be bad news for them.

His squad had scattered throughout the camp, some replenishing their ammo, some filling up their pockets with all the rations they could not knowing when they would be back. Cooper approached Masao and his bodyguards.

"What kind of training do those marines get anyway?" Garcia asked, still in shock from the incident.

"It's got to be battle fatigue," Cooper said, watching Major Irving skulk around. He opened up a map and laid it out on the ground. Soldiers from his squad gathered around.

"These guys in these hills here are on foot. No tanks can get in there. We're going to continue covering the back side - up this way. Get your gear ready. We move out in thirty." He avoided looking at the young faces surrounding him, not sure he could take seeing the disappointment on their faces. They were badly in need of sleep.

"What about these other goddamn squads, sarge?" one of his soldiers barked out, near the end of his rope and desperately needing a break.

"Soldier. These are our orders. And we're going to follow them."

While the squad prepared to move out, Masao sat and waited lost in his thoughts. He knew why the squad had to move out and felt that weight on his shoulders. Maybe he should suggest to Cooper that another squad absorb him for a while. Maybe he and Major Irving should just duke it out. Maybe—his thoughts were interrupted by Medic Galligan.

"Here you go, sarge." Galligan handed Masao a cup of hot coffee, already mixed.

"Thanks, John." Masao took the cup and sipped the coffee. "That's really good."

Galligan sat down beside Masao.

"How are you holding up, Abe? They haven't given you a lot of rest."

"You too, no?"

"Just came back from taking eight more back to HQ. In fact—" Galligan ran over to grab his pack, came back, and sat down. He pulled out some bread. Bread was unheard of on the line. Masao's eyes were wide with hunger, his mouth watered at the sight of the halved loaf with thick crust.

"Ohhhhh," Masao breathed out.

"Let's chow down," Galligan said with a smile as he ripped off a piece for Masao.

"That's awful nice of you. How did you get your hands on this?"

"Well, you know how HQ hoards all the good stuff. I just helped myself when nobody was looking. I figure we deserve it as much as they do."

"Heh!" Masao nodded and ate another bite. The steady diet of crackers, dried meat, and chocolate had gotten old weeks earlier. Nothing had ever tasted as good as this bread did. He wasn't even bothered by the dirt from Galligan's pack embedded in the white center. He just brushed it off. He closed his eyes and shut out the sounds of explosions in the distance so he could bring all his senses to his taste buds. He took in a deep breath.

"John, thank you."

"You bet."

❖　❖　❖

"That bread, boy, it tasted so doggone good," Masao said. A hellish battle around him—a morsel of bread. I didn't want to say a word.

"Let's go gamble, a-no?" This was a surprise. His eyes were excited, and his face looked youthful as he proposed the casino, even though our afternoon had been a little disjointed, and we were getting a late start. It would put me home at eight thirty or after, and I knew I would be incredibly tired the next day. But I couldn't, not in a million years, say no to him, this sweet, young-at-heart man.

He noticed my tired eyes. "Come on. I'll tell you a story about this one Japanese guy."

October 1944 – Peleliu

It was a particularly dark night. Masao and his bodyguards were dug in, weapons loaded and ready. Flares had been going up nonstop for the last few hours as the enemy resistance seemed to reignite itself daily. Another flare went up and, suddenly, shots were fired somewhere in line camp.

"Ehhhhhhh!" a voice squealed in the night. It was impossible to tell if it was an American or Japanese. A squeal is a squeal.

"I hope that was a Jap," O'Malley whispered, steadying his rifle in firing position and searching the camp. Another flare went up and commotion stirred from behind them.

"*It's coming from the supply hut!*" Garcia was in a squatted position ready to bolt toward the turmoil.

"*Who goes there?*" a voice called out in the darkness.

"That sounds like McCoy," Masao whispered, getting his sidearm in position. All at once, an explosion shook the ground and brightened the area behind the supply hut.

"*Take cover!*" Masao shouted. The four dropped to their bellies. Another flare went up and they wildly scanned the area looking for the enemy, certain they were being ambushed. Things went crazy. Other soldiers didn't take any precautions and started shooting haphazardly into the night.

"*What are they shooting at?*" O'Malley had his finger on the trigger looking for a target, any target.

"*Jack! Wait!!*" Masao yelled.

"*Wait for orders.*" Escola, too, urged O'Malley to hold his fire. The rapid fire continued lighting up the area with flickers of charge as bullets were fired from all directions. Finally, the commanding voice of an officer called out into the night.

"*Hold your fire!*" one of the tech sergeants shouted. But the fire continued.

"*Hold your fire, goddammit!!!*" another voice yelled.

"That was Coope," Garcia assessed. Masao nodded. The firing stopped. Another flare went up. There was no movement. The only sounds in the dark came from soldiers as they made jittery, nervous gasps.

"Shit. I hope none of our guys bit the dust in that chaos." O'Malley stated the obvious, unaware that he had been dangerously close to committing that very sin.

After a night of no sleep, the sun came up and shed light on the havoc of the previous night. Masao jerked awake; he had fallen asleep in a squatted position leaning against a tree. He spotted some soldiers gathered around behind the supply hut. Rubbing his eyes, he noticed Garcia was just waking up as well.

"The supply hut is still there," he motioned. "I'm going to go take a look."

"I'll go with you." Garcia got up.

Masao and Garcia joined Mess Sergeant McCoy and other soldiers near the body of a Japanese soldier. His head was completely blown off.

"How did this guy get so close?" Garcia asked McCoy.

"Not sure. Look, he's unarmed. No weapons."

"He had a grenade," Masao pointed out.

"He had K-rations in every pocket. He was stealing food. He could have blown us up with his grenade, but he didn't. He blew himself up, put the goddamn thing right in his mouth. He just wanted some food. Almost made it out of here, too."

"You've got too much heart for these bastards," another soldier retorted.

"Soldiers like us. Only without food or water."

"Well, that's gross," O'Malley said as he walked up to the mess.

Cooper joined in, looking at the dead imperial soldier with no head. "Any intelligence?"

Masao scratched his chin. "You kiddin' me?" But he knew he had to. He stuck his hands in the blood and brain matter, searching the soldier's pockets for anything useful. The only thing he found was a pack of cigarettes and those he kept for himself.

"The concerning thing is, his cave couldn't have been too far," Cooper surmised. "How the hell did he infiltrate our line, for Christ's sake? We've got to move this camp."

Summer, 2012

The summer had turned into an unusual scorcher. Masao, a native of the desert in California, loved the heat. I walked in, and he was ready to go. He was in dressy pants and an aloha shirt but had a sweater ready, knowing the casino would be air-conditioned.

"Hi!" I said, sitting.

"One time, we were approaching a cave…" This had not happened before, his jumping right in. This memory must have come to him sometime in the morning, and he had probably struggled to hold onto it for a few hours, in fear that if he lost it – it would be gone forever. He wasn't going to waste any time with niceties. He wanted me to hear this. I didn't even have time to get my tape recorder out.

I just listened.

October 1944 – Peleliu

Line camp continued to move every night. It was clear that U.S. soldiers were being watched closely by the enemy. The Japanese had been smart about designing the labyrinth of caves so that they had a bird's-eye view from hundreds of points on the island. Cooper's squad had just returned with some documents they had found in an abandoned foxhole. Masao was reading the worthless material before handing it off to one of the military couriers who would take batches of documents and letters back to HQ for further analysis. Galligan had handed him a hot cup of coffee that he was just finishing.

"*Cooper!*" The radio patrolman called out. Masao cringed. He knew this meant that they were going back out.

"Abe! Get your guys. There's another *goddamn* cave!" Cooper called out. "I don't know if there's an end to these damn caves, son-of-a-bitch," he muttered to himself.

Masao gulped the last of his coffee. Then he had an idea and looked around for Frank, the other Nisei interpreter attached to the 321ˢᵗ. Frank, as it had turned out, didn't have the Japanese skills the military needed. To make matters even worse for Masao, Frank wasn't at all military material, he was more of a desk-man. All the tech sergeants were aware of this and avoided taking Frank out to interpret on the line. Cooper had a lock on Masao and tried to keep him with his own squad at all times, something that pleased Masao most of the time. He liked Cooper and felt secure with his outfit, but wanted Frank to pull his own weight.

"Where's Kubota—can't he go out?" he asked Cooper as he reloaded in the ammo hut.

"Not on your life. Besides, he's already out, left an hour ago with Thompson's squad. And you should be thanking me, goddammit. All these prick tech sergeants want to attach you." Masao smiled at this, at Cooper's way of expressing himself. Masao had fit in nicely with Cooper and the soldiers in his squad. But for O'Malley, everyone seemed to accept him just fine.

After an hour of hiking they spotted the cave. When they came within twenty yards of its opening, they all crouched and hovered in the brush.

"Jesus. That's a small opening," Masao said in a low voice to Cooper.

"It's too goddamn dark in there to see what's waiting for us," Cooper said. "Come on." he motioned to Masao. The two shimmied closer. When they were within ten yards and somewhat shielded by small boulders, Cooper nodded toward the cave. It was the routine they had developed. Masao knew exactly what to do and what to say.

"Come out! You will not be harmed!" Masao called out in Japanese. Silence. Masao waited a few seconds and then called out again. "Come out! Leave any weapons inside! Hold your hands up so we can see you are unarmed!" There was, again, no response. Masao looked at Cooper.

"I don't hear anything. Do you?" Cooper asked. Masao listened then shook his head no.

"What do you think? It might be empty, or they're dead inside," Cooper shifted his weight, then jerked his head like he heard something. "Did you hear that?"

"No," Masao whispered.

"*Goddamn.* This jungle's playing tricks on my mind," he looked back at his squad and made a hand signal to check on the perimeter of the area.

The hand signal came back, area still secure.

"Let's throw in a grenade," Masao suggested.

"Those idiots back at HQ would shit in their clean uniforms if we destroyed intelligence," Cooper said, even though he liked the idea. "Fire a shot in," he ordered Masao. Masao fired a shot directly into the opening. Nothing. Not a sound, not a groan.

"I think it's empty," Masao whispered.

There was a long moment while Cooper figured out his next move. The soldiers behind them looked at each other.

"We have our orders, goddammit. I'm going in," he finally said. He motioned for O'Malley and Garcia to come forward. Cooper approached the cave. It was silent but for occasional jungle sounds. The four hovered around the opening.

"Give 'em one more chance," Cooper ordered. Masao nodded.

"This is your last chance. Come out, or you will be killed!" Masao called out in Japanese. Cooper waited another few seconds.

"Come on, you sissies. If I'm going to die, I want company," and with that, Cooper squeezed through cave opening and disappeared inside. Masao was next. He went in with ease.

Once inside, Masao struggled while his eyes adjusted to the dark. O'Malley came through the opening followed by Garcia. They all stood armed and ready to shoot.

"Stand guard!" Cooper called out.

The four stood in a small area at the opening of the cave. There was little light, but enough. They were astonished by what they saw.

"Oh my God," Cooper breathed out.

Twenty naval soldiers, lying on their backs, head to head, in full uniform. All still.

"O'Malley, make sure they're dead," Cooper said softly.

"They look dead," O'Malley protested.

"Make sure *goddammit*!" Cooper was jumpy. O'Malley got out a knife.

"O'Malley. Not that way," Cooper directed. O'Malley nodded, put his knife away, and went from body to body checking pulses.

"They're dead, all right. Cold."

At the back of the cave, seated in the middle of where the heads united, a lone Japanese naval officer sat in full dress uniform, slumped over.

"What about him?" Cooper nodded to the far end of the cave.

"Cover me." O'Malley stepped in between the dead bodies, making his way to the back of the cave. Within an arm's length, he reached out to tilt the officer's head up. His fingers reached the forehead, and he used the officer's hair to pull his head to an upright position but instead of the head tilting up, his entire scalp came off. Maggots fell out and dropped everywhere.

"*Ehhhhh!*" O'Malley yelped, jumping back. "*Shit!*" He frantically brushed the maggots off his hands as he stepped between bodies, stumbling to catch his ground.

"Poor devils. Out of food, no water, the enemy closing in. Christ…" Cooper shook his head.

❖ ❖ ❖

Outside, they sat near the cave opening and searched through documents, handing letters and books to Masao to sort by order of importance. Cooper was on the radio reporting in. "It appears to be some sort of mass suicide. A morphine overdose would be my guess. They must have stockpiled it."

"What about intelligence?" the voice on the radio asked abruptly.

"We've secured all weapons and documents. It looks like they burned the important stuff," Cooper rubbed his forehead and looked back at the cave opening. He'd often wondered how he would handle it if his squad was surrounded by Japanese forces. Would he suggest that they take similar measures and end things on their own terms? Or would they face the unknown, probably inhumane torture?

A few yards away Garcia and O'Malley sat near Masao. O'Malley jumped up as he spotted a scorpion crawling out from cover. He took a rock and crushed it with all his might. It took a while, the crustacean refusing to go easily.

"You ain't getting anywhere near my balls," he blurted as he squished it with his boot.

"Anything interesting?" Garcia motioned to the papers Masao was reading.

"Letters to their families," Masao answered while he kept reading the private and very sweet thoughts of a soldier to his beloved wife.

"How do you read that stuff? It looks like chicken scratch," O'Malley said. Masao smiled and kept reading. O'Malley looked around, bored.

"Hey, sarge," O'Malley said. This would be the first time he addressed Masao by his title instead of his last name. It got Masao's attention and he looked up from the letter that had been so enthralling.

"Hmm," Masao nodded.

"Your first name—Maseeo…"

"Masao."

"It got a meaning or anything?"

"I've never thought about that before. Let's see here now." He took a stick and wrote his name in kanji in the dirt. O'Malley watched him with interest. Masao pointed to each kanji as he interpreted. "It would be something like 'right man' or 'correct man.' Something like that." Masao used his foot to erase the characters.

"Correct man," Garcia pondered the translation. "That fits you."

Masao noticed a maggot on O'Malley's sleeve. "You've got a—" He pointed.

O'Malley saw it and brushed it off with a stifled squeal. "Shit! Get it off!"

"*Let's get back,*" Cooper called out.

"What about the cave?" a soldier asked. The protocol was to blast foxholes or caves apart so they could no longer be used. Cooper thought about it for a moment. His soldiers were all looking at him waiting for an answer. Nobody moved to ready a grenade as they normally would. Everyone had the same thoughts. It was a tomb. The soldiers had laid themselves to rest. It would be a travesty to disturb their thoughtful grave.

"There's no way out the back of it, this is the only way in or out. It's not a threat. Let's close it in a way that they can remain at peace." This was a direct violation of orders, but Cooper no longer cared. It was just one way he could hold on to a bit of humanity and his guys understood. Soldiers barricaded the cave opening with boulders and rocks, making it difficult for anyone else to enter.

On their way back to line camp, Cooper had received orders to fall back to HQ. Cooper muttered explicatives the entire two-mile trek, bitching about how he hated the officers and how didn't they know about advancing the line. Bufoy had commandeered the radio from HQ and had been asking Masao all sorts of questions about the intelligence uncovered at the cave. By the time they drew near HQ, every soldier in Cooper's squad was pissed.

"Cooper, where do you want these?" O'Malley asked, meaning the Japanese weapons they had been hauling.

"Shit. MPs, I guess. Let them deal with it."

Bufoy eagerly approached the tired and dirty unit as they neared HQ.

"No useful documents—again?" The first words out of his mouth made Masao's blood boil.

"Sir, as I said in my report—they burned anything of importance. Just personal letters, that's all we have," Cooper answered tersely. Bufoy was irritated he didn't have some intelligence that would give him a reason to award himself another Silver Star. "Sir, the mere fact that we discovered a mass suicide is indicative of a weakening enemy," Cooper reasoned.

"I'll be the judge of that, sergeant. You just follow orders. Now, let me see the letters." Masao handed the letters to Cooper who handed them to Bufoy.

"Abe scanned through them on the line, out there," Cooper pointed to the battle zone. His insinuation was obvious. But the insult fell on deaf ears. Not only was Bufoy arrogant, he was far too self-absorbed to listen to anyone of lesser rank.

"Well, maybe Abe needs to scan them again. More thoroughly this time. Abe, come with me." Masao and Cooper exchanged a look. Masao reluctantly followed Bufoy deep into the protected gut of HQ.

"Make yourself at home." Bufoy nodded for Masao to sit on mounted sandbags. Bufoy took a random letter from the pile of papers Cooper had handed to him. "Here, what's in this one." Masao took the letter and glanced at it; he had already read it.

"This one is about how much he missed his wife. He mentions the Yumoto Hot Springs. They must have visited there or something."

"All right, all right. Nothing about the war? What about their orders?"

"Nothing, sir. It's a love letter." Bufoy snatched the letter from Masao's hands and crumpled it up out of frustration. He threw it in a small burning fire. Masao watched as the words of a soldier to his love went up in smoke. He looked at Bufoy, who was selecting the next letter to immolate.

"All right, next one. There's got to be something worthwhile in one of these." He handed another letter to Masao who opened it. His heart ached for the imperial soldiers and their loved ones back in Japan. Had an honorable Japanese officer encountered the tomb, he most certainly would have taken these precious letters and made sure they were delivered. He would have given thought to the families of the men and provided them with the closure that they certainly craved. If the letters had been up to Cooper, the same might have happened. But with this Bufoy, this second lieutenant who seemed to have little regard for anyone but himself, all of these letters would perish in flames. Masao had to witness the entire letter-burning event, enduring insult after insult about how he had failed on the line. How he had failed to bring back intelligence that mattered. To make matters worse, he had to watch Cooper's squad leave HQ without him.

July 2012 - Bon Odori

Bon Odori is a summer festival providing a special place and time to honor ancestors who have passed on. People of all ages and ethnicities came from miles around to the Seattle Buddhist Temple to join in the festivities. The streets around the temple were decorated with colorful Japanese lanterns. Booths were set up along the sidewalks, offering crafts and delicious Japanese food. Masao made a nice comfortable seat out of his walker, and Alan and I sat on the curb and watched the parade of Japanese women in their kimonos perform a dance. Then the Taiko Drummers rolled out huge drums and played several numbers in a most choreographed and artful way. But the best part of the afternoon was watching Masao smile as he enjoyed the performances. The wonderful smell of *yakitori*, or grilled chicken, permeated the air along South Main Street by the temple and it made my stomach growl. Evidently, I wasn't the only one.

"Are you hungry?" I asked Masao.

"I could eat!" he answered, happy that someone else noticed all the food.

"You guys want yakitori?" We both nodded and that was all we needed to do. Alan would take care of the rest. I rested my arm on Masao's walker to get comfortable, held my face toward the sun, and closed my eyes to feel the warmth. Then I felt his gentle touch on my arm. I looked up at him and shielded my eyes so I could see him better.

"This reminds me of a time during the war." I shifted so I could hear him better. "One time, we were on orders to advance the line, and we came to a part that had been torn up realllly bad. There had been a recent *battle*, a-no? A lot of dead bodies lying around, blood everywhere." I nodded. "And-a, we smelled something…"

October 1944 - Peleliu

Masao was back with Cooper's squad. They hiked through burned-out brush until they entered a bowled area where there were signs of a treacherous battle: demolished terrain, torched trees, and scorched ground. Tractors were busy shoving enemy bodies into trenches while medics tended to the wounded and dead.

"No prisoners here," Cooper assessed.

"Doesn't look like it," Masao agreed. Cooper signaled for the radioman when Garcia came forward and stood next to Masao.

"Do you smell that?"

It was as if they were in a trance. "Yes, I do," Masao sniffed the air. He squinted to spot where the smell was coming from and noticed Naki and his bodyguards cooking something over a small fire on the other side of the valley. He started walking. Seeing Naki alive was almost secondary to following his nose.

"Where you going? Hey—*Abe!*" Cooper shouted as he followed.

"This won't take long." Masao motioned for his squad to come along. They arrived at the other side of burned-out valley where Naki was cooking rice over a small fire. A one-hundred pound bag sat nearby.

"Hey—Abe! Look what we found! Join us," Naki exclaimed, excited to see that his buddy was still alive. They shook hands and smiled while Masao stared at the steaming rice over the fire. Masao took his helmet off and filled it, eating it with his hand. Garcia squatted next to the fire and did the same. The rest of the squad stood around, bewildered.

"It's not like it's a sirloin steak, Abe," O'Malley barked out. But O'Malley's ration of shit didn't matter. The warm carbs took over. Masao and Garcia were in heaven as they stuffed their mouths.

"This is a brown people thing," Garcia said, spitting rice as he spoke because his mouth was so full. Naki was busy making more and motioning for the white soldiers to join in.

"Please, fill up. It might be weeks before you get hot food again!" It was as if he'd appointed himself host at a fancy dinner party, inviting his guests to fill up on extravagant food. In the middle of a war zone, cooked rice was about as good as it could get. Other soldiers finally joined in, eating until their bellies were full.

As Cooper's squad prepared to head out, Masao stayed with Naki until the last possible moment.

"Take care of yourself," Masao nodded at Naki as he grabbed his gear.

"You do the same." They shook hands and held on long before Masao joined Cooper's waiting squad.

It wasn't long before they were back in the jungle. "Did you get any of that rice to cook up later?" Cooper asked Masao. He had noticed Masao's face as he was eating the rice, content as a baby with a bottle.

"Nothing to carry it with."

"Guess not." Cooper checked his map. "You know, that's the first time I've ever had rice."

Masao was shocked. "No kidding." He studied Cooper. "Well, what'd you think?"

"Not much flavor, but it was okay I guess. At least I feel full. I haven't felt full since we left Honolulu. Come to think of it, there was rice on my plate at a restaurant there. But I didn't try it."

"You didn't eat any of it?"

"No, I thought it looked like maggots so I didn't touch it."

"Maggots! Where in the blazes are you from?"

"Idaho. Potato country. I miss potatoes. I hope I get to eat them some-day soon, Abe." Cooper checked the map as he walked. "I miss home." He looked at Masao who nodded in agreement. "Where are you from, Abe?"

"San Bernardino."

"You got a wife back there?"

"No wife. Not even a girl."

Cooper studied Masao. "I'll tell you one thing, if I had a daughter, I'd want her to be with a guy like you." This took Masao by surprise. He looked at Cooper who didn't realize the importance of his compliment.

"Thank you, sir." The sounds of battle were ever present.

"You married with kids?" Masao asked after a bit. His question seemed to hit a nerve. He saw Cooper's face twitch.

"I'm not sure." Masao listened and waited, not wanting to pry. "I was married when I left. But it's been two months since I've gotten a letter from her. And the last letter I got - something wasn't right. It had all the niceties, but no feeling. She didn't even sign it 'Love, Serena.' Just 'Serena.' Like she was a buddy or something." He looked off in the distance as he talked, not wanting to attach any feeling to his words.

"Maybe you're just imagining things. Since you're far away from her. And two months isn't a long time, especially since we're out here in the middle of nowhere."

"Maybe. But the mail's been coming regular. It's the only goddamn regular thing about this place."

Masao walked beside Cooper, silently.

"No. My gut tells me that she's moved on. That the home I left won't be there when I get back to Boise." Masao wasn't going to argue with anyone's gut feeling, especially since he so often relied on his own gut for guidance. He felt for Cooper, one of the best guys on the line. Trying to deal with a broken heart on top of the task of daily survival must have been excruciating for him. He wanted to give the guy some sort of relief.

"Hey Coope." He nudged Cooper who looked over. "You're right about one thing."

"What's that?"

"Grains of rice, they do look like maggots."

❖　❖　❖

After the Bon Odori celebration we went to Ginza. We sat at the sushi bar so we could banter with the sushi chefs.

Masao motioned to the chef, "*Unagi*." Fresh water eel. Ick.

"Unagi!" the chef affirmed as he went to work.

"Want to try some? It's realllly good, boy!" This caught the attention of the chefs and they looked at me, waiting to see if I would be adventuresome. They suspected not because Masao suggested some sort of sushi or sashimi every time we ate at Ginza, and every time I politely declined.

"No, thanks. I'll stick with my *tamago*." I waved him off and pulled my egg omelet *nigiri* toward my eating space as a defense against any attempt to place eel or octopus in front of me. While we waited for his sushi, Masao looked around and appeared to be momentarily lost in his thoughts. The chef set the unagi down in front of Masao who fixed his *shoyu* with *wasabi* and stirred it with his chopsticks.

"Every so often, during the war, they would send *replacement* officers." He looked over at me. "And, uh, most of the time, those guys were just— just..." he searched for the right word, "—*worthless*."

I smiled. This was going to be good.

October 1944

81ˢᵗ Infantry Division Headquarters, Peleliu

The fatigued squad was once again called back to division headquarters to bring documents from yet another cave they had secured. Cooper and Masao delivered the documents to the lead Nisei stationed at HQ and left before Bufoy could harpoon them with a lecture.

"Let's load up," Cooper said as he walked with a sense of purpose toward the ammo hut to catch up with the rest of the squad. "Ah, shit, look what's arrived." He nodded toward a batch of new replacement officers. They were clean-cut college graduates, virgins of battle, and assumed know-it-alls.

"Try to ignore them, let's get our gear and get the hell out of here," Cooper advised and walked faster. They passed a replacement officer who was a first lieutenant by the name of Doulas Miller.

"Hey! Soldiers!" Miller asserted himself. Cooper kept walking and Masao followed. Neither looked at Miller.

"Hey!! *Soldiers!*" he barked, his voice almost squeaking. He was clearly not comfortable with his position on the battlefield but had obviously been trained to be tough on soldiers of lesser rank.

Cooper stopped and turned toward Miller. He casually looked around and then pointed to himself. "Who? Me?" Cooper challenged Miller.

"You two. Get back here!" Miller insisted. Cooper hesitated, then took a few steps closer to Miller. Masao was in step with Cooper.

"Yeah?" Cooper scowled at Miller. *Please—piss me off, I beg of you*, he thought.

"You see this bar?" Miller asked, pointing to the Lieutenant bar on his clean, untarnished uniform.

"Huh. What is that, anyway?" Cooper's words were soaked with sarcasm. Masao resisted the urge to laugh.

"It's a bar," Miller said. "When you see this bar, it means *officer*. What are you supposed to do when you see an officer?"

"What *are* we supposed to do?" Cooper was getting heated. Masao wondered if this Miller guy would make it to his next sentence.

"When you see this bar, you're supposed to salute—I'm a first lieutenant. You are a tech sergeant, and *you*," he pointed his boney index finger at Masao, "I don't even know what you are." His words dripped with contempt.

"He doesn't know what you are, Abe," Cooper said light-heartedly to Masao. Then he gave Miller a steely look and leaned in toward him. "Okay, lieutenant, I want you to remember this. You see those hills up there?" Cooper nodded toward the torched landscape. Miller looked up.

"What about 'em?"

Cooper smiled. "Those hills are full of the enemy. Full of nips. And we're going to be up on that line. That's where we're headed now. You'll be on the line too—maybe tomorrow, maybe a week from now. And out there," he pointed hard to make his point, "out there, you're going to see a living hell. Charred bodies. Still smoldering, some of 'em. Soldiers, our men, clinging to life and knowing they're near the end. And around every goddamn corner, snipers are waiting." He let his words sink in.

"But here's the deal—don't worry about your front side. Those guys shooting at you can't shoot for shit." Cooper pointed to the first lieutenant's bar. "I want you to watch your back. People in back of the line have much better aim than the guys in front of you. Those guys are trained to kill, and they aren't going to waste any bullets. Don't worry about the front, you watch your back."

Miller was speechless. He wasn't sure how to decipher Cooper's message and Cooper saw that. "You're going to earn your bars out here in a different way. Soldiers are tired, wounded, starving, and hot. They aren't going to put up with little pricks in clean uniforms like you, barking out orders. Understand? Lieutenant. *Sir*." His last words nailed in his point. Miller stood mute as he watched Cooper and Masao march off.

In the ammo hunt, Cooper's frustration showed as he grabbed bullets and a few grenades.

"Salute my ass," he huffed under his breath. "I'd sooner salute that Jap who was stealing food from us a couple weeks ago." He stopped in his tracks and glanced at Masao, "No offense intended, Abe."

"None taken." Masao loaded up his belt with bullets.

"With any luck, he'll be shitting all over himself within the next couple of days when he gets sent out."

"Sarge, the way you handled him—I think he's shitting all over himself right now." Masao was gaining admiration by the day for Cooper; he was a soldier's soldier, smart about protecting his squad, not about to take chances but following orders and getting the job done.

❖   ❖   ❖

The sushi chef placed a plate of *saba* sashimi in front of Masao, who immediately dunked one in his wasabi mixture and stuffed it in his mouth. The most wonderful part about how Masao told stories was how he changed his voice to take on the persona of different people. For Cooper, his voice became gravelly and more authoritative, for his bodyguards he used his normal voice, and for this Lieutenant Miller, a voice that sounded pathetic. It made the recollection come alive.

"Heh! That guy was a little bit of a stupidshit. Who did he think he was, anyway? In his clean uniform, trying to be a goddamn *big shot*."

I smiled and took a bite of my pumpkin fried rice. "At least you had guys like Cooper and Galligan around. And your bodyguards sounded like good guys, except for O'Malley."

Masao was mid-swallow with his other saba roll when I mentioned O'Malley. He shook his head and wagged his finger. *Uh oh, I have something wrong.*

"O'Malley. He turned out to be a good guy," he corrected me.

"I thought he was racist. He said mean things to you."

"Heh! You can't blame him for that. It was just…the times."

I inhaled deeply with this last notion. Just the times…

Autumn, 2012

Another trip to Vegas had come and gone. We were going, on average, every two months. It was plenty for me and Alan, but not nearly enough for Masao.

"I think it's because our summer was so dry. Beautiful colors, a-no?" Masao noted the colorful foliage as we were on our way to the casino. Of all our conversations, I liked the ones that occurred in the car the best. It was just Masao and me, and privacy.

"Hey, Mas?" I approached this question with great care in mind. Masao had never, *ever,* brought up the memory of killing anyone. He looked over at me, his way of saying, "Go on."

"Did you ever…shoot anybody? The enemy I mean?" His face sank. This would be a hard topic to talk about, I could see it. His face clearly reflected the confusion and pain caused by taking another life to save his own.

"I remember the first guy…but… You kind of shut those things out a-no? It's not something you want to remember…taking a life." There was a long pause. I wasn't sure if he would continue or not. I knew I would leave it alone if he didn't want to talk about it. Minutes went by. We drove along in silence looking at the gorgeous autumn colors that lined both sides of the freeway.

"You know, during the war, we all had ah—diarrhea. A lot. The food was *shit*." I nodded, not sure where this was going but happy that he was talking. "And, ah, sometimes it came on at the worst times, a-no?" I nodded again. He wasn't smiling. This wasn't an amusing diarrhea story. This was not going to be funny.

October 1944 - Line Camp, Peleliu

Cooper's squad had another prisoner they had taken into custody. There were no documents of any kind in his cave, and the prisoner was so thirsty and hungry that he was lethargic. Masao sat the man down and McCoy brought over a plate of food and handed it to him. The prisoner looked confused.

"It's okay, eat it," Masao directed him in Japanese. The prisoner reluctantly took a few bites. Masao nodded. "In a few minutes, another soldier will escort you back to headquarters. You will be asked more questions there. There's nothing to worry about. You won't be tortured or killed," Masao continued, his instructions were rote at this point. McCoy handed the prisoner a canteen of water. This prompted Masao to drink from his own canteen.

"Hey, Mac, do you have any more water tablets? I feel like I'm just drinking mud," Masao asked McCoy.

"There's more coming from HQ. I'll save you a few." Masao nodded. Hearing the conversation from a distance, Galligan came over with a tin cup of steaming water and a coffee packet.

"Here you go, Abe."

"Thanks, John. I needed this." Masao fixed his coffee, savored a sip, and looked around the empty line camp. From the looks of it, there was Cooper's squad and one other squad that appeared to be about half the size of normal. Soldiers looked dejected if not depressed.

"Where's the rest of that unit?" Masao asked. Galligan noticed what Masao was referring to.

"Ah. Benson's squad. They lost half their squad a few days ago. Ambushed."

Masao felt for the remaining soldiers. To date, they had lost only one guy in Cooper's squad and that was on the first day on Angaur.

"And then there's the dumb shit who went souvenir hunting."

"What's that?" Masao was confused.

"Just some dumb shit who figured he'd use this time to find a sword or something. He left an hour ago and headed up that a-way, where it's supposedly secure. He's pretty stupid if you ask me. This whole goddamn island seems to be under attack. There's not one nook or cranny that's secure in my opinion."

Masao nodded. "He *is* a dumb shit."

In the distance the radio blared orders. "*Galligan! Wounded!!*"

"Shit. Guess I've got to go back to work," Galligan gathered his medic gear. Masao nodded, watching him close up a bag of supplies. His senses heightened, something didn't feel right to him. He looked around and tried to pick up where the bad feeling might be coming from. Galligan was just about to hurry off.

"*Galligan!!! Let's move out!!*" The fellow medic shouted.

"Hey, John." Masao got his attention just before he left. Galligan stopped and looked at him.

"Be careful out there."

"You bet," Galligan nodded.

Within an hour Cooper received new orders. Then the rain started. It poured hard and long until the hard ground had turned to thick mud.

Cooper's squad trudged quietly in the jungle. Everything was soggy as the men navigated rough terrain and swampland. The sound of the rain filled the space around them and muffled the sounds of explosions in the distance.

"Take five," Cooper stopped to check his map.

"Shit. I think I have diarrhea again. I'm going to find a spot," Masao said to Garcia. Fifteen yards away from the squad, Masao found a spot by a swampland that had formed from all the rainfall. While looking for a hidden place, out of the corner of his eye, he saw a bush move. He stopped in his tracks and squatted, his body frozen with fear and adrenaline. His heart was pounding so loud and so fast he was sure he would be detected.

Then he saw it: an imperial soldier with tree branches on his helmet. The soldier rose up from the brush at fifteen yards, scanning the dense foliage for his enemy target. Masao's breathing deepened. Sweat trickled from his forehead and mixed in with the raindrops hitting his face. *Is he alone?* He slowly pulled his sidearm out and cocked it. The sound was muffled by the rain. The imperial soldier looked young. Masao aimed his weapon right at the soldier's chest. *Shoot!!* He screamed to himself.

Suddenly, the enemy saw him and jerked. He didn't have a chance to draw his weapon. Masao had his sidearm pointed directly at him, ready to fire.

"You move, you're dead," Masao said calmly.

"I'd rather be dead than betray my country," the soldier spat back, thinking about how he was going to get out of this and wishing he hadn't been ordered for recon. He hated his military for sacrificing lowly soldiers like himself without a thought, and he was scared to death to be taken into American custody.

"If that's the way you want it," Masao took better aim. *Do it!!!* he tried to convince himself.

"You don't belong on their side." the soldier declared in a desperate attempt to save his own skin.

"I don't belong anywhere." Masao's own words surprised him. Maybe in the heat of the moment, the truth had finally come out. The imperial soldier lurched to shoot his weapon. Without flinching, Masao fired twice.

Back with the unit, O'Malley jerked his head around at the sound of the gunfire. "Abe!" He and Garcia took off in the direction of the gunfire, scared shitless that something had happened to Masao.

Masao watched as the imperial soldier fell back into the shallow pool of rain water. *Is he dead? Dear God, what did I just do?* He stayed in a squatted position until Garcia and O'Malley rushed in, assuming defensive positions. They looked around for other enemy faces.

"I still need to take care of business," Masao informed his bodyguards as he slowly rose up.

"We've got you covered," O'Malley assured him. Masao lit up a cigarette and went into the brush. When he came out, he glanced at his bodyguards. The rain stopped and the quiet became loud with the unthinkable. He went to the body and picked up the soldier's rifle. Blood was now coloring the water around the dead soldier, his body slowly settling into the swamp, his face breaking the surface.

Masao looked down. Beside the soldier's face was his own reflection in the still water. Two Japanese faces staring back at him; one dead, one alive. It was a long moment. *Who am I to kill this kid? He has parents who love him. They won't know for months, if not years, that their beloved son has died. They will never know that he died alone, in a jungle, on an island in the South Pacific. They will never know that he died at the hands of another Japanese.*

Garcia and O'Malley looked at each other. They could see that Masao needed time. There were levels to this that they would never understand.

Masao thought about checking the soldier's pack for food or cigarettes, then stopped himself.

He flicked his cigarette butt into his own reflection. "Son-of-a-bitch," he said under his breath.

"Abe. You okay?" Garcia asked.

"No." He handed the soldier's rifle to O'Malley. "Let's go."

And the clouds opened up with a vengeance.

❖　❖　❖

"I didn't like that. Nobody wants to take a life, a-no? Gee, that was a hard thing to get through." Masao looked out the window deep in thought. "That soldier, he was just a kid... I wouldn't have done it, but I wanted to live."

We drove along in silence until we were almost to the casino. Both of us needing the distraction of slot machines to pull us out of 1944.

"You know, the Japanese military..." He had one last thought as we pulled in to the valet area. "They didn't retrieve the bodies. Not a one. Our military, we buried our fallen guys, a-no? But not theirs. They just let their guys *rot*."

The three hours of gambling didn't alleviate Masao's heavy memories. I was sorry I had brought the subject up, not because I wasn't interested or didn't want to hear about it, but because I wondered if it had been too much for Masao to relive. We were on our way down the mountain when he picked up where he left off.

"That first one was realllly hard, boy," he said, intuiting my thoughts. "But after that, it got easier." He paused and seemed to digest the audacity of that statement. "That sounds funny, a-no?"

"Well, isn't it that way in war? You either kill or you are killed. Right?"

"That's right," he nodded, content that I was not going to judge him. "You know, that guy, I think he was recon for the Japanese military. He must have been, he was all alone out there. Either that, or he got separated from his unit. It wasn't long after that, our unit, we encountered heavy fire. And, ah, we lost a lot of guys. But we got a lot of theirs too."

I glanced at him before looking back at the road. "Do you feel like talking about that?" I wanted to hear if he needed to tell.

He needed to tell.

❖   ❖   ❖

Cooper, on the radio, glanced at the three as they re-joined the unit. He nodded at Masao, his way of saying "I'm glad you're okay." Every man on the squad was soaked through. They all crouched low to the ground, waiting for orders, scanning the dense brush for any movement, scouring the hillside for any hint of life. His bodyguards enveloped Masao between them.

"It feels like we're being watched," Masao whispered to Garcia.

"Shit. Don't say that. You're giving me the heebie-jeebies." Garcia sank lower in the brush.

Cooper hung up the radio and motioned that they were going forward. "There's a pocket ahead. We're going to circle them." Cooper ordered his men even though his instincts were telling him to retreat. The platoon fanned out in different directions, crouching in the tall, thick grass. It poured on them, sheets of rain coming down. Masao and his bodyguards kept moving out, keeping an eye on their comrades, feeling more and more insecure as the distance between them and the rest of the squad grew. They had advanced forty yards when machine gun fire erupted. They immediately squatted, their backs to each other.

"Shit!! Did they get anyone?!" Garcia blurted, his eyes wildly searching for the enemy.

"Hey!!" Masao pointed to an imperial soldier who had popped up from the grass a mere twenty yards from them and was now running for his life. He abruptly stopped when he saw the group of four still huddled on the ground. He aimed his automatic rifle directly at them. Without thinking, they fired off shots simultaneously. The soldier went down, riddled with bullets.

"He's hit!" Escola said. Then more machine-gun fire came at them from the other side in a shower of violent rounds. They all fired back. Masao was sure this was the end. Then the firing stopped as abruptly as it started.

"We got four!" a voice shouted out from sixty yards away.

"*Hold your fire!*" This voice was one they recognized, Cooper. Masao strained to see where Cooper was and spotted him. He was waving his hand, calling his squad back together. The four stayed low to the ground and made their way to him. They scanned the area around them with each step.

"Recon was right on the money that time. A goddamn miracle in itself." Cooper grabbed the radio. "Let's see what else they know." Masao strained to scan in all directions.

"Sounds like we're about to link up with the marines. They're moving along this line approaching Hill B." Cooper pointed to his rain-soaked map. "They're getting help from *our* guys. Three or four companies are up there already. We're ordered to move along this way — to take care of any enemy that might flee out the back side here." He looked at his men. All eyes were on him; he wanted to be smart about how they proceeded. He didn't want to lose any guys, but couldn't shake the bad feeling that he was about to. "Let's go. Stay low to the ground. They're coming out of nowhere and armed to the hilt."

Cooper's platoon stalked in the brush. They advanced into a shallow valley through severe terrain, hills flanking the sides of the small basin. The rain stopped and mist rose from the depths of the earth, the result of the moist ground heating up from the sun that was now breaking through the clouds. It was quiet, eerie.

"We're sitting ducks out here," O'Malley whispered.

Masao scanned the hillsides thinking that this would be the perfect place for an ambush. "This doesn't feel right."

The unit was isolated. In the distance from behind one of the hills, they heard the sound of relentless battle, spurts of machine-gun fire, grenades exploding, and mortar fire being launched with even louder blasts upon impact. In the small world of their hundred-yard vicinity, though, everything was quiet. Without the rain, their footsteps were no longer muffled. Every twig they stepped on cracked and seemed to echo throughout the valley.

"They're watching us," Masao breathed out. In a low position he ran to Cooper's side.

"Sir."

"I know. I feel it too," Cooper whispered back before Masao had a chance to elaborate. Cooper motioned for the unit to fall back.

"Screw orders. We're going to fall back and sit it out for a while. Over there," he pointed to an area that would take them out of ambush range.

Suddenly machine-gun fire came directly at them from the front as six enemy soldiers sprouted up from the dense brush. The three soldiers at the front of the unit were sprayed down in a split second, their bodies jolting backwards as they were ripped apart.

"*Take cover!!!!*" Cooper shouted.

Soldiers dropped to the ground and fired off shots in all directions. More incoming fire sprayed the area with rapid machine-gun fire as they scattered. The Japanese soldiers yelled out instructions to each other, wanting to eliminate this Yankee squad.

"*They're everywhere, goddammit!!*" Cooper shouted. The now separated and vulnerable unit was surrounded on two sides. The enemy was closing in.

Masao, understanding the instructions being shouted in Japanese, looked up and spotted the cave on a ridge where they were setting up bigger fire power. "*They've got a grenade launcher!!! Up on the hill!! Move!!!*" Masao yelled as loud as he could. He glanced at his bodyguards who were twenty-five yards away and camouflaged in thick brush.

"*Abe!!*" O'Malley motioned for Masao to make a run in their direction. O'Malley fired off his BAR toward the men closing in on the unit from the front. He hit three of their soldiers, the bullet-spray tearing apart their flesh, their bodies flying backwards. The other three imperial soldiers dove to the ground in opposite directions.

"*Goddammit.*" O'Malley ducked and squinted to see where the enemy was. Masao scurried to their position, diving in between them. He looked back to see a grenade hit the spot he had just left. Grass and rocks sprayed their faces.

"*Holy shit!*" Masao wiped his face and assessed the damage. He saw no soldiers from his unit standing. They were all either on the ground or, God forbid, dead.

"*THERE! Mi dios!*" Garcia pointed up to the ridge. An enemy soldier was loading the grenade launcher again. His target: them.

"*Holy shit!! The trees. HURRY!*" Masao pointed to the nearby tree line. They made a dash for it and jumped into a clump of trees. Masao tucked himself behind a trunk and took inventory of his bodyguards who were all there. The grenade launcher operator gave up on them and, instead, looked for another target.

"*We don't stand a chance without mortar,*" Escola surmised scanning the brush for the rest of their outfit.

"*The bazooka —*"O'Malley looked at Masao. "Stevens."

"He's out there, *shit!*" Garcia pointed, "*He's down.*"

"Cover me." O'Malley set his rifle down.

"Jack. Don't. You'll never make it," Garcia said.

"*We don't have a chance without it,*" O'Malley barked.

O'Malley readied a grenade. On the ridge Masao noticed that, in addition to the grenade launching soldier, other soldiers had emerged from other caves and were scanning the area and pointing, making all sorts of hand gestures and yelling out instructions.

O'Malley sprinted out to the retrieve the bazooka, throwing a grenade toward the hill. The grenade hit the ridge and rattled it. The imperial soldiers stumbled to regain their footing. Garcia and Masao covered O'Malley at the front, scanning for the enemy to emerge from the brush. O'Malley returned with the bazooka and tossed his BAR to Masao who hoisted it up.

"Let's see how brave they are now. Assholes," O'Malley hissed as he set up the apparatus to launch a shell.

Garcia continued to scan the area for the rest of the unit. He spotted them. Cooper and two soldiers were pinned under the ridge. Three more soldiers were twenty yards down the ridge, hovering behind some boulders.

"*There they are.*" Garcia pointed.

"Where's the rest of the outfit?" Masao feared the worst. Garcia and Masao frantically scanned for other soldiers while Escola and O'Malley finished setting up the bazooka. Neither had done it before.

"*There!*" They spotted the lone radioman out in the middle of the action, scared to death and trying to hide behind a Korrai shrub. Masao looked up. The enemy had spotted the radioman too and took aim with the grenade launcher. Masao couldn't bare the thought of the radioman's horrid demise.

"*Ruuuuuun!*" Both Masao and Garcia yelled to the radioman who heard them but didn't know what was about to happen. His body was frozen with fear. *Fffffttt.* The sound of a grenade being launched was unmistakable. The radioman looked up just as the grenade hit. Masao had never seen such a horrible sight. The radioman was alive one second, his body shredded into a thousand pieces the next. Blood, flesh, bone, fingers, hair, and bits of uniform ripped apart and cast in every direction, showering the area. Every soldier in Cooper's squad was a helpless witness to the horror.

"*Shit. Jack!!!*" Masao was angry at the sight.

"Almost there…" O'Malley looked around. "Get those assholes on the ground." He pointed to the movement in front of them. Imperial soldiers were closing in on Cooper and the other guys along the underside of the ridge. Masao spotted it and adjusted the automatic weapon.

"Eddie." He motioned for help. Garcia helped steady the bulky rifle. Masao sprayed the area where he had spotted the imperial soldiers, his body barely able to absorb the reverberation from the weapon.

"Did I get 'em?" Masao's breathing was heavy. He hadn't realized how hard a BAR was to maneuver. Before Garcia could answer, Masao fired again.

Garcia looked up on the ridge. The enemy soldier looked for his next target. *"O'Malley - it's now or never!"*

"I've got to move out some. *Cover me!*" O'Malley had to clear the trees to get off a good shot. Masao and Garcia stood in full view of the enemy—shooting unflinchingly. It kept the enemy soldiers from gaining ground. O'Malley had the bazooka set up and aimed it at the ridge. With all his might he launched the first shell then quickly ducked. "I don't know how to use this thing!" The bad shot bought some time. The enemy up on the ridge stumbled and scurried to arm themselves realizing they had a fight on their hands. Garcia and Masao ducked for cover behind the trees.

Machine-gun fire was coming at them from the ridge. Bullets hit the trees all around them. They all dove to the ground. Masao looked up at the ridge where the grenade launcher soldier had recovered; he was wobbly, but loaded the weapon again.

"Again, Jack!" The soldiers, pinned against the ridge, saw the plan. They waited for the right time to make a run for it. O'Malley was almost ready. He and Escola quickly positioned the weapon.

"*GO!*" O'Malley shouted.

Masao and Garcia again stood and aimed at the ridge. O'Malley fired off another shell. The blast knocked the enemy down. Garcia shot at the ridge. Masao aimed below so the isolated American soldiers could make a run for it.

"*RUN! DAMMIT RUN!!!*" O'Malley bellowed. O'Malley took the BAR from Masao's shoulder.

"*I got this,*" he handled the weapon as if it was a toy and fired relentlessly toward the front and the ridge, hitting two guys on the ground who yelped as they went down. Garcia, Escola, and Masao took whatever weapon they could and fired it at the ridge. It was hard to tell where the incoming fire was coming from or where it was aimed, but Masao didn't care. He just kept firing. The U.S. soldiers who were pinned against the ridge were half way to cover running for their lives. Cooper was in the rear.

Enemy fire changed its target when they saw the soldiers who were running for cover. First came machine-gun fire. The American soldiers dove for safety. Another Japanese soldier appeared on the ridge from a different cave opening. He was setting up another grenade launcher. O'Malley saw it first.

"*Son-of-a-bitch!!*" He threw down his gun and loaded the bazooka again, Escola assisted, cringing from the incoming fire that was hitting all around. Masao and Garcia ducked for cover as machine-gun fire turned on them again, this time with a vengeance. O'Malley got off the shell just as fire sprayed his area, miraculously missing him and Escola as they ducked. He loaded again and fired without any assistance. It was a direct hit on the ridge, taking out one of their grenade launchers.

"Way to go, Jack!" Escola shouted as he positioned himself behind a tree with his rifle. The pinned American soldiers made another run for it while Masao and the bodyguards shot with punishing accuracy toward the ridge. But with every soldier they took out, two more would come out from the depths of the volcanic hill. Incoming fire hit all around, shattering trees and the brush around them. Masao looked for Cooper, still in the rear. The men crawled along the ground trying to get to the safest place. Twenty-five yards away now, the soldier right in front of Cooper got hit in the back by a sniper's bullet.

"*Dickerson!!*" Cooper shouted as he caught up with him just in time to see Dickerson breathe his last breath, his body quivering, his head jerking back and forth until he went limp and lifeless.

"*Goddammit*," Cooper muttered. He looked up to see that his other soldiers had made it to cover.

Masao frantically motioned for Cooper to make a run for it. "*Come on, Coope! Come on!!!*" Without flinching, Cooper tore through the brush in an all out run to get to safety. In a moment that stood still for Masao, Cooper and he made eye contact. Cooper was now a mere twenty yards away. Their eyes locked just as Cooper was hit from behind multiple times. His eyes told Masao he knew he'd been sprayed with bullets. He knew this was the end. His body fell forward in a slump and hit the ground hard.

More incoming fire sealed the deal, tearing his body into shreds. Masao looked up at the ridge where the imperial soldiers were wildly shooting.

"*NOOOOOOOOOOOO!!!*" Masao couldn't believe his eyes. The remaining four soldiers dove for cover behind trees. Masao still stood, staring at Cooper, incoming fire hitting all around him. O'Malley reached up and pulled him down. The two hugged the ground, their faces covered in mud, blood, and flesh. Masao was in anguish, shaking his head and in shock.

"Let it go," O'Malley said in a low, empathetic voice. "But those assholes are going to pay for that." He shimmied over to the bazooka. Like a mad man, he reloaded and looked over at Masao and Garcia to give them the signal.

"*Now!*" He hollered. Masao and Garcia stood and shot at the ridge. O'Malley stood and fired off a shell. They all ducked and looked up at the ridge. A direct hit. Imperial soldiers dropped and fell off the ridge, their bodies thudding as they hit the ground below.

"*Again!*" Masao heard himself shout. O'Malley loaded another shell.

"*Now!*"

Masao and Garcia stood and aimed high and low. Other soldiers joined in, seeing that the plan had work. Another direct hit. The incoming fire slowed.

"*I've got one more!*" O'Malley shouted.

"*Use it! Get every last one!!*" Masao shouted back. O'Malley loaded again.

"*NOW!*"

What was left of the unit stood and shot at the remaining enemy. O'Malley fired off the shell. A direct hit, more yells of despair. More bodies flew apart. The remaining men in the unit hit the ground and waited for sounds, any sound that indicated the enemy was approaching.

Masao looked out in the valley, he spotted Cooper's body. He hated what he was about to do. He nudged Garcia, who was on the ground next to him, and pointed to Cooper.

"We need his map... and binoculars."

Garcia spotted the binoculars hanging off of Cooper's body. He knew Masao was right. Masao looked up at the ridge, it was secure for the moment.

"I'm going out." Masao started to move, but Garcia stopped him.

"Not you. I'll go." Masao thought about this and knew Garcia was right. Their orders were to protect Masao. If he'd been killed carrying out this task, Garcia, O'Malley, and Escola would pay for it. Garcia bellied out the twenty yards into the wide open to retrieve Cooper's binoculars. Masao and the others waited, aiming at the enemy front, ready to shoot. Masao spotted movement and braced himself. He looked at Garcia who had reached the body. He scanned the ridge, there was no sign of life. His eyes went back down the terrain on the valley floor. *They could be anywhere.* He thought he saw something move in the brush at seventy-five yards. Without hesitation, he shot at the spot. He looked at Garcia who was still at the body.

"What's he doing out there anyway?" he asked no one in particular. *"Hey! Hurry up!"* he called to Garcia. Garcia bellied back with the binoculars and map in hand.

"What the hell took you so long?"

Garcia showed him Coope's last letter, addressed to Serena Cooper. Masao thought about the conversation he had with him about Serena and wondered if this woman was even worthy of Coope's last words. "I want to be sure this gets delivered. I don't trust HQ—some of those guys seem like dumb shits to me."

Masao nodded.

"If you two ladies are done chatting we have more enemy out there. In case you didn't notice." O'Malley's voice was shaky. Masao nodded and squinted through the binoculars. He motioned for the men to circle close.

"Keep your eye on that area, about the one o'clock position from here. I thought I saw movement. Let's keep pushing forward, per our last orders, to the position on the far side. If we encounter live one, we have a reason to go back." He motioned the unit forward. The scant platoon, half its original size, fanned out and advanced cautiously. They started coming across enemy bodies.

"Make sure they're dead," Garcia said as he picked up an enemy rifle equipped with a bayonet. Another soldier did the same, and they used the bayonet to stab the dead Japanese soldiers, more out of revenge than to ensure death. They made it to the end of the valley without incident.

"What do you think?" O'Malley looked around as he asked.

"Let's keep looking."

Sniper fire abruptly came at them from the ridge. A bullet hit the ground next to Masao's feet.

"*Shit!!*" Masao jumped. The soldiers ducked and scanned the ridge. O'Malley hurled his rifle up and sprayed the ridge. There was an anguished cry. Then an enemy body dropped from the ridge. The soldiers slowly rose up from the brush. Masao jerked his head when he spotted something ahead. He motioned to be quiet and then signaled forward, pointing to the area. Masao led as they approached a clump of torched trees that would have made a perfect hiding place. He raised his handgun and held it out in front of him. He could barely detect movement, but it was there.

Masao's heart pounded. He glanced around and motioned for others to cover the area. O'Malley intuitively made his way around the other side of the charred tree trunk. Garcia stood to Masao's left, his gun ready. The other soldiers were nearby, standing guard, scanning the ridge. Masao looked at O'Malley who nodded. An enemy soldier was hiding inside, tucked away.

"You are surrounded. Come out and surrender," Masao shouted in Japanese.

"Go to hell!" The imperial soldier spat back.

"Quit with the tough guy talk. Come out with your hands up!"

"I'd rather die than surrender to you *Joes*!!"

"*What's going on, sarge? You two catching up on old times or what?*" O'Malley shouted.

"He's a stubborn son-of-a-bitch. Can you see him, Jack?"

"I'll move in closer," O'Malley said as he edged in closer.

"*Be careful, Jack!*" Masao didn't want to lose anyone else, especially not one of his bodyguards. O'Malley moved in behind the Japanese soldier. He was armed, wedged in between tree stumps. When he saw O'Malley, he panicked trying to aim his gun at the U.S. soldier.

"*Abe! Say 'Don't move'!! Never-mind. Don't move!!!*" O'Malley quickly walked toward the soldier and knocked his rifle away. Masao came close.

"Check him for grenades," Masao ordered. O'Malley patted him down.

"Nothing," O'Malley assured Masao. Masao was eye to eye with this imperial enemy, as before at the pond. Only this time he had no empathy. This time he had only hatred in his heart. The heavy rain started again.

"You're going with us," Masao instructed the soldier who had just become a prisoner.

"Just kill me here! On the battlefield! I don't deserve to live. I'm a disappointment to Japan!"

"What's he ranting about?" Garcia wanted to know.

"Some shit about not deserving to live."

O'Malley tossed down the enemy's rifle. "He was out of ammo."

Masao looked at the rifle on the ground, then back at the enemy prisoner, "You don't deserve to live after what you did to my guys back there."

The Japanese soldier smiled, but it was a sinister smile. "*Your* guys. Your *American* guys die like sissies. Especially your commander. He shouldn't have stopped. He could have made it. Heh Heh Heh."

Masao was filled with rage. He took his sidearm and shoved the nozzle into the soldier's forehead.

"*Abe!*" Garcia stepped forward so he was standing right next to Masao. "Sarge. We have our orders. Take them alive."

Masao held steady. "You don't know what he's saying."

"It doesn't matter. We have our orders."

The Japanese soldier stood defiant, unable to decipher English, though detecting what was happening.

"This piece of *shit* wants to die. And he deserves to die, *goddammit!*"

"Think, sarge. Think about it. It's going to be a lot harder on him to return to Japan," O'Malley reasoned.

"That's right. He'll be humiliated," Garcia added. They waited. Masao's arms quivered from the emotion, from exhaustion. The Japanese enemy kept his eyes locked with Masao, happy that he was sucking him down into a hate-filled vortex.

"Sarge," O'Malley said. Masao hesitated, then backed down and lowered his sidearm.

"Coward," the Japanese prisoner said under his breath. With that, Masao hauled off and punched the guy in the face. Others hustled in to stop any further assault.

"*Sir!!*" O'Malley shouted. This caught Masao by surprise. All the soldiers, their eyes were on him. He was the highest ranking soldier left. He was in charge. The most protected among the platoon, now the protector. "Sir," O'Malley restated, "we have our orders."

Masao nodded. He regarded the young faces around him. They were tired, war-torn, and dirty. All he wanted to do now was preserve the remaining lives of the unit. "Let's get him back to camp. We'll go along the south," He nodded in the direction that would give them the most protection.

❖   ❖   ❖

On the way back, Masao recognized the area they were passing through. It was the site of the cave that Cooper had left as a tomb days before. Masao was content knowing that he had served under a sergeant like Cooper, brave and humane. As they neared the cave that they had carefully secured with boulders, he realized something was different. Debris was scattered everywhere. There were pieces of shredded uniform, bits of paper, fragments of flesh and hair strewn about. Masao feared the worst. They came closer and saw it: another unit had come along and decided the cave was better off obliterated than left alone. What was left of Cooper's platoon stood at a distance from the destroyed cave. There were no words, only a few glances.

"Look what barbarians you are!" the prisoner snorted. Masao looked at him and his eyes filled with ire.

"Shut. Up." He looked at his soldiers, "Let's go."

The prisoner had been uncooperative all the way back to the line camp, trying to give signals to hidden comrades by talking loudly. Masao kept note of where he would erupt, sure signs that there were enemy foxholes nearby. The prisoner refused to give up any information about their command post or anything else. Masao thought about the radical Kunio. *This is what Kunio would be. Holding onto imperial bullshit to the very end.*

Back at line camp, Masao looked around for the highest ranking soldier, a tech sergeant by the name of Thompson.

"Sir," Masao said. Thompson looked up from his map.

"We lost Cooper?"

Masao nodded.

"Shit." Thompson rubbed his chin. "That's just - Christ." Masao couldn't help but feel responsible, even though he wasn't.

"The prisoner," Masao nodded toward the uncooperative Japanese soldier, "he was signaling on the way back. Here," Masao motioned toward the map. "It was right along here, this point, here, and down here." He pointed to different areas. "They might be hot spots, sir."

Thompson nodded. "Good job, sergeant." He nodded toward the sour-looking prisoner, "What's going on there? Uncooperative?" Masao nodded. The prisoner knew he was being watched.

"Just give me a grenade so I can end my life! I will not dishonor the emperor or bring shame to Japan!" he shrieked in Masao's direction.

"Shut up, asshole!" Masao called back in Japanese. "He wants a grenade to kill himself. I say we give it to him. Stuff it right in his mouth and let him have it. He's on my last nerve."

"Get the MPs. Let's get him back to headquarters ASAP," Thompson ordered. Masao nodded and started to leave. "Hey, soldier." Thompson stopped him. Masao turned. "Let's have you and your boys tag on to my unit from now on." This was a compliment and Masao knew it. He wasn't asking Masao to join his unit as an interpreter, he was asking Masao to join his unit as a soldier.

"Thank you, sir."

Masao spotted the MP by the ammo hut. As he passed by McCoy he signaled with a wave of his hand. It was understood—no food for this prisoner.

"Please take him quickly. He's making me crazy." He handed the prisoner off and then noticed that the camp felt empty. "Where's Galligan?" Masao asked. The MP shrugged.

On the perimeter of camp, waiting for their final ride off the battlefield, were the bodies of dead soldiers, lined up and covered. Masao hesitated, but knew he had to check. He stood looking down at the tattered plastic covering the bodies thinking about Cooper who was still out in the middle of the valley. He pulled the plastic back from the first body. Not Galligan. He pulled the plastic off the second corpse. Not Galligan. Then he found him: Galligan. His body was lifeless, his canteen still hung from his neck. The tin cup he used to offer Masao's coffee in was attached to his ammo belt.

"Christ." Masao squatted, overwhelmed by death. Before this day, death had been something that happened to other men, not his own.

McCoy had silently joined him. He laid his hand on Masao's shoulder. "Sorry about Coope." His voice had a calming effect on Masao. It was as if they were at a funeral on the mainland. Masao could barely hear the constant blasts coming from a distance.

Masao nodded. "How did this happen?"

"He went out after one of ours, some idiot, some souvenir-seeking idiot, and he bit it. We had to go get him and lost two more in the process."

"You've gotta be kidding me."

McCoy shook his head. The heaviness hit Masao as he sank into the ground next to Galligan's body.

"Who do we have to retrieve *our* guys," he asked in a desperate tone, referring to Cooper and the others. "They're still out there with those sons-of-bitches." Masao pointed frantically to the direction of the valley.

"More are on the way." McCoy said, patting Masao's shoulder, "Don't you worry, Abe."

❖ ❖ ❖

Masao, the best narrator on earth, made great sound effects for various weapons and explosives. It was both riveting and heart-wrenching listening to his account of the battle that had taken the lives of so many of his buddies. I was driving slowly so Masao could finish his story, but still, we were pulling into the garage of his retirement home. I parked and shut the engine off. Masao wasn't even aware of his surroundings; all he could see was the part of the war that claimed his comrades.

"When I was a-kneeling over his body, I wanted to take his cup," Masao looked over at me.

"The tin cup he always brought to you so you could make hot coffee."

"That's right. I wanted to have it. To remember the guy. He was a-realllly nice, boy."

I nodded.

"But, it would have looked kind of *funny*. You know, a soldier taking a-something from a dead guy's body. A Japanese guy—digging around. It wouldn't look right."

These Nisei men, brave soldiers, never felt completely equal to their counterparts.

He looked around and seemed startled. "Ah, we're home!"

"We are," I touched his arm, "Thank you, Mas, for sharing that story with me."

"Heh! I gotta thank *you!*"

Veteran's Day, 2012

The Seattle Chapter of the Nisei Veteran's Committee (NVC) is well-run, housed in a beautiful facility located in the heart of central Seattle, adjacent to Little Vietnam. The organization was established to support Japanese-American veterans of war who were excluded from other agencies that served veterans. The NVC offers various events and exhibits to celebrate the legacy of Japanese-Americans. Alan and I were especially excited to take Masao to the Veteran's Day occasion because we had a special birthday gift waiting for him at the NVC facility.

Months earlier, we had learned of the Japanese-American Memorial Wall located on the premises. At the far end of the parking lot, space had been allocated and designed to house hundreds of black granite tiles enshrining the names of Japanese-Americans who were either interned during World War II or served in World War II and/or other wars from the Spanish American War to the war in Afghanistan. All branches of the military were recognized.

The wall is approximately twelve feet tall and ninety feet long, extending the entire width of the parking lot. The overhead concrete beam was designed to accentuate the wall and meant to resemble traditional Japanese *tori* gates, structures that are spiritual in nature. The black granite tiles, similar to the tiles used in other memorial walls, provide a naturally reflective surface—creating an aura of tranquility. In keeping with the culture of Japan, it is sturdy and polished, but not pretentious or grandiose.

The wall is visually separated from the parking lot by five Japanese maple trees, interspersed with bamboo, shooting up a good ten feet. There is a wide path lined with pea gravel before the wall, and benches to sit and reflect are nestled near the trees. The designers did a wonderful job. The NVC Memorial Wall is peaceful, beautiful, and spiritual.

About one third of the wall holds tiles of war veterans, the other two thirds, tiles of Japanese-Americans who were interned at any one of the ten internment camps and/or eight Department of Justice prisons. Alan and I had purchased a tile, and we were excited to show Masao that his legacy would live on for decades, if not centuries. We were limited, though, on what we could have engraved. We couldn't reference the battles that he had fought in — Angaur, Peleliu, or Leyte. All we could include was his name, World War II, and MIS. But even so, we thought it was a spectacular gift.

We were an hour early and assumed there would be plenty of parking. As it turned out, we took the very last spot. Alan got Masao's walker, and I prepared an umbrella as it was a typical rainy November day.

"Let's go look over there," Alan suggested, pointing to the memorial wall. It looked stunning and attracted attention, even if you didn't know what it was, and Masao did not, yet it piqued his interest.

"What is that?" He started to roll his walker in the direction of the wall. The excitement built for me, and I think for Alan too. We knew exactly where his tile was, so we steered him to that particular column. What emotional response might we get from Masao when he saw his own name etched in the black granite?

As he got closer, we had to help him navigate the gravel with his walker. He examined the structure. "Gee, this is nice," he remarked. "All Japanese people…"

The designers would have been pleased. This was exactly the response they wanted, admiration and reflection. Masao rolled along and then came to the part where soldiers were honored.

"They have soldiers, too, a-no?" He continued rolling along, "Guys from the 442," he pointed to a tile or two. "Ohhhh…MIS," he noticed.

"Dad, look up there." Alan stopped him and pointed up high where Mas's tile was positioned. It took him a few minutes to see what Alan was talking about.

"Gee, is that me?"

I almost started to cry, knowing that at any second, Masao's gratitude would be overwhelming. At any moment, I felt that Masao would know how much I loved him. I glanced at Alan; he seemed to feel the same way.

"What's it say, anyway?"

"It says: Masao Abe…U.S. Army…MIS….World War II," Alan read it for him.

Masao looked at Alan. "Nothing about the battles? I—I fought in battles." He looked a little panicked.

This was a surprise.

"Mas, I asked if we could put those on there and they said no. Only the war and branch could go on there." My plan was quickly going awry. Where was the love? Where was the emotional burst of gratefulness that I was expecting?

"I was in battles. *Three* of them: Angaur, Peleliu, and Leyte." He counted the wars off with his fingers to prove his point. "It should be on there." He sounded anything but grateful — he sounded *cranky*!

Alan looked at me as if this whole fiasco was my fault. It *was* my fault. I was the brainchild behind this idea. I had coordinated with the NVC, I filled out the paperwork, and now I was getting all their newsletters. Maybe I should have been more aggressive with them; maybe I should have insisted that the battles were included. I frantically examined the other tiles and noticed that none of them had battles listed.

"But none of the tiles have battles. Don't you see?" I sounded like a little girl. But Masao had moved on. He had waved us off and was maneuvering the walker back to the pavement.

Back in the parking lot, more veterans were rolling themselves toward the entrance of the NVC hall, wearing their dress caps decorated with various war ribbons.

"Ohhhhh," Masao uttered in a startled tone, "My cap. I left it in the car."

"I'll get it," Alan assured him. And then I, the screw-up, continued to escort Masao into the building, Alan catching up at the last minute to hand him the dress cap that he immediately put on.

Masao had two military dress caps. One was olive green with gold embroidering that read *MILITARY INTELLIGENCE SERVICE VETER-ANS – HAWAI'I*. On the other side of the peaked fold, the MIS emblem was proudly displayed. Masao was not wearing this dress cap. In fact, I never saw him wear this cap.

The garrison dress cap he'd chosen to wear that day was dark blue with gold piping. *Disabled American Veterans*, or D.A.V. appeared on one side. The D.A.V. patch was placed just above and off to the side of the embroidered words *SEATTLE CHAP. 2*. Above the stitching, Masao had placed various pins he had collected: a D.A.V. pin with an eagle, a big V for veteran with an American flag, a World War II 50th anniversary pin that he had picked up in 1995, a Nisei Veterans Reunion pin from 1988 — NVR-Reno, his precious 81st Infantry Division pin that had the Wildcat in the middle, an MIS pin, and a Japanese-American Veterans Association pin.

On the other side of the cap's fold were all of his well-earned and well-deserved military decorations. Above the embroidered *LIFE MEMBER*, stitched into the lower part of the cap, and beneath the gold piping were all of his medals in cloth ribbon form, the kind you see soldiers wearing on the front of their formal uniforms.

The only metal pin on that side of Masao's dress cap was the Army's Combat Infantryman's Badge or C.I.B. Many soldiers felt that this pin carried the most respect and was considered the most important decoration a soldier could wear, indicating that individual had been in combat, had been an infantryman, and had seen battle. Rectangular, measuring one-inch-by-three-inches long, it has a light blue background. In the center is a silver musket surrounded by an elliptical oak wreath. Masao's C.I.B. was empty at the top center of the oak wreath indicating that it was a First Award. Had he been awarded more of these badges, stars would have been placed inside the wreath.

Below the C.I.B. pin were three rows of ribbons, neatly arranged by order of their importance and merit. In the first row, his Bronze Medal ribbon, his Army Commendation Medal ribbon, and his Purple Heart Medal ribbon. In the second row, his Army Good Conduct Medal, the American Defense Service Medal, and the American Campaign Medal. In the third row, his Asiatic-Pacific Campaign Medal flanked with two Bronze Battle Stars and a Bronze Arrowhead, his World War II Victory Medal, and his Philippine Liberation Medal that contained one Bronze Battle Star. He wore his service proudly.

I later learned the difference between all the Bronze Stars. His Bronze Star Medal, taking the first and most important place, was awarded for an heroic act and/or meritorious achievement in connection with operations against an armed enemy or while engaged in some sort of military operation involving conflict with opposing armed forces. The Bronze Star Medal was specifically awarded to soldiers not involved in aerial warfare, but who were involved in ground combat. Bronze Battle Stars, on the other hand, indicate that a soldier had participated in a specific battle and is worn on the campaign ribbon that the soldier also earned. In the case of Masao's Asiatic-Pacific Campaign Medal, he earned two Bronze Battle Stars for the conflicts on Angaur and Peleliu. Also attached to his Asiatic-Pacific ribbon is a Bronze Arrowhead, indicating his involvement in the amphibious assault on Angaur. He earned a third Bronze Battle Star for the battle on Leyte in the Philippines.

Inside the NVC Hall, people gathered in the converted basketball court. I had never seen so many rolling walkers, canes, and wheelchairs in my life, barring, of course, our trips to the casino. There were display tables lining the walls for vendors with various items to sell and offering cookies to eat. The middle of the basketball court was filled with chairs, and a projector was being set up to show a film that was narrated by none other than George Takei. I immediately noticed that Masao's dress cap was the only dark blue one in the room. The majority of other veterans in the room were wearing maroon caps with gold piping. I didn't think much of it. Masao's cap looked far more striking and military, it seemed to me.

I anticipated that he would be a complete and utter chatterbox, mingling with war buddies and catching up on old times. But nothing was further from the truth. He stayed to himself, near to Alan and me. I wondered if he was still disappointed about the tile, but he wasn't one to carry a grudge. He took a couple of cookies, and I was quick to get a napkin to hold them for him, still attempting to redeem myself from the tile catastrophe.

Other soldiers, with the maroon caps, gathered in groups and chatted. Masao would glance up at them every so often, but then would continue on his voyage around the room.

"Do you know any of these guys?" I finally asked.

He glanced around, careful to give me the right answer, looking for any familiar face in the crowd. "Gee, I don't think so. I used to know a couple of guys," he looked harder, "but I don't see them."

"Are there any MIS guys here?"

"Gee, I don't know, you know? All I see are the 442 guys."

"Are those the guys in the maroon caps?"

"Yeah, I think so." He was still looking. At least I felt like I was off the hook with the tile issue. He had moved on, long before I had, not giving it a second thought.

There were some announcements and some acknowledgments before the short film began. We found cushy seats to sit on. I, like a proud daughter, took pictures of Masao looking dapper in his dress cap. Before the film began I became aware of the subtle non-verbal communication in the room, the glances of the other veterans toward Masao. My emotions seemed to fine-tune the atmosphere. The 442 veterans – they appeared to have a mistaken idea about the MIS, and Masao seemed to be the only MIS soldier in the room. Their faces indicated their thoughts: the MIS men weren't 'real' soldiers. Everyone knew about the 442nd and the 100th Infantry Battalion, their valor, their courageous military efforts, the hundreds of Purple Hearts they had collectively earned through their bloodshed. But very few people, even in this circle of war heroes, understood that the MIS deployed soldiers to the South and Central Pacific. Even fewer were aware that these men were attached to Regimental Combat Teams in battle zones on various islands.

Part of this was, of course, because the MIS soldiers and officers were all sworn to absolute secrecy about their role in the military. The entire operation was under wraps. They couldn't breathe a word of it for three decades after the end of the war, not until 1975. However, in 1975, America was more enthralled with the disaster that was the Vietnam War than it was with World War II. It didn't care about a highly-secret operation that employed thousands of Japanese-Americans.

With every glance of one of the 442 guys in Masao's direction, I could feel it. The near condescension was almost more than I could bear. Evidently, and wrongly, they must have thought that Masao was one of the many MIS soldiers who had been stationed at one of the huge communications centers far behind enemy lines. Not to lessen the importance of those men, who intercepted chatter about military strategies and positions and helped to shorten the war significantly, but Masao was not far behind enemy lines. He was on the enemy line and had the ribbons to prove it. He was on the battlefield, same as the guys from the 442. But while soldiers in the 442 had each other, Masao had served in near isolation. Yet, not any of his ribbons, a list of his medals earned, deterred the detached way they looked at Masao. Confused by his C.I.B., and his Bronze Star Medal, not to mention the unmistakable Purple Heart, the 442 guys, not a one of them, interacted with Masao, instead, mingling amongst themselves.

Then I looked at Masao. His gentle face absorbed all the ignorance. He was used to this, I could tell. Here he was, a warrior who had seen the horror of war close up, a soldier who had looked into the eyes of his commander as he died on Peleliu, a guy who felt the loss of good and worthy men, and here he was, his service being discounted. No wonder he had been so insistent about including the battles of Angaur, Peleliu, and Leyte on his tile. No wonder he wanted that for all to see. It made perfect sense now.

"They don't know you served on the line," I whispered so only Masao could hear. He shook his head no, indicating that I understood. "They think you were a desk man." He nodded only one short but affirmative nod, indicating, "Exactly."

"Why don't they know about about guys like you?"

Masao looked around before whispering back, as though guarding his response. "Well, we couldn't talk about it. For thirty years, a-no?"

"How come?"

"Heh! The military didn't want us to," he paused, reliving a single point in history. "It was a secret, I guess. Secret operation. And now, now it's just a-lost. Our part, it's just a-lost."

The helplessness I felt for such an undeserved injustice and treatment from these 442 guys, not to mention from the military and society in general, started in my gut and worked its way up to my tightened throat. Every time I looked at Masao and his handsome face, wearing his striking cap, my feelings only intensified. My eyes started to sting. I got up in a hurry, trying to keep it together until I could find a place alone.

"Where are you going?" Alan said. "It's about to start!"

"Bathroom," I managed to say as I hurried out. The last thing I wanted was to have a nervous breakdown in front of everyone. I made it into a stall just in time for the floodgate to open so I could sob my way through my epiphany of Masao's reality.

After my meltdown, I cleaned myself up, had three cookies to ease the pain I was feeling, and found my way in the dimly lit room to my seat next to Masao. I offered him a cookie since I had taken a few more to get me through the seventeen-minute film. Masao accepted one and looked at me, noticing my eyes were still moist and blotchy. My damn thin, white skin; it was easy to tell when I had been crying.

He knew. He knew exactly what had just transpired. He felt it. I didn't have to say a word and neither did he. He just took the cookie, patted my leg, nodded, and continued to watch the short film that was mostly about the 442. He didn't need public recognition. For Masao, it was enough that I got it, that I understood the situation. What had frustrated him was this: outside, I didn't understand that his place during the war was specific and unusual, and now, in here, in this hall, I finally realized that his role in the war was, indeed, quite unique. His accomplishments were different from the soldiers of the 442, the 100th Battalion, and even other MIS soldiers.

And with that, his tile on the Memorial Wall remained without the battles of Angaur, Peleliu, and Leyte etched on it, and that was okay.

February 19, 2013 – Hawai'i

Since the Veteran's Day event at the NVC in Seattle, we had made it through the holidays by way of spending Thanksgiving in Vegas and Christmas Eve at the casino near Seattle. We were just wrapping up another trip to Hawai'i to see Doris. It had been remarkably enjoyable with great weather, nice visits with Naki, and wonderful food to eat. Masao was refreshed, having soaked in the bathtub every night of our trip with Alan's love and assistance.

We had gone to Haleiwa, on the north shore, and he indicated where the Japanese airplanes had come through the peaks of the mountains on Oahu on the morning of December 7, 1941. I took a picture of the naturally shaped V in the mountains to show him I was interested in recording his thoughts and memories. On the way to the airport, Masao had, again, shared all of his loving memories of Doris along the way, pointing out the oyster house and other places they enjoyed together.

"I miss her," he said softly on the plane while we were waiting for passengers to finish boarding.

I nodded. It had been three years and his pain was still as acute as ever. He longed for his beloved Doris and nothing on this earth would have a chance to fill that void. It was moments like these that were the hardest. I was never sure whether to try to pull him out of the depths of his aching heart, or to let him be. This time, though, I decided to pull.

"Hey, Mas?" He looked up. "You never did tell me about what happened after you lost Cooper. You never told me why you think O'Malley was an okay guy." I waited to see if he was in the mood to talk about the war.

"Heh! That was a long time ago! Almost seventy years, a-no?"

"It was a long time ago. But you know I love your war stories."

"Heh! Let me see now…" He pulled up the battle in his mind, that horrible battle that took Cooper away from him. "My tech sergeant, a realllly nice guy, boy. He was *shot*. Shot right in the back by that son-of-a-bitch Japanese guy." He looked at me to prove to me how serious this was. I was already convinced.

October 25, 1944 – Peleliu

Masao and his bodyguards trudged along with Thompson's platoon in the early morning hours. Their orders were to check out another cave with suspected activity.

"Man, I could go for more of that Honolulu surfing right about now," O'Malley said.

"You surfed, Jack?" Masao was surprised.

"Well…I tried. I fell on my ass a bunch of times and made it in once."

"How big was the surf?" Garcia was immediately suspicious of O'Malley's claims.

"I'd say about twenty footers or so," O'Malley winked as he laughed at his own ridiculousness. "Hey, at least I was out there. What were you two knuckleheads doing in Honolulu?"

"Well, I don't know about Eddie—but I was meeting all the local girls."

"You can say that again! There was this one doll, Eleanor, she was a knockout!" O'Malley whistled. "And she liked me, boy."

"Haole girl?" Masao was interested in this development.

"What?"

"You know. White," Garcia clarified.

"No, she was a local girl."

"Ah. Wahine," Masao figured.

"She wasn't that, but she was local," O'Malley insisted.

"The local girls *are* wahine, Jack," Masao explained.

"Look assholes, she was a local. What part of the island, I don't know. It was something like - Sawsun or Seasun or something like that." He strained to dredge up the name. "Sansan. Shit, I can't remember."

"Sansei," Masao smiled.

"That's it! Sansei. She's from Sansei! Where's that at, anyway?"

"Jack, Sansei isn't a place. She *is* Sansei. Sansei means third, as in third generation. *Japanese.*"

"*What?*"

"Eleanor is *Japanese.* She's Japanese, you dummy!"

"No way. You're full of *shit*, Abe. She's some sort of Hawaiian."

"Yep. Japanese-Hawaiian. You're in love with a Japanese girl!"

"Shit. Japanese…" O'Malley gave this some thought. "That's okay. Japs aren't so bad, after all."

The platoon returned to line camp by noon, empty-handed. The soldiers cooled off in the shade where they could find it. In the distance, Masao heard more orders by radio; another cave to be checked out. The other Nisei assigned to the 321st, Frank, happened to be nearby and Masao spotted him gearing up. Relieved that it was Frank's turn to go out, he sat down and lit up. Then he felt a tap on his shoulder.

"Hey, Abe," he turned to see Frank who had a worried look on his face.

"Yeah?"

"I need you to go out on this one."

"I just got back in!" Masao couldn't believe his ears. The nerve of this guy.

"Abe. I just have a bad feeling about this. I think - if I go out, I won't come back," Frank pleaded. Masao understood the power of gut feelings. He studied Frank's face. It seemed tender to Masao and filled with tension and fear.

He nodded. "All right, Frank. I'll go."

Masao alerted his bodyguards and while he was gearing up, a bad feeling came over him. Was it Frank who had spooked him, or was this his very own intuition trying to tell him something. He decided to visit the ammo hut and get extra weapons including two hand grenades and a rifle.

The platoon, headed up by a tech sergeant named Christensen, arrived at the suspected cave and surrounded it. A makeshift white flag hung on a blown-apart tree near the opening.

"Go ahead, Abe," Christensen ordered.

"Come out! You won't be harmed!" Masao called out in Japanese.

Fifty yards up the embankment on the torched landscape a Japanese Imperial Army soldier, who had dozed off at his post, jerked awake at the sound of Masao's voice. His camouflaged area concealed his post. He scrambled to the opening of his foxhole and peeked out. He grabbed his rifle and looked at the unit below through his scope. In the cross-hairs he suddenly stopped. A Japanese. In American uniform.

"Traitor," he hissed under his breath.

Down below, Christensen motioned for Masao to make one more attempt.

"Come out! Surrender! You are surrounded!" Masao shouted.

The imperial soldier bellied into his cave, loaded his rifle, and shuffled back to the edge. Beads of sweat formed on his forehead as he took aim. *Japan will be proud of me*, he thought. *My ploy worked, stupid Americans.*

Down below, it was quiet. Masao's intuitive radar was jumping off the charts. "Sir, this feels like a trap," he suggested as he looked around.

Christensen had his orders but felt anxious as well. He contemplated his next move.

Above, the imperial soldier fixed his site on the taller red-headed soldier, moved to the shorter Latino soldier, and finally set on the Japanese soldier. He honed in.

"You die first, Yankee," he spat as he squeezed the trigger.

Christensen decided to go in. "You three," he was pointing to three of his soldiers, his words suddenly interrupted. The blast of the sniper's gun alarmed the soldiers. Masao looked up just as the bullet hit him. It threw him off his feet, and he landed with a thud. Soldiers scattered and took cover. Masao, in the wide open, dragged himself behind a tree trunk. Blood was everywhere.

"*ABE!*" O'Malley shouted when he realized Masao had been hit.

Another shot was fired. One of Christensen's guys went down, his body jerked and trembled. Other soldiers ran in and pulled him out of sniper range.

O'Malley got to Masao. "*Shit*! It's my leg!" Masao was in excruciating pain.

Another shot. The unit rushed to get their wounded to cover. Masao's bodyguards surrounded him, ducking and searching for the best place to find cover.

"*Where's it coming from? Get him to cover, dammit!*" Garcia yelled in the midst of all the confusion. Another bullet hit close by. This time it shattered what was left of the tree covering Garcia. "*MOVE!*"

O'Malley dragged Masao, leaving a swath of blood as he pulled him into some brush.

"Where's the medic!? *Get the medic! Someone get the goddamn medic!!*" O'Malley was frantically looking around.

"*THERE!* Up on that ridge! *Get him!*" someone shouted when they spotted the assailant.

O'Malley strained to stop the gushing from Masao's thigh, feeling his way to the hole where the blood was escaping. Soldiers started firing at the ridge.

Masao began to lose consciousness, "I think my number is up..." his voice was weak. *Dying out here in the Pacific, in between the two worlds that have divided my soul...* Masao closed his eyes with this thought.

"Stay with me, Abe. Abe! *SARGE!*" Masao opened his eyes wide. He was confused and getting colder by the minute even though it was ninety degrees. The sniper fire continued. Garcia ran over and bellied down near O'Malley and Masao.

"We're sitting ducks here!"

"Don't you think I know that, goddamnit!? We gotta stop the bleeding!!" O'Malley took Masao's belt off his pants and used it as a tourniquet around the bleeding leg. Blood was spewing. Sniper bullets hit all around them. Dust and dirt was flying up everywhere.

"Awwww *Shit!*" In a brave but stupid move, O'Malley picked Masao up and threw him over his shoulder like a potato sack and ran for his life. Garcia followed shooting wildly toward the ridge. O'Malley made it fifteen yards and fell, struggling to hold on to Masao.

"*Did you get hit?*" Garcia shouted, jerking his head back and forth between the ridge and O'Malley.

"No, *goddamit!* I fell! My legs are shaking so bad." O'Malley got up, blood covering his uniform. "At least I think I fell. There's blood everywhere - I don't know if it's mine or his!"

"*Keep going! Keep going!*" They ran until they found cover. O'Malley laid Masao down and tightened the belt to try to stop the bleeding, then applied pressure with his hand. Other soldiers ran into the same area, carrying the body of the dead soldier.

"One dead and one injured!" Christensen reported on the radio.

"Hang on, Abe. Hang on." O'Malley used his entire hand to put pressure on the bullet hole. Garcia put his shirt under Masao's head.

"Hold on. Hold on." Garcia took Masao's hand, soldier style. Masao opened his eyes, saw his guys, looked at each one, and nodded.

❖   ❖   ❖

The Jeep screeched up on Beach Orange where medics were waiting. Masao's bodyguards pulled the stretcher off the Jeep and took it to the medic station. For a brief moment, the four were alone.

O'Malley squeezed Masao's hand. "Sarge." Masao opened his eyes. "Stay with us."

Masao searched the faces of O'Malley, Garcia, and Escola. "Did you get the bastard?"

"Hell yes, we got him," Escola assured Masao.

"You guys…you're good soldiers," Masao struggled to get out.

A medic came over and showed O'Malley where to keep pressure, "Right here," the medic pressed O'Malley's hand on Masao's leg.

"Okay, okay. I got it," O'Malley's voice quivered. He looked at the blood seeping through his fingers, the Japanese blood of Masao. He looked at Masao's face just as Masao opened his eyes and looked back. "Sarge. I was a complete prick to you. I'm so sorry." O'Malley fought his emotions. With that, Escola helped apply pressure on the wound and Garcia took Masao's hand.

Masao shook his head. "It's okay, Jack. We're just regular guys doing our best."

The four men had a brief moment of mutual admiration and respect, an expression of loyal brotherhood that can only shared between men who served together on the battlefield.

"Thank you." Masao managed to say before the medics rushed in and took over. O'Malley held Masao's hand until the last possible moment. The bodyguards watched as they loaded Masao onto the amphibian and the gate closed.

"I hope he makes it," Garcia sighed as he watched the amphibian crawl out of the surf and go afloat toward the transport ship. On Orange Beach, it was business as usual. Nobody was aware of or cared about these buddies and their emotional trauma. The three men watched the amphibian reach the transport ship, then they looked around and at each other.

"What do we do now?" O'Malley said. Nobody knew the answer.

Spring, 2013

Masao finished his fried egg sandwich and then fussed around to get ready. I meandered over to his wall of pictures and examined the one that appeared to have been taken on a battlefield. He was squatting, rifle in hand, in between two other soldiers, one Japanese-American and one Caucasian. As Masao rolled through the living room, I pointed to the photo.

"Where was this taken, Mas? Peleliu?" He looked up and saw the photo.

"Uh, no. Let's see now. That guy to my right is Bob Sakai, a reallllly smart guy, boy. And that Caucasian gentleman, I don't know who he is. Uh, let's see now. Not Peleliu, that was taken on, uh, Leyte. In the Philippines," he said as he pulled his shoes on.

"It's a really cool picture."

"Heh! We look a-tough, don't we?"

"I think you were pretty tough." I helped him get his jacket on. "You're still pretty tough."

"Heh! I'm a sad case, no? Can't even remember what day it is," he was referring to the fact that he hadn't known it was Tuesday until I walked through the door.

"Mas. You're ninety-six. You still cook, do laundry, and iron. Can you be just a tad easier on yourself?"

"Heh!" He waved me off.

As we waited for the glacially slow elevator, I thought more about Leyte.

"What happened on Leyte? You never told me about that."

The elevator door opened. "When are we going to Vegas?" he asked as he rolled onto the elevator.

"This Sunday."

"Oh…Sunday. Good." Vegas was far more important to him than Leyte. "You know, I don't remember much about Leyte, to tell you the truth," he began. "After I was shot, they sent me to, ah, what's the name now, ah, New Caledonia. I was there for a couple of months. Then they sent me to Leyte. In the Philippines. The local people, they hated the Japanese, boy, I'll tell you that much. Whenever they saw me, they would point and their faces, they would look – terrified." The brutality the Japanese military had inflicted on Allied Forces and the Philippine people was well-known.

"I've never seen anything like it," he was thinking out loud.

"Were you in battle there?"

"It was more like *mop-up*," he said as he looked at me. He knew I wouldn't have a clue what that meant. "Mop-up is-a like the cleaning crew, making sure there aren't any enemy soldiers left behind."

"Did you find any?"

He gave this some serious thought before he answered, "We found a few, a-no?"

"You took prisoners?"

"Maybe one or two. The orders had changed a little bit." The Allied forces were still pushing Japan back into itself, cleaning out Japanese forces from the Pacific Rim yet leaving a swath of destruction and death in the wake of military success. But the balance had tilted. With each group of islands freed from the Japanese, Allied commanders could feel victory approaching.

"I remember one Japanese guy, though, an officer. He was in really bad shape."

June 1945 - Leyte, Philippines

While he was still attached to the 321ˢᵗ everything felt different to Masao. The locals feared him and looked at him with loathing in their eyes. His bodyguards on Angaur and Peleliu now had different assignments; he hadn't even seen them since he left Orange Beach on Peleliu. His new bodyguards were aloof and distant. His leg bothered him most of the time, and he had been astounded that he had been ordered back on the line with such a serious injury that hadn't healed completely. But the commanders in charge were more determined than ever to drive the Japanese out of every stronghold, including the Philippines. They needed every available man.

He was attached to a platoon that had been ordered on mop-up behind enemy lines. Reports indicated there were still active pockets. The platoon crept along silently, listening for signs of life. Suddenly the platoon sergeant, a guy named Newberry, halted and crouched low, signaling everyone else to do the same. He motioned for the unit to stay put while he and two soldiers moved closer toward the sound, disappearing into tall grass that closed up behind them. The rest of the outfit waited, ready to fire.

"I need that interpreter!" Newberry shouted from a short distance. Masao followed his voice, wondering why his bodyguards weren't coming with him. He came upon the group in a small clearing where there was a Japanese officer on the ground, slowly bleeding to death. It looked as if he had been bleeding out for hours.

"What's he saying?" Newberry asked in his gruff voice.

Masao squatted down next to the officer. "He wants to know what you are saying," he asked, keenly aware of the man's agony.

"I was asking him to let me use his gun. I could end my life."

"He wants to use your gun, sir, to end his life."

Newberry softened. "I wonder where his unit is."

"Where is the rest of your outfit?" Masao took charge and asked.

"They fell back, under my orders." he pointed to a direction. "That way."

"Is that the direction of your command post?" Masao proceeded with his usual questioning. Then he realized that Newberry hadn't worked much with an interpreter, so he explained. "His unit headed that way. I'm asking if that's where the command post is." Newberry nodded.

"Our command post was there, yes." The Japanese officer was losing strength by the minute.

"Their CP was in the same area, sir," Masao interpreted.

"Shit. I'd like to get him some help but it would take half my guys to do it." Newberry's humanity appeared out of nowhere.

The Japanese officer looked back and forth wanting desperately to know what was being said. Masao noticed. "Sir? May I?" Newberry nodded. "My commander is thinking this through. He would like to get you some help."

He shook his head. "It's too late for help. Please. A gun with one bullet is all I need."

"Sir, he's pleading for us to let him end his life here."

Newberry wrestled with his thoughts. "You guys, head back with the others." His soldiers were bewildered. "Go on!" Newberry jerked his head, motioning for them to go. Masao looked at the Japanese officer who looked back at him. Masao nodded slightly.

They weren't yet back with the others when they heard a single shot ring out. They flinched and looked back. They knew what had just happened. Newberry couldn't have given an enemy soldier a loaded gun. He had to do the unthinkable — the unthinkable and the most humane.

❖　❖　❖

"I'll never forget that, boy… That guy was in bad shape, a-no? But the tech sergeant, he did what he had to do." And with that thought, he was lost in the past.

"You know, ah, Japan. It's the only country in the history, ever, to have a bomb, atomic bomb, dropped on it. Two, in fact." He held up two fingers to drive his point in. I slowly nodded. "Thousands of innocent people died. They didn't have to, a-no?" His heart was torn as it had been for most of his life.

"Hiroshima, then Nagasaki," he reminisced, "August 6th, and, ah, August 9th. I don't know why those damn Japanese guys just didn't surrender after the first one, you know?" It was quiet.

"Why those two cities?"

"I don't know. Those bombs killed a loooot of people, not just military. Tsch." It was quiet for a few minutes while he was back in 1945. I waited, knowing that there was more wisdom coming my way. "They had brought in a lot of young people, school-aged, a-no? To the city, to Hiroshima. From the country. Thousands of young kids, doing the work of men."

I thought about asking where all the men were but then realized – they had all been called to duty. Children were called to a different duty, to perform the jobs that would otherwise go to adult men and women.

"The girls, they had them working in a military factory, sewing military uniforms. Thousands of girls. The boys, they had them tearing down buildings to make, ah, breaks, what's it called now….ah, firebreaks. Because, ah, Hiroshima was one of the last major cities in Japan that hadn't been attacked by air raids. So they were expecting it, a-no? And, ah, they had these boys tearing down buildings so that when the air raids started, fires wouldn't spread." His emotions were evident. "And, ah, when that bomb dropped, those kids…they were all *vaporized* in a second."

My emotions were suddenly in my throat. I think it was because Masao felt such deep pain for the horror inflicted on so many innocent people, many of them children. It was infectious. I glanced over at him, he was still thinking.

"Thousands died that day, or within a few days after, a-no? Half the population of that city. Civilians." He looked over at me and saw that I was feeling it, the horror of the moment on August 6, 1945 at 8:15 a.m. I wanted to get my head around the destruction. It was hard to imagine what an atomic bomb did to the earth that it struck.

"Did it leave a huge crater? Is there a crater there now?"

"No no. It exploded above the city. I don't know, maybe five hundred meters above it, I can't remember. And, ah, it just flattened everything for a mile or so. And caused damage all over." He paused, and then another memory surfaced. "One gentleman, he was a-waiting on the steps of a bank near the exact place of the bomb. And, ah, when the bomb a-struck, he was just instantly burned up. But, ah, what was left on the concrete steps was his shadow. That was all that was left of him. A shadow."

I heard myself gasp. He looked at me and nodded. "Just a shadow. You can see those a-steps if you go to the museum there. You and Alan should go someday."

I nodded. "You were still in Leyte? When the bomb dropped?"

"Yep, that's right, Leyte."

"Did you know at the time? That the bombs had been dropped?"

He nodded and looked away. I could see the emotion swelling inside him and felt horrible for bringing up such a painful memory.

"All I could think about was my mom."

April 9, 2013 - Good-Bye Vegas

"When are we coming back?" Masao asked. He was like a little kid. I glanced at Alan who looked like he was about to have a hissy fit at the mere notion of making more Vegas travel plans.

"Let's give Alan a couple of days to settle down. But probably June."

"Ohhhh… June. That's too long." We looked out the window as the plane took off, leaving Vegas below us until the next time. After the beverage service I noticed that Masao wasn't napping as he often did when flying, and I wondered if he would talk more about the war.

"Hey, Mas?" He turned and looked at me. "Where were you when the war ended? Leyte still?"

"Yep, Leyte," he nodded, "I remember that. That was a good day, boy."

August 10, 1945 - The War Ends

Masao was attached to a different platoon and was, again, feeling isolated. Soldiers were exhausted by seeing death play out in front of them day in and day out, and longing for home. Nobody cared that Masao was the lone Asian in the unit. Everybody had the same goal in mind - to get back to family and to where things made sense.

They were squatted down while the tech sergeant looked at his map. Suddenly a shout came from the hills.

"*The war is over!! The war is over!!*" an American voice yelled out to the world.

"What the hell?" The tech sergeant jerked his head around and motioned for the radioman, "Get on the horn and find out what the hell is going on."

Within moments it was confirmed. Celebrations erupted all over, men popping up from camouflaged positions they had held, coming out from nowhere, yelling and cheering.

"Men, we're going to play this safe," the tech sergeant ordered his unit as he heard the distant celebrations continue. "Those idiots are like moving targets, *goddamit*. The Japs may not yet know they've surrendered, and even if they do, what do they have to lose to kill a few more of us? Hold your heads low until I get orders to fall back." The tech sergeant's wisdom paid off. There were reports of men letting their guard down and being picked off even after the war was technically over.

❖ ❖ ❖

Once back at the military base, Masao was eager to pack up and get back to San Bernardino to figure out his uncle's situation. For the next several weeks, he watched soldier after soldier being honorably discharged. After weeks, it was finally his turn. He had been summoned to the captain's office on base. He'd never seen other soldiers processed this way but didn't give it much thought or care, he just wanted to get to California.

"Sergeant Abe, you MIS boys did a fine job out there." The Captain began.

"Thank you, sir."

"You and your comrades have been crucial to the military success in the Pacific. Remember that."

"Thank you, sir."

"You're now considered what the military calls an essential. And it's my duty to tell you what your next orders are," the Captain said with a fair amount of empathy in his voice. He knew this would be a shock.

"Orders, sir?" *Is this a joke?*

"I'm afraid so. You ship out for Tokyo on eighteen September. You'll be on the first transport ship to arrive for occupation efforts."

"*Japan!* Sir. With all due respect, I have enough points to be honorably discharged just like the other guys," Masao pleaded. He was right. The point system for an honorable discharge was a calculation based on the number of battles in which a soldier had fought, the number of children he had, and other factors. The cut off score was seventy-five points. Masao had eighty-two.

"I understand." The captain felt for Masao. He was certain that Masao just wanted to settle, just like all the other GIs, and he was sure that Masao wanted to settle on United States soil, not the defeated ground of Japan. "Be assured, thousands of other American soldiers will be there as well, including MacArthur himself."

"I'll be wearing a U.S. uniform in Japan," Masao said.

"Yes." The captain understood the complication. He would still be the target of hate, only now it would be directed at him as an American in Japan, a different kind of traitor.

Masao learned that three of his Nisei interpreter buddies had been given the same news. On September 18, Masao boarded the military transport vessel for the seven-day voyage to Japan. He would be in the first wave of American soldiers to dock in Japan.

❖ ❖ ❖

"In one minute we were at war, in the next minute, we weren't," Masao recalled.

"What about the Japanese soldiers? What happened to them?"

"Heh! I don't know. The Japanese military just *left* them there. Poor devils. They never stood a chance." He lingered in the memory for a moment then glanced at Alan who was dozing off and nudged me. "Hey, when are we going back to Vegas?"

I just smiled, "Soon, very soon." After a few days, Alan did make travel arrangements for June. That eased Masao's restless heart.

Tatsuo Abe, Mataemon Abe, Yasoshichi Abe, circa 1920.
Courtesy of the Abe family photo collection.

Tomie, Masao, and Yasoshichi Abe in San Bernardino.
Courtesy of the Abe family photo collection.

Tomie Abe with son Masao.
Courtesy of the Abe family photo collection.

Masao Abe, first row, fifth from right, 1921.
Courtesy of the Abe family photo collection.

Star Cash Grocery, Yasoshichi is second from left, his younger brother,
Tatsuo, on left, holding pole.
Courtesy of the Abe family photo collection.

Form 500 A
U. S. DEPARTMENT OF LABOR
IMMIGRATION SERVICE

List **15**

LIST OR MANIFEST OF ALIEN PASS

ALL ALIENS arriving at a port of continental United States from a foreign port or a port of the insular possessions of the United States, and all aliens arriving at

S. S. "Shinyo Maru" — Passengers sailing from Yokohama

No. on List	HEAD-TAX STATUS.	NAME IN FULL Family name.	Given name.	Age. Yrs. Mos.	Sex.	Married or single.	Calling or occupation.	Able to— Read.	Read what language [or, if exemption claimed, on what ground].	Write.	Nationality. (Country of which citizen or subject.)	†Race or people.	Last permanent resider Country.	City or to
1	TAX 631·348400 Mar.15, 1928	Abe	Yasoshichi	35	M	M	Merchant	Yes	Japanese	Yes	Japan	Japanese	Calif.	San Fr
2	TAX 631-35133 Nov 20, 1928	Abe	Tomiye	33	F	M	Wife	"	"	"	"	"	"	"
3	USC	Abe	Yoshi	6	F	S	Family	No	-	No	U.S.A.	"	"	"
4	USC	Abe	Yuri	3	F	S	"	"	-	"	"	"	"	"
5	USC	Kuwashima	Yoneo	17 8	M	S	Student	Yes	Japanese	Yes	"	"	Japan	Tokio
6	TAX	Ikeda	Junkyo	30 5	M	M	Missionary	"	"	"	Japan	"	Calif.	Los Ang

Passenger List departing from Yokohama, Japan, November 28th, 1925.
Courtesy of the National Archives, Riverside.

Yasoshichi, Masao (with glasses), Jiro (in front of Masao), Mataemon (grandfather),
Yoshiko, Tayo Anzai (grandmother), Yuriko, Yoichi, Tomie, circa 1931, Senoue, Japan.
Courtesy of the Abe family photo collection.

 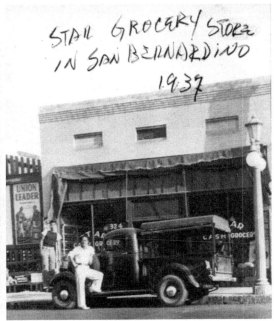

Left photo: Masao with buddy Susumu.
Right photo: in front of Star Cash Grocery.
Courtesy of the Abe family photo collection.

Tatsuo, Masao, Yonekatsu during one of their traveling adventures.
Courtesy of the Abe family photo collection.

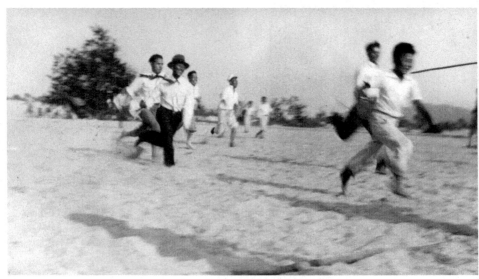

A race at the Santa Ana River annual picnic.
Courtesy of the Abe family photo collection.

The people of Little Japan, San Bernardino, Masao kneeling in front.
Courtesy of the Abe family photo collection.

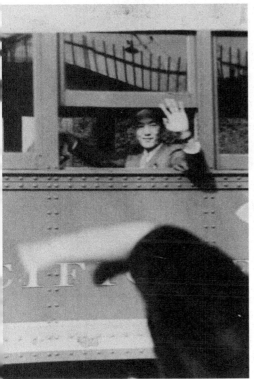

September 10, 1941 Masao leaves for boot camp.
Courtesy of the Abe family photo collection.

President Roosevelt's visit to Camp Robinson, 1942.
Courtesy of the Franklin D. Roosevelt Presidential Library.

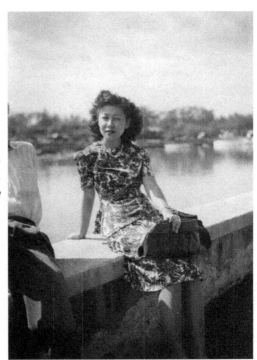

Doris Kimie Okada on Oahu, circa 1943.
Courtesy of the Abe family photo collection.

Doris with friends; she is second from the left.
Courtesy of the Abe family photo collection.

The 81st Infantry Division ten-man Interpretation/Interrogation Team.
Back row: Saburo Nakamura, 322nd RCT, Kei Kitahara, 323rd, Robert
Sakai, HQ, Tomio Ichikawa, 322nd, James Kai, HQ and Team Leader,
Hiroki Takahashi, HQ.
Front row: Masao Abe, 321st, Shiuso Chojin, HQ, Shiro Sakaki, 323rd.
Not pictured: Frank Kubota, 321st.
Courtesy of the Abe Family photo collection.

Amphibious Assault on Angaur, September 17, 1944.
The 81st Infantry Wildcat Division in World War II, National Archives.

Troops Arrive on Anguar.
The 81st Infantry Wildcat Division in World War II, National Archives.

T3 Saburo Nakamura, 322nd Regimental Combat Team, interrogates
a Japanese Imperial Army soldier.
The 81st Infantry Wildcat Division in World War II, National Archives.

T3 Hiroki Takahashi, 81st Infantry Division Headquarters, checks out
an enemy cave on Peleliu, 1944.
The 81st Infantry Wildcat Division in World War II, National Archives.

Masao stands for inspection, third from right.
Courtesy of the National Archives.

On Leyte, Masao, center, Robert Sakai, right, unidentified soldier, left.
Courtesy of the Abe Family photo collection.

Orchard in Fukushima, Japan. Yasoshichi Abe on the ladder,
Tomie below.
Courtesy of the Abe family photo collection.

Doris on her way to Japan.
Courtesy of the Abe family photo collection.

Doris in Japan.
Courtesy of the Abe family photo collection.

Doris in Japan surrounded by Japanese children who had never seen
a Japanese-American woman before.
Courtesy of the Abe family photo collection.

Doris Okada and Masao Abe, Japan, circa 1946.
Courtesy of the Abe family photo collection.

Masao and Doris Abe at their granddaughter Taryn's wedding.
Courtesy of Kathie Abe.

Masao and Alan in Vegas.

Masao Abe and Saburo Nakamura, "Naki", February 18, 2012, Hawai'i.

Masao on Veteran's Day, 2012.

The Memorial Wall, Seattle Nisei Veteran's Committee.

Lady Columbia at the Punchbowl Cemetery.
Courtesy of the Abe family photo collection.

Masao's service.
Courtesy of the Abe family photo collection.

Masao's urn at the Punchbowl Cemetery. November 6, 2013.
Courtesy of the Abe family photo collection.

Masao Abe with his Congressional Gold Medal.
Courtesy of Kathie Abe.

PART III

THE FINAL JOURNEY

NOVEMBER 6, 2013

THERE WASN'T A RAIN CLOUD IN THE SKY AS WE DROVE TO THE PUNCHBOWL, Masao's urn sitting between Alan and me on the front seat. We entered the cemetery and parked at the administration building just inside the entrance. The first thing you notice when coming into the Punchbowl cemetery is Mall Drive, a road that cuts through the center of the crater. It is flanked on either side with Chinese banyan trees and envelops a wide swath of perfectly cut, lush, green Hawaiian grass punctuated by plots between the two one-way roads. At the end of Mall Drive, a white marble memorial rises up seventy feet and perfectly extends the width of Mall Drive. Like the entire cemetery, it is symmetrically placed.

The climb up the stairs to the marble memorial reveals several side courtyards that were built to honor the missing. Each Court of the Missing contains four tall, narrow structures that appear to be solid white marble. Each face of each structure contains nine white marble tablets etched with names of missing soldiers. At the center of the four structures sits a plumeria tree. There are close to thirty thousand names represented in these courts that are designated to specific wars.

The monument, commissioned by the American Battle Monuments Commission, contains as its centerpiece a thirty-foot statue of Lady Columbia who stands on a ship's bow. She carries with her the hearts of all the mothers who lost their children in battle. Below her and above the sacred pool, President Lincoln's words are inscribed: "*THE SOLEMN PRIDE THAT MUST BE YOURS TO HAVE LAID SO COSTLY A SACRIFICE*

UPON THE ALTAR OF FREEDOM," referring to a mother who lost five sons to the Civil War.

Behind Lady Columbia, a non-secular chapel is open for all to pray and/or meditate. A gallery of maps extends out on each side of the chapel displaying the locations in the Pacific that were the sites of battles during World War II. Sadly, Angaur and Peleliu were not among the featured battles along this wall of maps.

Just off to the side of Lady Columbia's memorial area and in between her and the columbarium is a small courtyard called the Committal Court. This is where the ceremony for Masao would be held. We had handed off the urn to the cemetery administrator who was handling everything with expertise and care.

Family and friends were gathered. Most of us stood, but there were chairs for the elderly among us and Masao's sons, Patrick, Michael, and Alan, who were seated front and center. Masao's urn was placed on a small table covered with a green cloth and draped in a thick, red fabric on all sides. Both of his dress caps were laid on the top. Flowers decorated each side of the table. There was a portable roof to shield guests from the sun.

I stood at a distance, not wanting to intrude on the family and wanting to capture the last moments with Masao on film. I noticed soldiers in full dress uniform and white gloves off to the side. Two other soldiers opposite them were lined up one behind the other. The soldier in front held Masao's urn, the soldier behind him held Masao's flag.

The service began with the two soldiers who carried Masao's urn and flag, marching in sync to the table, each of their movements well-rehearsed and perfect. One soldier carefully set Masao's urn down while the other held the folded flag above it, as the last token of the military caring for one of its fallen. They each saluted. Then they carefully unfolded the flag to its full length and stepped over so that the flag was now unfolded across and above Masao's urn. The soldiers on the other side of the courtyard moved into position, one of them standing at attention and saluting, the other stepping back from the courtyard, facing away, and holding up his bugle to play taps. Everyone stood.

CHAPTER 10

THE BEGINNING OF THE END
JUNE 4, 2013

"Herrroooo?" Masao answered the phone. *He must have been sleeping*, I thought. He sounded groggy.

"Mas?"

"Herrroooo?"

"Mas? This is Sandie."

"I—herrooo-wann—nooo—fllll—." He was completely incoherent.

I became alarmed. "Are you okay?" I pulled out of my parking spot in a hurry.

"Wannn—fllll—ahhh—slllll—." I couldn't make out a word. *Oh my God oh my God*. My heart started pounding.

"Masao. I'm going to call you back. Okay?"

"Ooookkk."

"I'm going to call you back. Just—soon." I hung up and dialed Alan's sister-in-law, Stephanie, while trying to drive at the same time. Thank God she answered.

"Steph? It's Sandie. Something's wrong with Masao. I'm on my way over there but can you please go check on him right now?" She could hear the panic in my voice.

"Sure thing. I'll head over there right now." She lived close to the retirement home and would be there within minutes. My heart raced as I merged onto the freeway. I dialed Alan.

"Something's wrong with your dad. I'm going over there but I called Steph. She's on her way there too."

"Okay, well, call me when you get there. He's probably just tired."

Alan didn't seem too concerned but something in my gut indicated urgency.

For the next week, Masao's not feeling well persisted and worsened. I badgered Alan and his brother until they took him to the emergency room. They knew their dad—he was a stubborn guy and didn't like going to the doctor. But my senses, every one of them, told me that he needed the care of a doctor. This wasn't something that was going to go away on its own. He was getting weaker and was having trouble walking, even with his walker.

As it turned out, he had come down with pneumonia. He was admitted to the hospital where he stayed for days. Instead of the casino, I would visit him in the hospital, often with food from his favorite restaurants. Sometimes he would have an appetite for it, and sometimes he wouldn't. Sometimes, he was strong enough to eat on his own, and other times, we would help him eat.

One day when I arrived, there were already visitors in the room and Masao was awake. Alan, Mike, and Stephanie were all trying to get him to eat something suggesting different things off the hospital menu or from local restaurants. He just kept shaking his head, he wasn't interested. *At least he has the strength to refuse*, I thought. Then I had an idea.

"What about a fried egg sandwich?" I asked him. He looked at me like I was on to something.

He nodded. "That sounds good." Everyone else in the room looked at me like I had some sort of extra-sensory perception. I did not. I had just seen him eat a lot of fried egg sandwiches. Since I was last to arrive, I was the last to leave that day. I stayed with Mas while he ate part of the fried egg sandwich and watched him doze off and on. Just as I was about to leave, he woke up and looked alert.

"Where's a-Alan?"

"He went home," I patted his knee, "How are you feeling?"

"Oh, so-so." I nodded and waited to see if he was going to nod off again. "When are we going to Vegas?" Alan had cancelled our trip the day before. It was evident that Masao was not strong enough to walk on a plane.

"Well, uh, when you're strong enough." I didn't have the heart to tell him the trip had been cancelled.

"Oh, this month, a-no?"

"Uh—I hope so! We need you to get better so we can go."

"Ohhhh." He sounded dejected. I had to think fast, I didn't want him to get depressed.

"Hey, Mas, where did you meet Doris? Was that in Hawai'i, after the war?"

"Noooo," he quickly corrected me, "I met my wife in *Japan*." He looked at me knowing I would be confused.

"I didn't know she was in Japan."

"Heh! Gee, that was a long time ago, now. Seventy years...I arrived in a place called Aomori, in the north." My ploy worked, we were going back to 1945.

September 25, 1945 – The Occupation

The transport ship maneuvered through the Tsugaru Straits. Its destination was Aomori, a port tucked inside Mutsu Bay in the very northern part of Japan. Masao and Naki stood at the rail watching the shore approach.

"You're going to have to show me around, old boy. Introduce me to your family and friends." Naki nudged Masao with his elbow.

Masao smiled and lit up a cigarette. "My friends. I wonder what happened to them. They all went into the war. I doubt any of them made it," Masao concluded. He noticed as Japanese locals scurried from the dock area and closed themselves up inside their homes, afraid for their lives. "I never thought I'd be coming back here as an American soldier."

Naki looked at his friend. He couldn't begin to understand what Masao was feeling. What kind of fate had been dealt to Masao, bounced back and forth between two countries that would end up as enemies? Forever feeling like a foreigner, never feeling as if he had a home.

"Does your mom know you're here?"

Masao shook his head. "No." He flicked his cigarette into the sea and watched it swirl in the dark water. Like the cigarette, his feelings swirled, not knowing which end was up, not knowing how he should feel being reunited with his family.

His family. He'd been apart from them more than he had been with them.

Soldiers took the train from Aomori to Tokyo, which the military would soon occupy in great numbers. Masao was assigned to the U.S. Army censor operation and worked at the post office following certain dignitaries' mail. He and Naki would take a Jeep to drive around town when they had free time, the military giving them free reign.

Seeing Japan and all the destruction wasn't easy. Witnessing the current situation of Japan's people was heart-wrenching. But the hardest thing for Masao to contemplate was a visit with his family. The last time he'd seen his parents had been in 1936, almost a decade earlier.

For Masao, reuniting with his parents felt complicated.

❖ ❖ ❖

It was a crisp October, morning and Tomie was helping Yasoshichi in the orchard. They had received periodic letters from Tatsuo, who was still in a Department of Justice (DOJ) facility in America. He had kept them loosely informed as to Masao's whereabouts in the world. Tomie had fretted when she heard Masao had been shot, praying, hoping her oldest child would somehow survive. She had spent many sleepless nights fearing for his safety and worried that he would fall into the hands of the Japanese military.

She kept herself sane by focusing on her remaining children. Her oldest daughter was grown and had married and her youngest child, Yoichi, was still a teenager. While she was devastated that Japan had endured not one, but two atomic bomb attacks, she was more than relieved that Japan had finally surrendered. At least her youngest son wouldn't have to face conscription.

The air was refreshing on this particular morning, and it was quiet in the village as she took apples from Yasoshichi who was handing them down from the top of his ladder. Then she heard something. It was a vehicle of some sort, but the engine sounded unlike anything she had ever heard before. It stopped near their home. She shielded her eyes from the morning sun and strained to see.

For some unknown reason, Tomie's heart started pounding. She instinctively dropped the apples and walked toward the vehicle, hoping that her senses were accurate. Her heart seemed to pull her toward the car.

Then she saw him. Her Masao. Her body went limp with emotion when she saw her oldest son step out of the strange looking car. He didn't notice that she had already extended her arms out. He didn't notice that her maternal energies had already wrapped him inside her heart and held him tight. Tears welled in her eyes as each step brought her closer to him, to the little boy she had abandoned when he was nine, to the young adult they forced to leave Japan when he was nineteen, to the man that he had now become.

She stepped on a twig and it cracked. Masao heard it and looked over to see his mother, her arms stretched out in front of her, her gait short but swift.

The soldier, the warrior, the survivor of bloody battles, now felt as if he was nine all over again. As they embraced, Tomie held onto her son tightly, sobbing tears of joy and love, sorrow and regret, and relief.

"My Masao…oh…Masao…" she sobbed as she held him even tighter. They didn't want to let go of each other for several moments.

Yasoshichi looked on. His reunion with his son would be different. He knew Masao harbored deep resentment toward him for the decisions he had made as a father. Yasoshichi had regrets, many of them. But he, for one moment, did not regret sending Masao back to the States before the Japanese military could grab a hold of him. The only chance Masao had for surviving World War II was in the hands of the U.S. military. Masao's presence here now had proven that. *Hate me all you want*, Yasoshichi thought. *It's a cross I'm willing to bear.*

After several minutes of embracing his mother and reconnecting with her love he so missed, he turned to his father and extended his hand to shake. His father held out his hand in return.

"Hello, father," Masao's Japanese was as perfect as ever.

"Son. I'm very glad to see you," Yasoshichi greeted Masao with a smile.

March 1946 - Honolulu

With the war over, things in Honolulu slowly returned to normal. Doris still worked as a civil servant. She and Stanley were still dating and Doris hoped he would commit to her soon. When Stanley announced that he was applying to go to Japan to work as a civil servant, she, at first, had been beyond disappointed. But then he suggested that she apply as well. She thought this was a magnificent idea. Maybe in Japan their relationship would solidify at last.

It took some badgering of her parents to let her go, but she eventually got her way. She found a group that was heading for Japan, one that had solid supervision and guidance and that eased her parents' concerns. Stanley had left two months before her, but she would be on her way soon. Not only that, she would be flying on a jet airplane, something she had never done before. She was more than excited the day she left Honolulu. She desperately wanted to join Stanley to start their adventurous life together in Japan.

April 1946 – Tokyo

The Japanese government voices had instilled fear into the hearts of the citizens regarding Allied Forces. They warned that the occupying American troops would be brazen and would take the Japanese girls away; they would be savage on all accounts. But when American troops arrived with medicine, food, and clothing, Japanese locals started to emerge from out of nowhere.

Masao and Naki were acutely aware of the locals and lack of supplies. Every time their plentiful rations of cigarettes and alcohol were distributed they would take a Jeep, drive to the shipyards, and share with the workers who were getting off their shifts. Most of the time, Japanese locals were happy to see the U.S. uniform. Still, some people spat at them, wondering how Japanese men could possibly wear the uniform of the enemy.

The Japanese imperial soldiers who survived the war had returned to Japan in shame. None of Masao's childhood friends made it back alive. Miyoko had long since married, Masao heard. On the brighter side,

Cooper's outfit, or what was left of it, made it out of the war alive. His bodyguards were all awarded with Bronze Stars, two of them with Silver Stars. Masao thought it well-deserved. He missed his guys from Angaur and Peleliu and thought of them often.

❖　❖　❖

Back at the Post Office, Masao continued to censor mail. The airplanes and ships full of civil servants, mostly women, continued to arrive on Japan's shores. Many of the women were looking to link up with a soldier and settle down. Some of the women came under the notion of civil service but were really there as working girls. Masao had little interest in any of them even though they had plenty of interest in him.

Naki had met a Japanese girl and was spending a lot of time with her at the expense of his buddy-time with Masao. While his feelings of loneliness had subsided since he had reconnected with his family, Masao still felt something was missing in his life. He envied Naki for finding a girl with whom he wanted to start a life.

❖　❖　❖

A smiling Doris descended the stairs of the airplane. She spotted Stanley and couldn't wait to get to him. She ran to hug him, and he hugged her back, but it felt different. When he turned his cheek to avoid her kiss on the lips, she knew something was up. Stanley took her to dinner to break the bad news.

"I've met a girl," he said with little empathy.

Doris thought she was hearing things. "What do you mean you 'met a girl'? I'm your girl."

"I found a Japanese girl. And…," He looked at Doris to gauge her reaction. "I think she's the one for me."

"You found a Japanese girl? I'm a Japanese girl! I'm the Japanese girl who *followed* you here from Honolulu!" Her voice reflected her disbelief, her shock.

"Doris, please calm yourself. She's…" He smiled as he thought about how to describe his new girl. "She's a *real* Japanese girl."

Doris was angered by that insult. "A *real* Japanese girl, huh? You know what you are? You're a damn bastard, that's what you are!" Her voice was loud.

"This is exactly what I'm talking about. Shizuko would never behave in this manner. Using profanity and yelling."

"Yelling? *YELLING?*" Doris shrieked, drawing attention in the restaurant. "What's going on with you, pal? Why are you talking that way?" Her eyes teared up, her voice turned soft, "This isn't the Stanley I know. And love."

"I'm a changed man," he looked at Doris with uncaring eyes, daring her to challenge his statement. "Shizuko. She made me see the real me."

A mixture of seething and heartache filled her beautiful face. "You don't know *who* you are." She got up, collected her belongings, resisted the urge to throw water in his face, and walked out.

Back in the hotel room, Doris was surrounded by a group of girls who consoled her. She sobbed helplessly for days until the group leader, Mrs. Okasako, found her a nice civil servant job that would help to get her mind off Stanley. Within her first week in Japan, Doris was longing for home.

❖　❖　❖

"A new group is coming through," Naki nodded in the direction of the new group walking toward them. Masao looked at him, disinterested in the husband-seeking girls coming from America.

"More pan-pan girls," Masao responded, brushing off the notion that he would find anyone of interest.

"They're not all working girls," Naki insisted. Masao gave this some thought and decided to glance at the new group making its way through the post office. He spotted Doris right away. She was different, not giggly like the other girls were. She seemed — *angry*. While the other girls darted their heads around in search of officers to glom on to, Doris seemed to look off in a daze, eager to get down to business so she could get her mind off of whatever was ailing her. Masao studied her while she was introduced to the clerk who would give them their assignments and show them how to perform the tasks. She went right to work, kept to herself, and concentrated on the mail she was sorting.

"That one looks interesting," Masao said in a low voice to Naki. Naki looked up as Masao made the slight nod in the direction of Doris. Naki watched Doris for two seconds before he made his assessment.

"Are you crazy? She looks like she's the type who would bite your head off."

Masao just smiled, "That's okay."

He waited for a while before he moseyed over to her desk. She didn't see him approach. He lit up a cigarette and then offered one to her. That was when she noticed him for the first time. She accepted the cigarette and the light.

"I'm Masao," he said.

She looked at him as though she was going to burn him with the cigarette, "Hi, Masao." Her voice had anything but enthusiasm in it.

"You know, you don't look like the typical girl who comes here."

She set her mail down. She was annoyed to be taken off her task and was not interested in this soldier's opinion of her. She sighed and sat back, meaning – go ahead, I'll listen to your babble.

"Well, the typical girl who comes here is like a pan-pan girl. You know, a working girl." He thought he was being funny and smiled, anticipating a connection.

But instead of smiling back, she pursed her lips together and put out her cigarette, extinguishing the gift, the offer, Masao's gesture to be friendly. "Listen here, Masa, or whatever your name is. You just mind your own *goddamn* business and *leave me alone.*"

Not the response he anticipated.

He slowly backed away and returned to his desk. Naki had been a witness to the epic failure but had to ask anyway, smiling at his buddy's attempt. "How'd it go?"

Masao looked at Doris over his glasses and studied her. "I have a good feeling about her."

❖   ❖   ❖

"That's what she said to me, 'You mind your own *goddamn* business,' heh!" Masao chuckled as he remembered their first encounter. "I liked her right away."

I reveled in Masao's wonderful and vivid memory. This was not the Doris I had known. This young Doris was someone I would have wanted to hang out with. I would have wanted to watch her put people in their place and would have admired her for saying things to others that I never could.

"Doris was sassy!"

"Heh! She was," he chuckled. His recollection of their first meeting had warmed his heart. "I knew she was the one…"

July 9, 2013

He was awake when I walked in with his breakfast and eagerly accepted the coffee I brought, sucking it down with big gulps. He took a bite of the donut, and I sat down so I could be close to him.

"Did I tell you about the time I asked my wife to marry me?" His thoughts were frequently with Doris. I hoped it wasn't because he was near the end.

"No, you never did." I leaned forward to show my interest.

"It was in Japan, that was a long time ago…"

"Tell me about it. It must have been magical."

"Magical! Heh! We were on a bus!"

Summer 1946 - Tokyo, Japan

Doris had thawed toward Masao, and they began to see each other. She wanted to tour Japan and Masao had access to a Jeep so it was a good combination. They traveled all over the country together, meeting Masao's family and visiting the Japanese relatives Doris had never met. The more time they spent together, the stronger their connection grew.

One evening they had gone to a show in town. They took the bus and were on their way back to Doris's place. They sat together, holding hands. Masao reached into his pocket and pulled out a ring.

"Doris," he said sincerely, "would you consider marrying a soldier like me?" Doris looked at Masao, surprised and delighted by the ring he was holding.

"I would love to marry you, Masao."

❖　❖　❖

"Heh! I almost fell off the bus chair. I was so surprised that she would marry a bum like me!" His love for Doris was so deep you could feel it.

"What are you talking about? You were a catch, just like she was!"

"Nah. She was pretty. So pretty. Too pretty for a guy like me. Until the day she died, a-no?"

I nodded that I agreed with that completely. "She was pretty."

I stayed until he was almost asleep. "Mas," I tapped him and whispered, "I'll see you tomorrow."

"Okay, thank you," he said as he dozed off.

July 16, 2013

I stopped at Ginza to pick up food for Masao who had been moved to a long-term care facility. The sushi chefs smiled when I walked in. The owner came out to greet me. The Mexican guy from the back, Juan, who always came out to say hi to Masao, came out to say hi to me. They all wanted an update.

"He's still in the long-term facility. But the food there is horrid," I reported.

"He likes fish head." the owner was already taking care of business and getting Masao's favorite dishes ordered. I didn't have to do a thing. They didn't even charge me for it. They just packaged things up, with the greatest of care, and sent me on my way.

Visits with Masao were becoming heart-wrenching. He was withering away in front of our eyes. Still, he would have the occasional day where he was alert and perky, and those days would give me hope. This was one of those days. I walked in and he was awake, his bed cranked up so he was almost in a sitting position, and the TV was on.

"Hi!" I was happy to see that he was awake and alert.

"Hey, Sandie." He spotted the take-out sack. "You brought a-food?"

"I did! From Ginza. They made a special order for you," I unwrapped the containers from the bag and set each one down in front of him.

"Ohhhh, boy, that looks good." His eyes devoured the food. It made me happy that he was hungry and that I picked food he would eat. And to have a coherent Masao to converse with, that was a gift.

"You want tea?"

"No, water is fine." He was dribbling food down his chest so I helped him with his napkin.

"I'm a sad case, a-no?"

"You're just trying to get better, that's all." I sat down and watched him enjoy the fish head, something he ordered many times at Ginza, a dish I did not understand and never wanted to try. In his better days, Masao would tease me about eating the fish eyeballs, knowing I would be completely grossed out by the notion.

"Hey, Mas? Can you tell me about your Uncle Tatsuo? What happened to him after the war?"

"My uncle, he was a realllly good guy. Everyone loved him. He ended up living in, ah, the *barrio*. Heh! He was a good guy. He saved every penny and sent it back to Japan. Then the war happened and all his money –gone. Just like that."

"Did he still have the little store?"

"Nope. Let's see now. What happened to that store..."

1946 - San Bernardino

The internment camps and Department of Justice prisons were closing one by one, sending their incarcerated back out into society. Tatsuo had been moved from the Sante Fe facility, where Masao had visited him before shipping out, to yet another DOJ detention center in Crystal City, Texas. Tatsuo and Yukie had been separated for years when the War Authority finally approved Yukie and her two young daughters to join Tatsuo at Crystal City.

Upon their arrival, Tatsuo's daughters looked at their father as though he was a complete stranger. He was a stranger to them. He had never met his youngest daughter and hadn't seen his oldest daughter since she was an infant. They welcomed a third child, a son, while incarcerated at the Crystal City facility.

Now that they had been given clearance to leave the prison, they would return to San Bernardino to start all over again. They were thankful they had a home to return to, grateful to Masao for putting the house in his name. At least they had a place to land; the overwhelming majority of Issei and Nisei did not.

San Bernardino had changed significantly. There was not even a hint of the Japanese legacy that had long occupied Third Street. Every last shop that had been owned and operated by Tatsuo's friends was gone. Many of the previous Japanese residents refused to come back at all.

His little grocery store, still under the ownership of his former manager, was run-down and losing money. The manager, Larry, refused to turn the ownership back over to Tatsuo. So, Tatsuo found a job as a custodian, worked hard and saved his money, and eventually found a site for a new grocery store in the barrio where he felt welcomed by the warmth of the Latino and African American communities.

❖   ❖   ❖

Masao smacked his lips as he finished his fish head. I handed him a napkin and cleared the containers.

"That was good. Thank you."

"You're welcome," I said as I wiped a piece of rice off his chin, happy that he had eaten and hoping this was the beginning of his recovery.

I didn't know, then, that this would be the last meal I would see him eat.

July 23, 2013

I showed up with another one of Masao's favorite meals, steamed clams, salad with pesto dressing, and garlic bread. We had become such regulars at several restaurants that Masao was noticeably absent as a patron. People missed him.

"Hi, Mas," I whispered when he woke up.

"Hey, Sandie." His voice was weak.

I showed him the bag of food. "It's from Brier Pizza!" He appreciated that I picked out his favorite foods, but nothing appealed to him.

"No thanks," he waved me off. This was becoming more and more typical. He wasn't eating anything.

"How about the salad?"

"Nah." He woke up a little more and looked out at the sunny day. "Is it nice outside?"

"Yeah. Want me to open the window a little bit? Get some fresh air?" He nodded, so I cracked the window for him. I pulled a chair close to his bed and sat where I could occasionally pat his legs. That was more for me than for him, it somehow felt good to be in physical contact with him. He felt the breeze and woke up a little more.

After an hour of dozing off and on, he woke up and reached for his coffee cup. It was empty.

"You want coffee?"

"Okay. Or tea…" Tea it was. I sprung into action and returned within moments to find him sitting up a little more.

"Gee, what day is it anyway?" he asked after he had taken sips of his tea.

"It's Tuesday. July 23rd."

"Did we go to Vegas?"

"Well," I wasn't sure what the heck was going on with this question. "We went to Vegas in April. And we were supposed to go in June, but we just need you to get a little bit better."

"Ohhhhh," it was a dejected oh. He had missed a trip to Vegas. Nothing could be worse. But what troubled him was that he couldn't remember. Things must have been very fuzzy for him. "I'm a sad case, no?"

I smiled and patted his knee. "You are not a sad case."

He looked at the bag of food I'd brought. "Take that and give it to one of the nurses."

"Are you sure?" He nodded, so I found one of the nurses he flirted with and offered it to her. When I came back, he was asleep again. I sat down with my book, every once in awhile glancing at his peaceful face as he slept. Suddenly, he moved his lips like he was trying to say something. I leaned in to hear, fearing for the worst, but he would just doze off again. He coughed and it woke him up.

"Doris?" His voice was frail.

I leaned forward so he could see me. "She's not here, Mas. Were you dreaming about her?" He was incoherent and looked around in a bewildered state before dozing off again.

Maybe Doris is tugging on him to join her in the ever-after. Maybe my tugs to keep him here are no match. Maybe he isn't going to get better and walk out of this horrid place on his own. Maybe this was where it will all end, where I will have to say good-bye to the kindest, wisest man I will ever know.

I couldn't stand the thought. I had to leave. My emotions were getting the better of me and I didn't want Masao to see me like that.

"Mas?" I whispered. He barely woke up. "I'm leaving." He nodded that he understood. "I'll see you in a day or two."

"Okay, thank you." His voice was scarcely audible.

"No. Thank *you*."

July 25, 2013

I showed up with his favorite coffee drink and donut. I was prepared for the worst, but was pleasantly surprised to see Masao awake and with the TV on.

"Hi!"

"Hey, Sandie."

"I brought you something," I set the coffee and donut down in front of him.

"Nah. I don't feel like eating." I wasn't going to argue. I sat close to him and glanced at the game show he had on the TV. He had never watched game shows before. *He must just want the noise*, I thought.

"You been to casino?" he asked in his weak voice.

"No. It's no fun without you."

"Heh! You gotta go without me. Unless they can wheel this bed there." My mind sprung into action, thinking of how I could wheel him in his hospital bed to the casino. Then I realized it probably wasn't possible. I had never seen a hospital bed at the casino.

"You know my uncle...gee, now. What's his name again?"

"Tatsuo?" His mind was not as sharp as it had been a mere few days ago.

"Yeah, Tatsuo. He was a realllly nice guy. He used to do nice things for people. He tried to put me through college, a-no? But I was a knucklehead about it. But he put his, ah, kid brother through dental school. At the University of Southern California." He looked at me as he talked, making sure I had this down.

"That's a tough school."

Masao nodded. "My uncle. He took care of everyone else."

I softly nodded and patted his knee, "I think you must have taken after him."

1947, San Bernardino

Deep in the barrio in San Bernardino, Tatsuo had found a small building to open his new grocery store. Since the old Star Cash Grocery had been run into the ground and no longer existed, Tatsuo took the name back. He was open for business but still setting up and loading inventory onto shelves. He felt right at home in the barrio, filled with people of various ethnicities. Working away, he hardly noticed as Ben Miller entered through the front. Ben was carrying something wrapped in a tattered old burlap sack.

"Ben! My old friend. Good to see you. Come in, come in," Tatsuo welcomed Ben.

"It's good to see you back here." Ben's voice was shaky. He had aged since Tatsuo had last seen him. "We were all worried about you and your family."

Tatsuo nodded, he appreciated Ben's concern. "Here, have a seat. It's good to be home. I missed all of my customers." Tatsuo had to help a slightly unstable Ben sit on a stool. "And I missed seeing you, dear friend, from time to time. Uh, I don't have the back set up for you just yet. Although we don't have to be so secretive in this neighborhood, do we?" He chuckled at the newfound freedom. But Ben was shaking his head. It wasn't whiskey he was seeking. It wasn't food. He didn't want anything from Tatsuo.

"I'm not here for that. I have something for you." Ben handed Tatsuo the burlap sack. Tatsuo took it, confused. He unwrapped it to find his wall clock from the old store along with the photo of himself, Yasoshichi, and their father. Tatsuo was more than astonished.

"From my old store!? But—how?"

"Oh, I have my ways." It was a triumph that Ben was able to save these two items and Tatsuo knew that he must have taken an enormous risk to do it. Ben's thoughtfulness washed over Tatsuo in a heartfelt wave, warming his entire body with gratitude. Usually the giver, it was clear that Tatsuo's presence in this new community was greatly valued.

"That's...Thank you, Ben."

And Tatsuo was home, at last.

❖ ❖ ❖

Masao dozed off to the good memories of his uncle Tatsuo. I stayed with him until Alan showed up after work.

"Did he eat?" It had become the first question any one of us asked each other. I shook my head no. "Jesus. He hasn't eaten in days." I couldn't bring myself to face the reality of what that meant. I just wasn't ready to go there.

"Hey, Alan? Did he ever talk about the war with you guys?" Masao was most likely tight-lipped about the war even with his own family. Like all the other MIS soldiers, he kept the details to himself.

"Sometimes, sure," Alan thought about this. "I remember him talking about how after the war it was hard for him to eat. He didn't have an appetite. I guess the sick smell of all the dead bodies, you know - the stink that had infiltrated his nostrils, just stuck with him. He couldn't shake it for years. Sometimes, the smell would come back for no reason at all. He would just have to get up from the dinner table and leave."

I looked at the sleeping Masao. "What else?"

"I don't know. Jeez. He just seems to really like to talk about the war with you more than anyone." I sat back with that. My face contorted as I tried to hold in the emotion that leaked out despite my efforts to hold them inside.

I had to leave the room.

Alan found me outside on an isolated bench where I had collected myself. He rubbed my back to comfort me. "He's lucky he has you around. You know? You listened to him and took notes on everything, recorded his thoughts. You listened, and he loves that. He loves you."

"*Goddamit. Shut up. Just shut up,*" I started to sob again. Alan was completely confused. Here he thought he was comforting me and it had the opposite effect.

"What's wrong? What'd I say?"

"Shit," I said, mopping up my tears and snot, "It's not him who's lucky," I choked out. "It's me." I looked at him. He was clueless. "Don't you see? I'm the lucky one."

Sunday, August 4, 2013

He barely woke up when Alan and I entered his room. He had been moved and had an inside bed, no window. In these facilities, the window is often the only source of life ongoing. Without that glimpse the place was beyond gloomy. It was depressing. We stayed for a couple of hours, and Masao woke up for very brief moments before dozing off again. Alan checked with the nursing staff and, as we assumed, he had not eaten a bite.

"Well, let's get going," Alan announced before saying loudly to his dad, "I'll be back tomorrow, Dad." Masao barely nodded. Alan looked at me. We both knew the end was near. "I'll meet you out front. I have to use the restroom." That meant I had a few extra minutes with Masao. I sat down and patted his knee over the covers and watched him sleep.

"I'm leaving now, Mas," I gently said, knowing that Alan was probably waiting at the front door. To my surprise, Masao woke up, reached for my hand and held it tightly.

He held it tightly for several seconds.

"I'll be back tomorrow or the next day, okay?"

"Okay, thank you."

And then he let go of my hand, put it back under the covers, and dozed off. It was a hard thing to do, to leave him that afternoon, leaving him in that dingy room with no natural light. Leaving the warm feel of his hand in mine, leaving him, very possibly, for the last time. I pulled myself out of that room, out of the facility, and into Alan's arms.

Tuesday, August 6, 2013

I was glad to be done with the morning cross-fit class and eager to check my phone for messages. There were two and I had to look at them twice, blinking my eyes as I read.

"Dad's not doing well. I'm on my way up there now," the first text read. That was at 9:20. I quickly scrolled to get to the next message; it had come at 9:35.

"Dad just died."

I felt like the air was suddenly sucked out of my lungs. I couldn't breathe. At the same time my legs felt as though they had been cut off at the knees. The next thing I knew I was kneeling at my car, frantically trying to find my keys and pulling air into my lungs while the tears poured out. My friend, Ruth, aware of my connection with Masao and his condition, and the class instructor Dillon were trying to help me. They were wondering if I should drive at all. All I could do was nod and choke.

I just wanted to get to Masao. All I wanted to do was get to Masao. Everything was a blur.

I called Alan simply because I didn't know what else to do. "Where are you?" My voice was frantic. My words, halfway stuck in my throat, begrudgingly coming out one at a time.

"I'm at the bottom of the hill," Alan's voice sounded equally as distressed. The bottom of the hill meant that he would be with his dad within minutes. Meanwhile, I was a good forty-five minutes away. It somehow felt reassuring knowing that Alan would be there, would be with the lingering spirit of Masao. I sobbed all the way there, driving as fast as I could.

At the entrance of the facility, family members gathered. Everyone had arrived before me and there I was in my sweaty workout gear. I saw Alan, and he walked me into Masao's room where more family was gathered. I sat down in the chair next to his bed and it was there that I broke down. I looked at his still body. No sound would come out of my mouth. I could only inhale in gulps. I rested my hand on his arm and continued to suck air in while tears dropped out, one after another.

My sobbing was deep. Someone handed me tissue, someone else was rubbing my back. I noticed that I was far more visibly upset than anyone else in the room and felt foolish for a fleeting second. Alan was crying, but wouldn't allow himself to sob. I noticed Katharine, Masao's granddaughter, across the bed.

"Was anyone with him?" I tried to get out. Nobody understood me.

"What?" Katharine asked compassionately, straining to make out my words. She was crying too. *Thank God I'm not the only one*, I thought.

"Was he alone or was someone with him?" I managed to get out.

Stephanie stepped in to assure me. "I think one of the nurses was with him." She didn't sound too convincing, though.

"Are you sure? Someone was with him?" I couldn't bear the thought of him dying alone. This soldier, this warrior, this wonderful man who had served his country heroically, he deserved to die surrounded by love.

Stephanie nodded. "He wasn't alone."

"Okay," I blurted out in between bursts of sobs. At the time I couldn't think of anything but my broken heart. I couldn't think of anything but the incredible loss I felt, the void that would now fill my life in the absence of my good friend Masao. Later, I wondered what his family thought of me. Did they see me as a hysterical woman? Or did they understand the depth of my feelings toward Masao. In the end, it didn't matter what they thought. In the end, it only mattered what Masao thought.

August 6th. I didn't connect the date until later. Masao left us on August 6, 2013, sixty-eight years to the day after the bomb was dropped on

Hiroshima. If it's true that we decide when to leave, then this made sense. Masao's heart had forever been shared between two countries that he loved. That he died in the U.S. on a day that was so historically significant for Japan was more than a coincidence.

It was the perfect day for Masao to depart.

CHAPTER 11

HIS FINAL JOURNEY
NOVEMBER 6ᵀᴴ, 2013

IT WAS THE FIRST TIME I NOTICED THAT ALL THREE SONS WERE EMOTIONAL. The playing of taps. The urn sitting in front of them. The finality of it all. It must have been heart-breaking for them. I looked at Alan, and my heart broke even more.

What would we do without our Masao? Life just wouldn't be the same without his stories, without his wit, without his sass.

As the bugle player played the last note of taps, there wasn't a dry eye in the courtyard. Everyone remained standing while the two soldiers who held the flag now folded it with great precision and care, placing three bullet casings, symbolic of three volleys and representing duty, honor, and country, inside the folded flag. Once it was folded back into the triangle with the stars on the outside, the soldier kneeled down and the flag was presented to Michael.

The soldiers marched out of the courtyard and everyone remained still. Then, from the very back row, a woman came forward with beautiful leis draped from her arm. Her footsteps were light as she came forward and stood in front of the three brothers. They looked up.

One by one, she placed a lei around the neck of each brother, afterward gently touching their shoulder. When she came to Alan, I sensed both warmth and sorrow enveloping him — her love and his grief. The finality of it all was evident on Alan's face, in his eyes, on his shoulders that were tucked around his heart. Then the woman turned to Masao's urn and placed her last lei, ever so carefully, around it. After the woman made her way to the back row, Masao's family came to his urn with their meticulously selected leis, one at a time. Young and old alike, they placed their last token of love around his urn and said their good-byes.

The funeral director then showed us the way to the columbarium where Masao would be laid to rest in the same niche where Doris was patiently waiting for him. We all gathered around as the grounds worker respectfully unscrewed the face of the niche, placed Masao inside, and closed it back up. The leis were laid in front along with flowers. The only comfort my aching heart had was that Masao was with Doris at last.

I stood off at the side and watched Masao's family and friends as they comforted each another and fussed over the flowers. *There must have been some reason that all of this came together the way it did. There must be some reason that I intersected Masao's life when I did.* It was the perfect meeting of souls; he had a fascinating story to tell and, for whatever reason, I was fortunate enough to be a listener. Why he chose me to tell it to, I'll never know. Maybe it was because I had joined the family late in his life, so I didn't have any preconceived notion of Masao, and he didn't have any of me. We had several precious years of friendship and there was not much that contaminated the friendship. I think that is what made it so special.

I watched the cemetery worker screw in the last bolt, sealing up Masao and Doris's niche forever. I liked to think of them together in the mid 1940s when they blissfully traversed Japan as a pair, providing Masao with a sense of belonging that he so longed for and giving Doris a sense of adventure she craved.

As for me, I convinced myself of one decision in that moment at the Punchbowl watching the niche close up.

Masao's legacy was one that must not be forgotten.

EPILOGUE

In October 2010, President Barack Obama signed an order to honor World War II Japanese-American soldiers with the coveted Congressional Gold Medal. Masao proudly accepted this great honor at a ceremony in Seattle where he and other soldiers from World War II were recognized. As wonderful as that medal is, what might be more important to Masao's generation is social recognition. Receiving an award from the highest office in the land is one thing, but having acknowledgment, or even better, appreciation from your own generation, and your children's generation, and their children's generation is quite another. It's the collective awareness of those quiet heroics that make this country great.

The generation of Nisei that lived through the World War II era was among the greatest. They gave up everything, quite literally, to prove their loyalty. All the suspicion about Japanese-Americans was for naught. After all the investigations, all the evacuations, all the injustice levied against an entire race, only ten people living on American soil were found guilty of espionage or fifth element activity. All of them were white.

When Nisei and Sansei soldiers were finally discharged from the military, they weren't allowed to join veterans associations. Masao wasn't even issued a lapel button, a standard issue for soldiers. Yet, this group of citizens was the first to provide a strong voice on behalf our Muslim Americans after 9/11, and to this day, to prevent any hysteria that would have led to the same injustice they had once endured. This is the importance of history — to learn from our shortsightedness, to grow as a people, and to become stronger by listening to those who have gained wisdom through endurance.

No generation understands this more than our Nisei.

BIBLIOGRAPHY

"A History of Japanese Americans in California: Terminal Island." *National Park Service, U.S. Department of the Interior.* Last modified November 17, 2004.
< https://www.nps.gov/parkhistory/online_books/5views/5views4h87.htm >

"A More Perfect Union." *Smithsonian Institute, National Museum of American History, Behring Center.* Accessed May, 2014.
<http://amhistory.si.edu/perfectunion/non-flash/index.html>

Action at Angaur. Produced by the Army Pictorial Service Signal Corps, 1945.

Adler, David Gray. "Minidoka and Flagrant Violations." *The Blue Review,* 2013. Accessed March, 2014. <www.thebluereview.org/wwii-japanese-incarceration/>

Aimone, William F. *A personal reflection on the author's life before, during, and after World War II.* Written post-war, no date indicated.

Aimone, William F. "The Nisei and the CIC." *Japanese-American Veterans Association (JAVA) Newsletter,* March/April, 2003.

"Alien Detention Center." *Historical Museum at Fort Missoula.* Accessed April, 2014.
<http://www.fortmissoulamuseum.org/aliendetention.php>

Ano, Masaharu. "Loyal Linguists: Nisei of World War II Learned Japanese in Minnesota." *Minnesota History 45, no. 7* (1977): pages 273-287.

Antill, Peter. "Peleliu, Battle for (Operation Stalemate II) - The Pacific War's Forgotten Battle, September-November 1944." *History of War Military History Encyclopedia on the Web.* Accessed May, 2014.
<http://www.historyofwar.org/articles/battles_peleliu>

Bailey, Ronald H. "The Incredible Jeep." *World War II magazine,* September, 2009. Accessed May, 2014 <http://www.historynet.com/the-incredible-jeep.htm>

"Behind Barbed Wire at Amache." *University of Denver Museum (DUMA) Online Exhibit.* Accessed April, 2014. <http://www.du.edu/behindbarbedwire/history.html>

Blair, Bobby C., and John Peter DeCioccio. *Victory at Peleliu: The 81st Infantry Division's Pacific Campaign.* Norman, Oklahoma: University of Oklahoma Press, 2011.

Brown, DeSoto. *Hawaii Goes to War: Life in Hawaii from Pearl Harbor to Peace.* Honolulu, Hawaii: Editions Limited, 1989.

Conn, Stetson, Rose C. Engelman, and Byron Fairchild. *Guarding the United States and Its Outposts.* Washington, D.C.: Center of Military History, United States Army, 1962. Accessed April, 2014.
<www.history.army.mil/books/wwii/Guard-US/ch8.htm>

Cook, Haruko Taya, and Theodore F. Cook. *Japan at War: An Oral History.* New York: The New Press, 1992.

"Decorations and Medals." *The Institute of Heraldry, Office of the Administrative Assistant to the Secretary of the Army.* Accessed May, 2014.
<http://www.tioh.hqda.pentagon.mil/Catalog/HeraldryList.aspx?CategoryId=5&grp=4&menu=Decorations%20and%20Medals&hilite=ribbons>

Dower, John W. *Embracing Defeat: Japan in the Wake of World War II.* New York: W.W. Norton & Company/The New Press, 1999.

Dower, John W. *War Without Mercy: Race & Power in the Pacific War.* New York: Pantheon Books, 1986.

"Essay: Relocation and Incarceration of Japanese-Americans During World War II." *The University of California as part of the Japanese-American Relocation Digital Archive (JARDA) project, California Digital Library.* Accessed April, 2014.
<https://calisphere.org/exhibitions/essay/8/relocation/>

"Executive Order 9066: The President Authorizes Japanese Relocation." *History Matters.* Accessed March, 2014. <www.historymatters.gmu.edu/d/5154>

"FDR and Japanese American Internment." *Franklin D. Roosevelt Presidential Library and Museum.* Accessed April, 2014.
<www.fdrlibrary.marist.edu/archives/pdfs/internment.pdf>

Gayle, Gordon D. Brigadier General. "Bloody Beaches: the Marines at Peleliu."
   Official U.S. Marine Corps Marines in World War II Commemorative Series.
   Accessed May, 2014.
   <http://www.marines.mil/Portals/59/Publications/Bloody%20Beaches%20
   The%20Marines%20At%20Peleliu%20%20PCN%2019000313700_1.
   pdf?ver=2012-10-11-163203-753>

Hirohata, Joyce, and Paul T. Hirohata. *Nisei Voices: Japanese American Students of the
   1930s - Then & Now.* Oakland, California: Hirohata Design, 2004.

Ichihashi, Yamato, Ph.D. *Japanese Immigration: Its Status in California.* San
   Francisco: The Marshall Press, 1915.

Ishimaru, Stone S. *Military Intelligence Service Language School: Camp Savage,
   Minnesota 1942-44.* Southern California: Military Intelligence Service Club, 1992.

Japanese Relocation. Produced by the U.S. War Department, 1943.
   <https://archive.org/details/Japanese1943>

Johnson, Robert Flynn. " 'Manzanar': The Wartime Photographs of Ansel Adams."
   *Photographic Traveling Exhibitions presented at the Jundt Art Museum at Gonzaga
   University, Spokane, Washington.* January, 2014. Accessed March, 2014.
   <www.p-t-e.org/manzanar/text.pdf>

"Lessons from the Past: Japanese-Americans." *Chicora Foundation, Inc.* Accessed
   May, 2014. <http://www.chicora.org/Japanese-Americans.html>

McNaughton, James C. *Nisei Linguists: Japanese Americans in the Military Intelligence
   Service during World War II.* Washington D.C.: Department of the Army, 2007.

"Military Intelligence Service (MIS)." *Go For Broke National Education Center.*
   Accessed February 1, 2010.
   <http://www.goforbroke.org/learn/history/military_units/misls.php>

"Military Intelligence Service Language School at Fort Snelling: Overview."
   Minnesota History Center, Gale Family Library. Last modified July 14, 2016.
   <www.mnhs.org/library/tips/history_topics/120language_school.html>

MIS - Northwest Association. *Unsung Heroes: Military Intelligence Service, Past-
   Present - Future.* Seattle, WA: MIS-Northwest Association, 1996.

"National Memorial Cemetery of the Pacific." *U.S. Department of Veterans Affairs.*
   Last modified February 9, 2016. <http://www.cem.va.gov/cems/nchp/nmcp.asp>

Nielsen, Michele, Curator of History/Archives, San Bernardino County Museum. Email message, January 19, 2010.

Odo, Franklin. "100th Infantry Battalion." *Densho Encyclopedia*. Accessed March, 2014. <http://encyclopedia.densho.org/100th%20Infantry%20Battalion/>

"Patriotism and Prejudice: Japanese Americans and World War II." *National Park Service, U.S. Department of the Interior.* Accessed April, 2014. <https://www.nps.gov/goga/planyourvisit/upload/MIS-bulletin_6-07_medium.pdf>

Sands, Diana, Developmental Director of the Fort Missoula Museum. Email message, March 27, 2014.

"Santa Fe (detention facility)." *Densho Encyclopedia*. Accessed April, 2014. <http://encyclopedia.densho.org/Santa%20Fe%20(detention%20facility)/>

Sledge, E.B. *With the Old Breed.* New York: Ballantine Books, 2007.

"Terminal Island." *California Japantowns.* Accessed April, 2014. <www.californiajapantowns.org/terminalisland.html>

"Terminal Island Japanese Memorial." *San Pedro Peninsula Chamber of Commerce.* Accessed April, 2014. <www.sanpedro.com/spcom/terminal-island-japanese-memorial.htm>

"The 1930s and War Economy." *National Graduate Institute for Policy Studies.* Accessed May 8, 2010. <http://www.grips.ac.jp/teacher/oono/hp/lecture_J/lec09.htm>

"The 321st Infantry Moves North." *Ibiblio; online public library.* Accessed May, 2014. <https://www.ibiblio.org/hyperwar/USA/USA-P-Approach/USA-P-Approach-23.html>

The 81st Wildcat Division Historical Committee. *The 81st Infantry Wildcat Division in World War II.* Washington: Infantry Journal Press, 1948.

"The Lost Village of Terminal Island." *Terminal Island - Our Stories.* Accessed April, 2014. <www.terminalisland.org>

"The Points System or Advanced Service Rating Score." *Custermen.* Last modified October 25,2008. <http://custermen.com/AtTheFront/Points.htm>

"The War, At Home, Civil Rights: Japanese Americans." *Public Broadcasting Service.* Accessed April, 2014
<www.pbs.org/thewar/at_home_civil_rights_japanese_american.htm>

"Timeline." *Densho Encyclopedia.* Accessed April, 2014.
<http://encyclopedia.densho.org/timeline/>

"Timeline." *Go For Broke National Education Center.* Accessed February 1, 2010.
<http://www.goforbroke.org/learn/history/timeline/1943.php>

"Traditions of O'ahu: Stories of an Ancient Island. Ka'ahupahau." *Asia-Pacific Digital Library, Kalamaku Press.* Last modified September 11, 2010.
<http://apdl.kcc.hawaii.edu/oahu/stories/ewa/kaahupahau.htm>

Webber, Paul M. "Camp Robinson - WWII." Accessed April, 2014.
<http://home.pcisys.net/~pwebber/31_id/text/camp_robinson.txt>

Weber, Mark. "The Japanese Camps in California: World War II West Coast Camps for Japanese-Americans." *The Journal of Historical Review 2* (1981): 45-58. Accessed March, 2014. <www.ihr.org/jhr/v02/v02p-45_Weber.html>

"What was the 442nd Regimental Combat Team?" *The 442nd Regimental Combat Team Historical Society Digital Archives.* Accessed April, 2014.
<www.the442.org/442ndfacts.html>

Wong, Morrison G. *"The Japanese in Riverside, 1890 to 1945: A Special Case in Race Relations."* Ph.D. dissertation, University of California, Riverside, 1977.

"World War II Harbor Defenses." *National Park Service, U.S. Department of the Interior.* Accessed April, 2014.
<https://www.nps.gov/goga/learn/historyculture/world-war-ii-harbor-defenses.htm>

"World War II in the San Francisco Bay Area." *National Park Service, U.S. Department of the Interior.* Accessed April, 2014.
<https://www.nps.gov/nr/travel/wwIIbayarea/pre.htm>

ABOUT THE AUTHOR

SANDRA VEA was born and raised in Seattle, Washington. She attended the University of Washington for undergraduate studies, Western Washington University for graduate studies in Education, and Seattle University for graduate studies in School Counseling. Sandra is a public educator and a life-long learner. She enjoys spending her spare time reading about and researching American events that are not well known but are of significant historical value and contemporary relevance.

CPSIA information can be obtained
at www.ICGtesting.com
Printed in the USA
LVOW01s0036060217

523303LV00008BA/234/P